Fig 7, 27, 24

PHYTOHORMONES

EXPERIMENTAL BIOLOGY MONOGRAPHS

PACEMAKERS IN RELATION TO ASPECTS OF BEHAVIOR. BY HUDSON HOAGLAND

NEUROEMBRYOLOGY. BY SAMUEL R. DETWILER

THE EGGS OF MAMMALS. BY GREGORY PINCUS

AUTONOMIC NEURO–EFFECTOR SYSTEMS. BY WALTER B. CANNON AND ARTURO ROSENBLUETH

PHYTOHORMONES. BY F. W. WENT AND KENNETH V. THIMANN

Other volumes to follow

PHYTOHORMONES

BY

F. W. WENT, Ph.D.

Professor of Plant Physiology
California Institute of Technology

AND

KENNETH V. THIMANN, Ph.D.

Assistant Professor of Plant Physiology
Harvard University

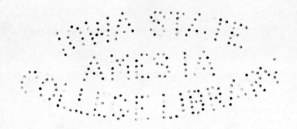

NEW YORK
THE MACMILLAN COMPANY
1937

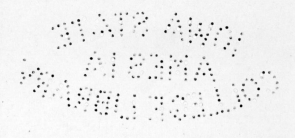

Dedicated
to the memory of
F. A. F. C. Went and Herman E. Dolk

Oats, peas, beans and barley grow,
Oats, peas, beans and barley grow,
Can you, or I, or anyone know
How oats, peas, beans and barley grow?

—Old English Nursery Rhyme

ACKNOWLEDGMENT

It is a pleasure to express our thanks to the many colleagues who have aided in one way or another the preparation of this monograph. Dr. J. van Overbeek and Mr. C. L. Schneider have carried out a number of special experiments; Dr. J. Bonner, Dr. J. van Overbeek, and Dr. A. J. Haagen Smit have made numerous valuable suggestions and criticisms of the manuscript; and Miss E. M. Wallace has spent much time in the preparation of the drawings. Finally a number of co-workers and students have been kind enough to allow the citation of their unpublished results. In many cases this has made possible the discussion of papers published later than the autumn of 1936, although we have made no attempt at completeness beyond this date. Thanks are due to Prof. F. Kögl for the samples of auxin and biotin used in some of the unpublished experiments cited here. Thanks are also due to the authors of a number of papers and the editors of the journals in which they appeared for permission to reproduce figures. The source of these is acknowledged below the figures in each case.

F. W. WENT
KENNETH V. THIMANN

June, 1937

TABLE OF CONTENTS

PHYTOHORMONES

CHAPTER I

INTRODUCTION

The field of plant hormones is perhaps now at the stage of its most rapid development. The number of facts is becoming so large, and their distribution through the literature so scattered, that there is a danger of losing sight of the general trend. We shall attempt not so much to give a detailed historical account as, rather, to present the field from the point of view of workers in it. Where matters of hypothesis are concerned, our personal views will necessarily be emphasized, but opposing views will be given an opportunity for the reader's consideration. In matters of fact, as also in regard to credit and priority, every attempt will be made to give as fair and accurate an account as possible, both of the experiments and of the concepts of the different workers. For the sake of completeness many new experiments have been included. These are designated as u (unpublished). Some idea of the amount of work which has been done in this field may be gained from the statement that the contents of this book are based on actual measurements of the responses of about one million plants. The growing interest in the field is exemplified by the fact that the bibliography includes references to 77 publications dated 1936. Since equally detailed and critical treatment cannot be accorded to all of this material, we have naturally laid emphasis on what appears to be the most important work.

A. OUTLINE OF THE BOOK

Our review will deal only with the hormones of higher plants. We shall first trace the development of the leading

1

idea that correlations in plants are due to the influence of special substances (Chapter II).[1] We shall try to show how experiments along four different and apparently unrelated lines,—correlation proper, organ formation, tropisms, and normal growth,—have gradually come together and been unified into a complete picture of hormone activity as we now know it. Next we shall consider the methods for the assay of these substances, treating them in sufficient detail for experimental use (Chapter III). Since most of these methods are founded upon cell elongation, and all other work has had its foundation thereon, it is natural to consider cell elongation in some detail first.

The best demonstration of the effectiveness of these assay methods has been the working out of the chemical nature of the active substances (Chapter VII). The success of the chemical attack has made it possible for all the experiments described subsequently to be checked by use of the pure compounds; this has had the effect of making the conclusions clear-cut and has avoided the difficulty of working with unknown extracts and mixtures.

Parallel and simultaneous with work on the above lines, the rôle of the active substances in various aspects of plant growth has been elucidated (Chapter V), beginning with their formation (Chapter IV) and movement in plant tissue (Chapter VI). The latter phenomenon is of special interest, firstly because it offers an example of a naturally occurring substance whose movement can be followed quantitatively throughout the plant, and secondly because of the causal relation between the polarity of this transport and the well-known polarity of plant structures. One of the most interesting aspects of the subject has been the attempt to analyze the various reactions intervening between the auxin and its final effect,—growth (Chapter VIII). In this, knowledge of the chemical nature of the substances has played an essential part. In close connection with problems of cell elonga-

[1] References such as VIII *G* or III *C* refer to chapter (Roman numbers) and section (letters).

tion and transport come the tropisms, particularly the reactions of plants to gravity and light, insofar as they are caused by unequal growth (Chapter X).

Further, these same active substances play an important rôle in a number of other correlations in plants, particularly in the formation of roots (Chapter XI), in bud inhibition (Chapter XII), and in the stimulation of cambial activity (Chapter XIII). There are also a number of other phenomena not so well understood.

Finally the findings and general conclusions will be compared with those from other fields, bringing the work on plant hormones into the realm of general physiology (Chapter XIV).

B. DEFINITIONS

The definition of *hormone* which we propose to apply is this: *a hormone is a substance which, being produced in any one part of the organism, is transferred to another part and there influences a specific physiological process.* This is essentially the definition of Bayliss and Starling (1904): "the peculiarity of these substances (hormones) is that they are produced in one organ and carried by the blood current to another organ, on which their effect is manifested" (Bayliss, 1927, p. 712). There is, of course, no blood stream in plants, but, as Bayliss emphasizes, "these hormones are characterized by the property of serving as chemical *messengers*, by which the activity of certain organs is coördinated with that of others." [1] There is no strict necessity for the production of the hormone in specialized organs, since even if all the cells of the plant should produce it, the phenomenon of polarity would bring about its specific distribution. In general, however, the points of production and response are spatially separated.

To avoid the possibility of confusion with animal mechanisms the term phytohormones has been introduced for

[1] The conception of hormones has recently been somewhat broadened (see Huxley, 1935).

such substances in plants. However, since in this book we shall deal only with the plant kingdom, the prefix can suitably be dropped. Thus our conception of hormone is essentially that of a correlation carrier, where correlation (as used in regard to plants) is defined as the influence exerted by one part of the plant upon another,—not in the sense of statistical correlation, but in the sense of causal relationship.

In the beginning of the work in this field, the noncommittal terms growth substance, Wuchsstoff, growth regulator, and growth hormone were used, but as our knowledge developed, it became clear that the substances causing cell elongation must be regarded as a separate group. Since recent work indicates that this group is heterogeneous, the term *auxins*, first suggested by Kögl and Haagen Smit (1931), will be arbitrarily restricted to those substances which bring about the specific growth reaction which is conveniently measurable by the curvature of *Avena* coleoptiles. Whenever used in the physiological sense, the terms growth substance (g.s.) and growth hormone will be used throughout this book in the sense of auxins. The term *Wuchsstoff* in particular has been used for some of the growth substances of lower plants, such as Bios, but it cannot be too strongly emphasized that only those substances whose activity is determined on higher plants, preferably by the standard methods which are described in Chapter III of this book, can be termed auxins.

C. Previous Reviews of the Field

The rapid development of the field has resulted, as would be expected, in the publication of a number of reviews and summaries. Such reviews have rarely more than temporary interest, and many of these are already only of historical value (Babička, 1934; Cholodny, 1935a; Kögl, 1932, 1932a, 1933, 1933a, 1933b, 1933c; Laibach, 1934; Loewe, 1933; Malowan, 1934; Pisek, 1929; Snow, 1932; Söding, 1927, 1932; F. A. F. C. Went, 1927, 1930, 1931, 1932, 1932a, 1932b, 1933, 1933a).

The newer and more extensive reviews are those of du Buy and Nuernbergk (1932, 1934, 1935), Erxleben (1935), von Guttenberg (1932, 1933, 1934, 1935, 1936), Heyn (1936), Jost (1935), Kögl (1935, 1935a, 1936), Haagen Smit (1935), Stiles (1935), Thimann (1935, 1936b), Went [1] (1935b, 1936a), and F. A. F. C. Went [1] (1934, 1935).

The most complete account which has appeared up to now is that of Boysen Jensen (1935, translated and extended by Avery and Burkholder, 1936). We do not feel, however, that Boysen Jensen's publication makes our book superfluous, for several reasons. In the first place, it does not attempt to do more than review the past work, while in this book our aim is rather to analyze and integrate the material. In the second place, its scope is restricted largely to the rôle of hormones in growth and tropisms, while, as was stated above, the field has recently developed in quite different directions, which necessitates a revision and broadening of our ideas. Lastly, it appears from book reviews (Söding, 1935b; Umrath, 1935) that one of the principal impressions which the book has made is in regard to the question of priority in the discovery of the auxins. We feel that the gradual unfolding of the current conceptions and the coöperation of different workers has made it impossible to credit any one person with such a discovery, and it is to be hoped that the reader of this book will gain the impression of a steady and collective advance rather than of individual contributions.

[1] References to Went (without initials) refer to F. W. Went, the papers of F. A. F. C. Went being cited with initials.

CHAPTER II

DEVELOPMENT OF THE HORMONE CONCEPT

A. CORRELATION AND FORMATIVE SUBSTANCES

The idea that the phenomenon of correlation is brought about by substances or "saps" is by no means new. No detailed consideration need be given to the very vague idea of Malpighi (1675) nor to the artistic conceptions of Agricola (1716) of a *"materia ad radices promovendas."* Careful experiments, however, were carried out by Duhamel du Monceau (1758), whose sound scientific reasoning led him to conceive of correlation as brought about by two saps, one moving downward, the other upward. The former was elaborated in the leaves and, after passing downward through the cortex, was used for the nutrition of the roots. If, however, this downward stream were intercepted by ringing or other means, it caused the swellings, callus, and root formation which he observed above the point of interception (see

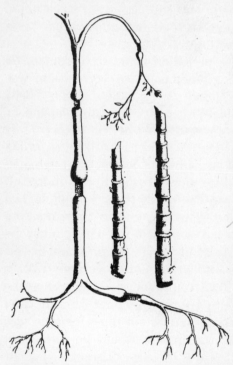

FIG. 1. The first published drawings of correlations in plants. Swellings occur above but not below ring wounds, and in isolated pieces of bark they are most marked when leaves or buds are present. (From Duhamel du Monceau, 1758.)

6

Figure 1). So much stress was laid on the root formation that the swellings and callus were considered as "being much of the nature of roots" (Bk. IV, Ch. V). During the next hundred years the physiological concept of correlation seems to have been lost, the emphasis being placed on morphology, *i.e.* upon the inherent nature of the tissues themselves. The discovery of sieve tubes by Hartig and von Mohl led them to the opinion that there was indeed a downward-moving sap, and this was later proven by Hanstein (1860). The content of this sap, however, was studied from the viewpoint of organic food materials rather than that of its correlating functions.

At this time began the period of rapid development in plant physiology. The phenomenon of correlation was studied in greater detail and Sachs (1880, 1882, 1893) brought forward a complete theory, a modern version of Duhamel's views, which covered most of the known facts of morphogenesis and correlation, and can still be regarded as a modern treatment of the subject. Sachs' great achievement was that he applied the laws of causality to morphology. His starting point was the thesis that "morphological differences between plant organs are due to corresponding differences in their material composition, which must be already present at the time of initiation, even though at this stage chemical reactions and other crude methods fail to show any differences." To account for these differences he assumed the existence of root-forming, flower-forming, and other substances, which move in different directions through the plant. For example, the former would be formed in leaves, and would move towards the base of stems. If a cut be made in a twig, this will be "an obstacle for further downward movement," and roots will be formed above the cut. Light and gravity were assumed to affect the distribution of these special substances. With only two assumptions: 1, the existence of organ-forming substances which, in minute amounts, direct development, and 2, polar distribution of these substances,—a distribution which may be modified by external forces such as light and gravity,—correlations, normal development, galls and monstrosities were brought into one picture.

In his very remarkable publications on galls Beijerinck (1888, 1897) elaborates the idea of "growth-enzymes."

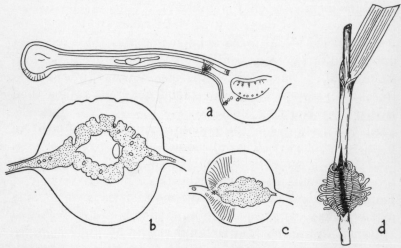

FIG. 2. a, b, c, gall of *Nematus capreae* on leaf of *Salix*. a, egg deposited with some mucilage in mesophyll of young leaf; b, mature gall before hatching of larva; c, gall in which by accident no egg has been deposited. The mucilage excreted by the gall-wasp has caused formation of an almost complete gall. This excretion is the first published example of an organ-forming substance. (From Beijerinck, 1888.) d, gall of *Cecidomyia Poae* on stem of *Poa*, showing excessive root formation. (From Beijerinck, 1885.)

While he originally thought (1886) that "it can not be doubted that nutritive stimuli must be considered as the primary cause" of root formation when parts of plants are cut off from the parent-plant, he afterwards modified his views in the direction of those of Sachs. In the case of the *Capreae*-gall on *Salix* (Beijerinck, 1888) he considers the development of the gall (see Figure 2) to be caused by "a protein, whose action differs from that of ordinary proteins, which only form an equivalent amount of protoplasm, and resembles that of an enzyme, whose effect is quantitatively of a different order of magnitude from the amount of active material." Thus we have to do here with a "material stimulus" (or as we should say now, a stimulating material) (1888, p. 132). Beijerinck designates this protein as a "growth enzyme." Later (1897) he extended this view to the development of organisms in general, and stated that "form is determined by liquid substances, which move freely through considerable numbers of cells in growing tissues" (1897, p. 203).

Except for these observations of Beijerinck no direct evidence for the existence of such special substances as Sachs had postulated was obtained for nearly 40 years. On the other hand, at about the same period, the existence of polarity in correlation phenomena was proven, both for whole organs, and for each separate cell of a transplant, by Vöchting (1878, 1884, 1892, 1908). His work, however, is primarily concerned with inherent morphological polarity, rather than with its physiological basis.

After the time of Sachs and Vöchting most of the studies on correlation laid emphasis on nutritional factors. Goebel (1908), for instance, in discussing quantitative correlations, says "of the numerous organ initials, many remain undeveloped because the building materials, which they need for their development, go to others which can 'attract' these materials more powerfully." Similar views, involving also the nitrogen content of the plant, *i.e.* "the carbon: nitrogen ratio," have been generally held by American workers (*cf. e.g.* Kraus and Kraybill, 1918). While their experiments show that there is a parallelism between a given carbon: nitrogen ratio and a given type of growth, no causal relation has been shown to exist.

B. Tropisms

About 1880 it began to be realized that tropisms were to be regarded as a special kind of correlation phenomenon. This aspect of tropisms was particularly emphasized by C. Darwin (1880). Both for roots and shoots he was able to show that the effects of light and gravity are perceived by the tip, and that the stimulus is transmitted to the lower regions, which then react. "We must, therefore, conclude that when seedlings are freely exposed to a lateral light, some influence is transmitted from the upper to the lower part, causing the latter to bend" (p. 474). In regard to geotropism of roots, he concludes "that it is the tip alone which is acted on, and that this part transmits some influence to the adjoining parts, causing them to curve downwards" (p. 545). At first Darwin's statements met with much opposition, but Rothert (1894), working with phototropism of shoots, confirmed completely the separation between the zones which perceive and those which react. The connection between these processes was envisaged by Fitting (1907) as being due to a polarity set up by the light stimulus, which "spread out" from cell to cell.

Fitting's work was closely followed by the experiments of Boysen Jensen (1910, 1911, 1913) which showed that a

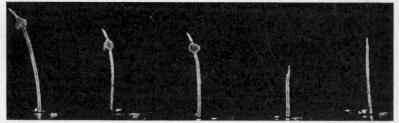

FIG. 3. First experimental demonstration of transmission of the phototropic stimulus across a wound gap. Five *Avena* coleoptiles were decapitated, and the tips replaced upon the three plants to the left, the wound being covered with cocoa-butter. Two plants to the right as controls. On illumination of the tips only, from the left, the plants with tips replaced show curvature in the base, the controls not. (From Boysen Jensen, *Ber. d. bot. Ges. 31:* 559–566, 1913; and *Growth Hormones in Plants*, tr. Avery and Burkholder, McGraw-Hill, 1936.)

phototropic stimulus can be transmitted across a wound gap. Boysen Jensen cut off the tips of *Avena* coleoptiles and stuck them on again with gelatin (see Figure 3). He then illuminated the tip only and showed that curvature appeared not only in the tip but also in the base. From this he concluded that "the transmission of the irritation is of a material nature produced by concentration changes in the coleoptile tip." He was led to assume such concentration changes by comparison with Lehman's model of a nerve, in which the electromotive changes of a chain of zinc sulfate concentration cells were compared to the transmission of stimulus. The "material nature" of the transmission seemed not to be purely physical, but "on the other hand, various considerations make one think that the transmission is of a chemical nature."

Under the influence of Pfeffer and of the application of zoölogical concepts, it is clear that Boysen Jensen visualized the transmission of the phototropic stimulus as a complex chain of reactions. This is exemplified by his interpretation of it in terms of the transmission of irritation in a nerve. He assumes that the light causes a differentiation between the bright and dark sides of the coleoptile tip; this constitutes an "irritation" of the dark side, and this irritation "leaves the dark side of the tip to travel down the dark side of the coleoptile." Finally, this irritation "sets free," in the lower part of the coleoptile, an acceleration of growth. This separation into perception, transmission, and reaction made it impossible for him to conceive that all three were realized through the same agency. While his experiments prove that the transmission of the irritation is a transmission "of substance or of ions" he did not postulate that this was a special, growth-promoting substance, and it was left to Paál to show that the material nature of the transmission was due to a special substance which is active in promoting normal growth. It will be clear to the reader that the above analysis does not at all support Boysen Jensen's claim (1935, 1936) that "the existence of a growth substance in the *Avena* coleoptile during phototropic curvature was demonstrated" by his experiments.

C. BIRTH OF THE GROWTH HORMONE CONCEPT

Because of the importance of Boysen Jensen's experiment, it was repeated and extended by Paál (1914, 1919), who, after excluding the possibilities of the base being influenced by scattered light, by contact stimulus, or by the asymmetrical weight of the bending tip, confirmed Boysen Jensen's finding. Varying the conditions of the experiment, he showed that the stimulus could cross a layer of gelatin, but not cocoa-butter, mica, or platinum foil. His next important step was to show that, even without light, curvatures could be induced in the base by the simple process of cutting off the tip and replacing it on one side of the stump. This makes it clear that "the tip is the seat of a growth-regulating center. In it a substance (or a mixture) is formed and internally secreted, and this substance, equally distributed over all sides, moves downwards through the living tissue. In the growing zone it causes symmetrical growth. If the movement of this correlation carrier is disturbed on one side, a growth decrease on that side results, giving rise to a curvature of the organ" (Paál, 1919). This puts the whole problem on a new basis, namely the control of normal growth by a diffusible correlation carrier. Here, for the first time, the idea of a *growth* hormone enters botanical literature. Paál then suggested that "this correlation carrier, which, under normal conditions continually moves downwards from the tip along all sides, is, upon illumination of the tip, either interfered with in its formation, photochemically inactivated, or inhibited in its downward movement, through some change in the protoplasm, these effects being greater on the lighted side."

Paál thus established the theory that the growth of the coleoptile is controlled by the tip through the agency of a diffusible substance, and this was confirmed by the careful growth measurements of Söding (1923, 1925). Working not with curvatures but with straight growth, Söding proved that replacement of the cut tip would restore the greater part of the growth reduction which is caused by decapitation. Further, the success of Paál's work led to a search for a direct demonstration of the postulated growth-promoting substance. Stark (1921) introduced the method of applying small blocks of agar on one side of decapitated coleoptiles, the agar being mixed with various tissue extracts, but in no case did any of these promote growth, only inhibitions being observed. The same failure to extract the growth-promoting substance from coleoptile tips was experienced by Nielsen (1924) and by Seubert (1925). However, Seubert was able to prove that agar containing saliva, diastase, and malt extract caused a promotion of growth. This was the first evidence that growth-promoting substances exist outside the plant.

Stark (1921), Stark and Drechsel (1922), Gradmann (1925), and Brauner (1922) attempted to explain tropisms in terms of special stimulus substances, or "Tropohormones," but with little success, and shortly afterwards Cholodny (1924, 1926, 1927) and Went (1928) developed the view of Paál and attributed all tropisms to asymmetric distribution of the normal growth-promoting substance (cf. X B).

D. Isolation of the Growth Hormone

Success in obtaining the active substance from the coleoptile tip was finally achieved by Went (1926, 1928 [1]). Using the findings of Paál and adapting the method of Stark (see III B), he placed coleoptile tips upon blocks of agar, and then placed the agar on one side of the stumps of decapitated coleoptiles. The result was a curvature away from the agar block (negative curvature). His fundamental improvement in technique was to measure this curvature, which was proven to be proportional, within limits, to the concentration of the active substance. This test, the "Avena test," was then used to determine some of the properties of the substance, which was shown to be thermo- and photostable, as well as readily diffusible. From the diffusion rate its approximate molecular weight was determined. Went interpreted the normal growth of the coleoptile in terms of the action of this growth substance in conjunction with other limiting factors. For the asymmetric growth involved

[1] Published November, 1927.

in phototropism he obtained evidence that an asymmetric distribution of the growth substance occurs, this being the cause of the curvature. In recent years a large literature on this subject has developed. The later work, which will constitute the body of this book, need only be briefly referred to here. First of all must be mentioned the chemical investigation of the active substances, auxins, which, mainly in the skillful hands of Kögl, Haagen Smit, and Erxleben, led rapidly to the isolation in pure form of three highly active substances (this work will be discussed in Chapter VII).

The occurrence and distribution of the auxins has been investigated by Söding, Thimann, Laibach, and others. In this connection the fact that the auxins have no specificity of action was first demonstrated by Cholodny, and confirmed abundantly by Nielsen, Söding, Uyldert, and others. The investigations of van der Weij have brought light to many remarkable facts concerning the transport of auxins in the coleoptile, particularly the strict polarity of its movement.

Since the approach to knowledge of the auxins was through tropisms, it is natural that one of the main applications of the acquired knowledge of these substances should be in the explanation of tropisms. The investigations of Dolk, Cholodny, and Dijkman have shown that asymmetrical distribution of auxin under the influence of gravity quantitatively accounts for geotropic curvature. This rules out any need for assuming the action of "tropohormones." In phototropism the situation is somewhat more complicated, but the main lines have been elucidated by Cholodny, Boysen Jensen, du Buy, and van Overbeek. In roots, the studies of Cholodny, Snow, Boysen Jensen, and others have made it clear that the effect of auxin is to inhibit, not to promote, elongation, and this makes it possible to explain geotropic behavior of roots along the same lines.

Many attempts have been made to elucidate the mechanism of the growth-promoting action. Heyn and Söding succeeded in showing that one of the ultimate effects of auxin is a change in the properties of the cell wall, which allows extension to take place.   The intermediate stages between the entry of auxin and its final effect have been investigated by Thimann and Bonner.

Following the discovery of the growth-promoting activity of the auxins, it was found that many well-known correlations in organ development are brought about by the same substances.   As mentioned above, Sachs assumed that root formation is due to a special root-forming substance.   Experimental evidence to support this view was brought forward by several investigators, particularly by van der Lek.   Proof that a special substance is indeed concerned was obtained by Went and Bouillenne, and the isolation of this active substance by Thimann and Went led to its identification with the auxins, an identity which was independently confirmed by Laibach and others.   Another phenomenon long known as a typical correlation is the inhibitory effect of the terminal bud of a shoot on the development of lateral buds (Goebel, Dostál, Reed, Snow); this effect was shown by Thimann and Skoog to be due to auxins, produced in the growing bud.   Still other important correlative phenomena, such as cambial growth, swelling of the ovary of orchids after pollination, petiole abscission, and callus formation have since been shown to be brought about by auxins (Snow, Laibach).

The interrelations between the fields of organ formation, correlation, tropisms, and growth have been summarized in the chart, Table I, which shows how these four lines of approach have gradually come together, and how each investigator's contribution has been merged into a more and more complete system.   Exceptions must be made for Beijerinck and Loeb, whose work, although of importance, had little influence on the development of this field.   The soundness of their views, however, must now be acknowledged. The placing of an investigator's name between two vertical lines indicates that his work linked up these two lines; thus Boysen Jensen showed that tropisms were a correlation

TABLE I

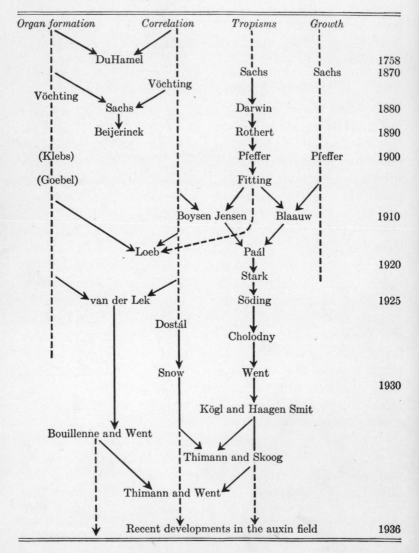

phenomenon, and Blaauw that they were a growth phenomenon. The vertical line beginning with Paál is intended to be symmetrically placed between the three lines of correlation, tropisms, and growth. It goes without saying that such a chart is to a considerable extent arbitrary in its selection, and large numbers of valuable studies are of necessity omitted for one reason or another. An important point brought out by the chart is the true internationalism of these researches, the 27 investigators listed belonging to 10 nationalities.

E. Other Hormones in Higher Plants

The first investigator actually to work with hormones and active extracts in plants was Fitting (1909, 1910). He also was the first to introduce the word hormone into plant physiology, considering hormones merely as stimulative substances, without stressing the importance of their transport. He was able to show that the swelling of the ovary, and other phenomena of post-floration in tropical orchids, are due to an active substance which could be extracted from the pollinia.

As mentioned above, Laibach was able to identify this substance (with a high degree of probability) with auxin. An effect of perhaps similar nature has been shown by Swingle (1928) to be exerted in the development of the date fruit by the embryo ("meta-xenia"). Evidence for other types of hormones was obtained by Haberlandt and his pupils in a series of investigations, principally on cell division. Their fundamental experiment was the demonstration (Haberlandt, 1913) that in small pieces of the parenchymatous tissue of the potato tuber, cell division only occurs in the presence of a fragment of a vein containing phloem tissue. This influence was also shown to be exerted on the parenchyma if the phloem was separated from it by a thin film of agar. In addition Haberlandt was able to show that cell division is promoted by the presence of crushed cells (1914).

In experiments with leaves of succulents and kohl-rabi, Haberlandt (1914, 1921) and Lamprecht (1918) also showed that cell divisions could be induced by spreading upon the cut surface some of the crushed tissue of other leaves. Haberlandt concluded (1913) that cell division was determined by two substances, one coming from the wound ("wound-hormone"), and the other from the phloem tissue ("lepto-hormone"). The latter was assumed to be present to a lesser extent in some other tissues. Subsequent investigators have tried to extract these hormones and to identify them with known substances (Reiche, 1924; Wehnelt, 1927). Their methods of testing were not specific enough to allow the drawing of any definite conclusions, but Jost (1935a) has confirmed and extended some of their results (cf. XIII A), and Umrath and Soltys (1936) have made a partial purification (see below).

Further, Bonner (1936), using Wehnelt's test not as a measure of cell division but simply of growth, has demonstrated that tissue extracts contain a growth-promoting factor not identical with auxin. By the addition of alcohol extracts of tissues to a culture medium he has obtained growth of undifferentiated parenchyma cells in vitro, which closely approached true plant tissue cultures.

The experiments of Jacques Loeb (1917–1924) on correlations in Bryophyllum occupy a very isolated place in the literature. He studied regeneration, bud growth, and geotropic behavior in isolated leaves and stems. At first his explanations were based upon Sachs' ideas, as for instance: "There must, therefore, be associated with the material which causes geotropic bending also something which favors the growth of roots, and this may be one of the hypothetical substances of Sachs" (1917a, p. 118). Subsequently he transferred the emphasis to more general factors of nutrition, controlled by simple mass action, as for instance: "These facts show that the regeneration of an isolated leaf of Bryophyllum is determined by the mass of material available or formed in the leaf during the experiment" (1923,

p. 852).   The same views were developed with respect to geotropism and bud inhibition.   The greater part of his results fit in very well with our present knowledge of the rôle of auxins and can be explained on that basis.   The somewhat similar experiments of Appleman (1918) on the development of shoots in pieces of potato tubers led him to postulate both growth-promoting substances, present in the tuber, and growth-inhibiting substances formed in the growing buds.

Another interesting case of correlation by the transmission of a substance was discovered by Ricca (1916).   He found that the well-known transmission of excitation in the sensitive plant, *Mimosa*, takes place in the vessels by means of a substance, secreted into them upon stimulation and carried principally with the transpiration stream. Snow (1924, 1925) afterwards found that there are three types of stimulus involved, only one of which is due to a diffusible substance.   Fitting (1930) investigated the action of pure substances of biological interest in stimulating *Mimosa* and found a number of compounds, especially α-amino-acids and anthraquinone derivatives, to be active.   Their action, however, is not identical with that of the *Mimosa* leaf extract.   The active substance in the leaf extract itself was shown to be heat-stable by Umrath (1927) and attempts to purify it have been made by Fitting (1936a) and by Soltys and Umrath (1936).   The latter workers have succeeded in obtaining a highly purified extract, from the properties of which they conclude that the active substance must be an oxy-acid with a molecular weight of about 500. They have also partly purified a similar oxy-acid active on the leaves of certain sensitive *Papilionaceae* (Umrath and Soltys, 1936), and this, it appears, may be identical with the substance active in the Wehnelt test.

Although their hormonal nature in the strict sense is questionable, mention must be made here of those substances causing the onset of protoplasmic streaming in *Vallisneria* leaf cells.   In the first place Fitting has shown

that, just as is the case with auxins, a number of different
substances can bring about the effect (Fitting, 1927, 1929,
1932, 1933, 1936b). In the second place, as with the activity
of auxins on *Avena*, some of them are active in extremely
high dilution, and the activity of different substances varies
widely.   Thus, N-methyl-l-histidine stimulates streaming
at 1 part in 10^9, or about 10^{-8} mol.; aspartic acid, asparagine,
histidine, and some other amino-acids are active down to
10^{-7} mol.; alanine, serine, and phenyl-alanine down to
10^{-6} mol., while glycine, proline, and glutamine have very low
activity.   Some, *e.g.* tryptophane, are completely inactive.
A number of non-nitrogenous acids, including galacturonic
acid, are active down to 10^{-3} to 10^{-5} mol.   In the amino-
acids activity decreases with increasing distance between
the carboxyl and amino-groups.   Neither peptides nor
amines have much activity, so that, presumably, amino-
groups only confer activity if they are accompanied by
an acid radical.

Small changes in the molecule greatly affect the activity;
thus, N-methyl-l-histidine is five times as active as l-histidine
itself. These differences may, of course, be caused by different rates of penetration into the cells, and not by true
differences in "sensitivity" of the protoplasm for these
compounds, as is probably the case for the different activity
of auxins (see VIII *G*).

CHAPTER III

THE TECHNIQUE OF AUXIN DETERMINATIONS

Practically all of the facts known about plant hormones and most of the theoretical conclusions are based upon the *Avena* test, which in itself again is based upon growth in length of the *Avena* coleoptile. It will be well, therefore, to begin by considering this object.

A. MORPHOLOGY OF THE AVENA SEEDLING

Upon germination of the seed the primary root begins to grow out and is followed, within one day, by two lateral roots. Meanwhile the shoot also starts to elongate. It consists of the growing point, a very short stem with two partially developed leaves, and a surrounding sheath, the coleoptile (see Figure 4). Between the coleoptilar node and the insertion of the scutellum there develops an internode, generally called the "mesocotyl" or in older literature "hypocotyl," whose length is dependent upon the treatment of the seedling.

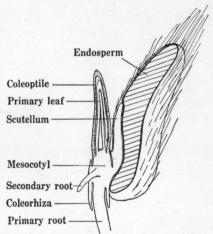

FIG. 4. Longitudinal section through *Avena* seedling after 30 hours' germination, at the beginning of the period of rapid elongation.

If the coleoptile be considered as one cotyledon and the scutellum as the other, then this internode is truly the mesocotyl (= between cotyledons). If, on the other hand, the coleoptile be considered as the first true leaf, then this mesocotyl is simply the first internode (or epicotyl) (see

21

Avery, 1930, and Boyd and Avery, 1936). Since the term mesocotyl has been generally adopted in physiological literature, we shall retain its use.

The growth of the coleoptile, which is a hollow cylinder with a solid conical top, takes place almost entirely in the

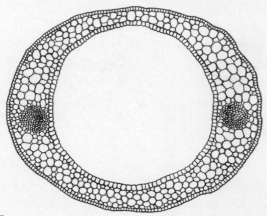

FIG. 5. Cross section through *Avena* coleoptile at 5 mm. distance from the tip. The dorsal side faces the seed.

longitudinal dimension. In its early growth, up to a length of 1 cm., cell divisions of the parenchyma accompany the elongation (Avery and Burkholder, 1936). The epidermal cells, however, cease dividing at a very early stage and grow only by extension. From a length of 1 cm. up to its final length (5–7 cm.), cell divisions are practically absent (see also Tetley and Priestley, 1927) and growth is entirely by cell elongation. On this account the coleoptile is a particularly suitable object for studies of growth uncomplicated by cell division, and whatever conclusions are drawn from it apply only to cell elongation.

In transverse section, the coleoptile is elliptical, with the short axis in the plane of symmetry of the seedling. Two small vascular bundles run up on either side (see Figure 5). The cells at the tip of the coleoptile are morphologically distinguishable from the others by the fact that they do not elongate and are almost isodiametric (see Figure 6). The epidermal cells of the extreme tip stain somewhat more

heavily than the rest and are presumably richer in protoplasm. The region of isodiametric cells is limited to the
uppermost 0.5 mm. of
the length of the cole-
optile (du Buy and
Nuernbergk, 1932).
The growth of the
primary leaf closely
follows that of the
coleoptile, so that un-
der normal conditions
the coleoptile is almost
completely filled. At a
length of 50–60 mm.
the coleoptile is broken
through, near the tip,
by this leaf, which
then starts to grow
very rapidly (see Fig-
ure 27). At this time
the growth of the cole-
optile ceases. The
whole period of growth
lasts about 100 hours

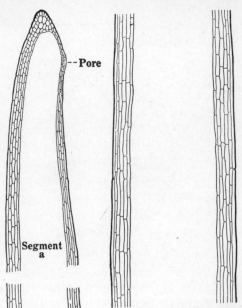

FIG. 6. Longitudinal section through mature
Avena coleoptile. Left, tip; right, middle zone,
which has greatly elongated. (From Avery
and Burkholder, *Bull. Torrey Bot. Club 63:*
1–15, 1936.)

at 25° C, and the maximum growth rate, which is reached at
an age of 70 hours, is approximately 1 mm. per hour (Figure 27). This mode of growth, beginning slowly, rising to a
maximum and then decreasing again to zero, has been called,
following Sachs, the "grand period." Coleoptiles 25–35 mm.
in length, which are growing at the maximum rate, are
generally used for experimental purposes.

During the growth of the coleoptile from about 20 mm.
on, the uppermost 2 mm. scarcely elongate at all. The
zone of maximum growth is first located near the base and
migrates upwards so as to remain about 10 mm. below the
tip. At about 40 mm. length, the growth of the most basal
zones ceases altogether (see V A).

B. Evolution of the Avena Test Method

By placing the cut tip asymmetrically on the stump, Paál (1919) showed that the growth of the lower zones is accelerated by a diffusible substance coming from the tip. His experiments were carried out with seedlings of *Coix*, and were afterwards confirmed on *Avena* by Nielsen (1924). This conclusion was confirmed by the careful measurements of growth made by Söding (1923, 1925). He compared first the growth of the stump, after decapitation, with the growth of the corresponding portion of the intact coleoptile. In the first 5 hours the growth was only about 40 per cent of that of the intact control. If, however, the tip were replaced, the growth of the stump was accelerated to 60–70 per cent of that of the intact control, thus proving that the decrease in growth after decapitation was not primarily due to any effect of the wound, such as the "wound substances" of Stark (1921). On the other hand the accelerating effect of the tip must be due to its secretion of growth-promoting substances. Söding states: "Since these substances certainly also influence growth in the intact plant, I propose to call them growth hormones." Cholodny (1924) carried out a similar experiment on *Mais* coleoptiles, in which the growth of coleoptile stumps on which the tips had been replaced was, in 3–4 hours, 144 per cent of that of the untreated stumps.

When the growth measurements were continued beyond the first 5 hours, however, a new phenomenon appeared. In a representative experiment Söding obtained the following average growths in mm. (Table II).

TABLE II

	FIRST 5 HOURS		NEXT 13 HOURS	
	Total growth	Mean/hr.	Total growth	Mean/hr.
Decapitated	0.66	0.13	2.76	0.21
Decapitated, tip replaced	1.23	0.25	1.78	0.14
Intact	1.61	0.32	3.52	0.27

It will be seen that after the first 5-hour period the growth rate of the decapitated plants has increased again. If now the uppermost zone of these plants was cut off and placed upon freshly decapitated stumps, the growth of such stumps was accelerated, just as by tips. Other cylindrical zones of the coleoptile, similarly placed upon freshly decapitated stumps, had no such effect. Thus the uppermost zone of plants which have been decapitated for some time behaves like a tip in that from it diffuses a substance which accelerates the growth of the stump. This is the "regeneration of the physiological tip," and, as we shall see later, it explains the earlier observation of Rothert (1894) that tropistic sensitivity returns some hours after decapitation.

The regeneration was studied in greater detail by Dolk (1926), from whose paper the curve of Figure 7 is taken. It

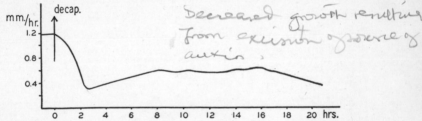

Decreased growth resulting from excision of source of auxin.

FIG. 7. Growth rate of *Avena* coleoptiles after decapitation. Ordinate, mm. elongation per hour; abscissa, time from decapitation in hours. (From Dolk, *Proc. Kon. Akad. Wetensch.*, Amsterdam, *29:* 1113–1117, 1926.)

will be seen that immediately after decapitation the growth rate begins to fall, but after 2½ hours (at 21° C) a sudden break in the curve occurs and the growth rate rises to about 50 per cent of that of the intact plant. This sudden rise can be completely eliminated by a second decapitation 2 hours later, in which the uppermost 1 mm. of the stump is removed (Dolk, 1930). This proves that the rise is really due to regeneration of the production of growth hormone in the uppermost zone of the stump. It may be pointed out that this regeneration is not accompanied by any morphological change in the uppermost cells of the stump (Tetley and Priestley, 1927; Perry, 1932).

The above experiments provided evidence for the existence of the growth hormone in the coleoptile, and experiments of Beyer (1925) gave similar evidence in the case of *Helianthus* hypocotyls. Attempts were therefore made to prove the existence of this substance directly by extraction. Stark (1921) crushed up coleoptiles, mixed the extract with warm 5 per cent agar, and when the mixture had solidified, he divided it into small blocks and placed them one-sidedly upon the cut surface of decapitated coleoptiles. The decapitation was done by removing the tip without cutting it completely through, so that the primary leaf remained intact and could be used as a support for one side of the agar block. However, in all his experiments, embracing several hundred plants, only *positive* curvatures were obtained, that is, curvatures towards the applied block of agar. Extracts of stems or hypocotyls were similarly inactive. Hence no growth-promoting substance was extracted in this way; the explanation for the positive curvatures will be given later (III *C* 6). An important technical improvement was then introduced by Stark and Drechsel (1922), who pulled the primary leaf loose, breaking it at the base so that it did not grow further, and thus did not lift off the agar block. The differential growth rate of the leaf and coleoptile is caused by the decapitation, which only reduces the growth rate of the coleoptile itself.

Nielsen (1924) and Seubert (1925) modified the experiment of Stark by crushing only the extreme tips of the coleoptiles, but, except for one experiment by Seubert, failed to obtain any growth-promoting extract. Seubert, however, was able to obtain growth promotion—that is, negative curvature—with agar blocks containing diastase, pepsin, malt extract, or saliva, and, in one experiment only, with concentrated press juice from coleoptiles.

Starting from the facts that the growth hormone is able to diffuse through gelatin, and that only the tip actually produces it, Went (1926) [1] showed that the substance could

---

[1] See footnote to page 5.

be "trapped" in the gelatin. He cut off a number of tips of coleoptiles, placed them for some time on gelatin, removed them, and placed the gelatin one-sidedly on the cut surface of freshly decapitated coleoptiles. For the preparation of the test coleoptiles he used essentially Stark's technique. However, as measure of the growth-promoting activity, he used, not the percentage of plants which curved, but the actual degree of curvature. The reason for this is that in any group of plants one or two will fail to curve due to experimental faults, and these should not be included in the mean. The percentage of plants which curve thus measures the efficiency of the technique rather than the growth-promoting activity. With this method he was able to show, amongst other things, that heating the gelatin for a short time at 90° C did not inactivate the substance, which cannot therefore be an enzyme. These fundamental experiments provided final proof of the material nature and stability of the growth-promoting substance of the coleoptile, and laid the foundation for further work. In a more detailed publication (Went, 1928), the *Avena* test method for determination of the growth hormone was worked out quantitatively. Since this method has been so extensively used as the basis of all phytohormone work it will be well to treat it here in detail.

C. THE AVENA METHOD IN ITS PRESENT FORM

1. *Dark Room and Equipment*

Although it is not strictly necessary to maintain darkness and constant conditions for carrying out qualitative work with *Avena* curvature, nevertheless for quantitative study the conditions outlined below must be strictly adhered to. Söding (1935) has used the *Avena* test in diffuse daylight with uncontrolled temperature, but under these conditions the sensitivity of the plants is very much less, and there is no strict proportionality between concentration of the active substances and curvature produced (see van Overbeek, 1933, 1936a).

For quantitative work, the temperature should be maintained constant: probably 25° C. has been the most used, but a somewhat lower temperature is more nearly optimal. The actual growth rate of the coleoptile, however, has its optimum close to 30° (Silberschmidt, 1928). Most of the data which we shall quote refer to 25° C.

The maintenance of constant relative humidity is of great importance for a number of reasons: if the humidity is too high (above 90 per cent), guttation, i.e. exudation of water from the cut surface of decapitated coleoptiles, frequently occurs; this wets the whole cut surface, and may either wash off the agar block or may spread the substance which diffuses out of the block on to all sides of the plant. If, on the other hand, the humidity is too low, the agar dries out, which frequently leads to a failure of contact between block and cut surface.

It is, of course, possible to maintain a suitable humidity in small chambers, inside a dark room, by merely lining them with wet filter paper. This is not, however, convenient for work on any considerable scale. Suitable thermostats and humidifiers have been described by Nuernbergk (1932). With the recent advances in the field of air-conditioning a completely air-conditioned room is easily obtainable and is very suitable for hormone work.

The effects of temperature, humidity, and some other factors have been worked out for a number of varieties of *Avena sativa*, as well as for some other plants, by Silberschmidt (1928).

The *Avena* coleoptiles are exceedingly sensitive to light of the shorter wave-lengths (< 550 mμ). This, if it falls on the plant from one side, causes phototropic bending, while, if symmetrically distributed, it causes a decrease of sensitivity to the applied auxin. Hence all manipulations must be carried out in orange or red light. Corning light filters 243 or 348, or Schott's O.G. 2, are very suitable to cut out the phototropically active wave-lengths from incandescent lamps. If no phototropic experiments have to be carried out in the dark room it is advisable to have the walls painted in a light shade.

C. 2. *Preparation of Test Plants*

Since most of the experiments in this field have been carried out with the genetically pure line of oats known as Victory oats (Segrehafer or Siegeshafer) it is advisable that further work be continued with the same strain.[1] Other lines have been used by various workers, perhaps the most notable being Gul Naesgaard in Denmark.

The standard procedure for the preparation of the plants is as follows: The seeds are freed from their husks (glumes) and soaked in water for 2–3 hours. After this period they are laid out, groove downward, on wet filter paper in Petri dishes in the dark room. They are allowed to germinate in this way for about 30 hours, during which period it is advisable to expose them to some red light, to suppress subsequent mesocotyl growth (Lange, 1927; du Buy and Nuernbergk, 1929). Origi-nally the seeds were planted in a mixture of sand and leaf mould, but more re-cently, for the sake of uni-formity and convenient handling, planting in water has been substituted. If the seeds are to be planted in such soil or in washed saw-dust, however, they should be inserted at an angle of about 45° with the vertical,

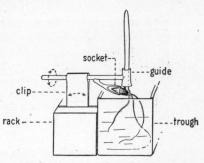

FIG. 8. *Avena* seedling growing in glass holder with roots in water con-tained in the zinc trough. The adjust-ments available are indicated by arrows.

in order that the shoot may emerge straight. The sand or soil should be so wet that further watering is not necessary, as this will displace the seeds. If, on the other hand, it is too wet the sensitivity of the plants is reduced (Boysen Jensen, 1935). The depth of planting is also important and the shoot should be about 8 mm. below the surface; if too shallow the seeds will be pushed out by the developing roots.

For water culture convenient glass holders were devised by Went (1928) and a modification of his design is now in almost universal use (see Figure 8). The holders are coated thinly with paraffin, which prevents water from creeping into the guide and makes the fitting of the seeds into the

[1] Obtainable from Sveriges Utsädesförening, Svalöf, Sweden.

sockets somewhat easier. They are fixed in rows of 12 by means of brass clips which fit into grooves in a wooden rack; the clips are free to move, stiffly, in a vertical plane, while the holders can be rotated and thus any adjustment of the growing plant is possible.

The germinated seeds are inserted into the sockets in such a way that the shoot comes under the center of the guide, and the roots point downwards. The whole rack, with its 12 seeds, is then placed with the roots at the surface of water contained in a zinc trough. The most usual dimensions are: rack 25 × 25 × 200 mm., trough 35 × 35 × 200 mm. About 48 hours after planting, the coleoptiles are 20–30 mm. long and ready for use. They are selected for straightness and uniformity, and

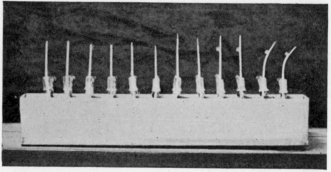

FIG. 9. Row of 12 *Avena* seedlings as Figure 8. Left to right: 2 intact, 2 decapitated, 2 decapitated for the second time (primary leaf protruding), 2 from which primary leaf has been pulled loose, 2 with applied agar block, 2 showing curvature.

since the holders are removable, rows of 12 good plants are assembled. It is advisable to bring all shoots into the strictly vertical position some 2 hours before use (see Figure 9).

In the preparation of the test plants the first operation is to cut off the extreme tip with a razor (B, Figure 10). In the subsequent period a large amount of the growth hormone present in the stump is being used for its residual growth, and the test plants become more and more sensitive to any hormone which is applied (van der Weij, 1931). After 3 hours the topmost 4 mm. of the stump is cut off (C–E, Figure 10). This can be done by making an incision

on one side of the coleoptile without cutting the primary
leaf; the top of the coleoptile is then bent so that it breaks
at the incision and the topmost part is pulled off. Special
decapitation scissors (Figures 11, 12) which cut the coleoptile on two sides without touching the leaf are very convenient for this, because with the closed scissors the cut-off

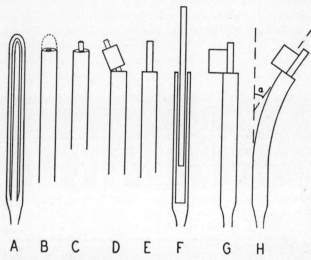

A   B   C   D   E   F   G   H

Fig. 10. Diagrammatic summary of procedure in the *Avena* test, showing the
stages photographed in Figure 9.

portion can be removed in the same movement. The primary leaf, which now protrudes for 5 mm. or more, is then
pulled gently so that it breaks at the base and is partially
drawn out (F, Figure 10); this can be conveniently done
with cork-tipped forceps (Figure 11). If the cut surface is
very wet it should be dried with filter paper. The small
block of agar to be tested is then placed on one side of the
cut surface, resting against the leaf, so that it is held in
place by capillarity. The period elapsing between the
second decapitation and the application of the block does
not usually exceed 20 minutes.

To record the curvatures a piece of bromide paper is
placed behind the plants; they are then illuminated from

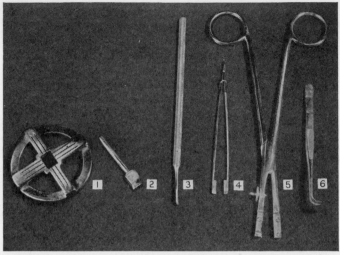

FIG. 11. Convenient tools for the *Avena* test. 1, frame for dividing agar rectangles into 12 equal blocks with safety razor blade; 2, stamp for cutting the rectangles 8 x 11 mm. from agar disc or sheet 1–2 mm. thick; 3, spatula for application of agar block; 4, corktipped forceps for pulling primary leaf loose; 5, decapitation scissors (see Figure 12); 6, forceps for planting in glass holders.

one side. The curvatures are measured on the resulting shadowgraph (see Figure 22) by means of a celluloid protractor with rotating arm (Figure 13). The angle measured is that between the tangent to the extreme curved tip and the straight base.

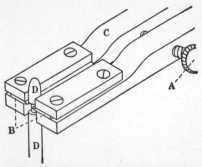

FIG. 12. Cutting end of decapitation scissors. A, adjusting screw to regulate opening between knives; B, strips of safety razor protruding 4 mm. beyond brass holders C; D, plant being decapitated.

Söding (1934) has described a method depending on the same principle, but measuring the curvature on the plant itself by placing it over the protractor.

Purdy (1921) has developed a method, which has been adopted by Boysen Jensen and by Nielsen, of measuring the increased growth on the side to which the agar block has been applied.   Instead of measuring the angle (which is directly proportional to the difference in growth), the radius of curvature, r, thickness of the

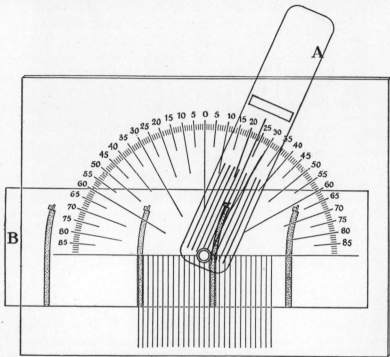

Fig. 13. Measurement of *Avena* curvatures. The vertical lines on the base of the transparent celluloid protractor are brought parallel to the uncurved base of the plant on photograph, B, while the lines on the moving arm, A, are brought parallel to the extreme curved tip. The angle (23½°) is read directly. (From Went, *Rec. trav. bot. néerl. 25:* 1–116, 1928.)

plant, t, and length of the curved zone, l, are measured (see Figure 14). Then the difference, d, between the growth on the two sides is expressed by $d = \dfrac{tl}{r}$. Assuming a thickness of 1.5 mm., a d-value of 0.1 mm. corresponds to 4° curvature, 0.5 mm. to 19°, and 1.0 mm. to 38.5°. This procedure involves the making of three measurements, of which, however, t is taken as constant. Satisfactory measurement of the other two, r and l, depends upon the assumption that the curved zone is a circular arc. It is, however, apparent from Dolk's (1930) measurements of plants curved under the influence of auxin that this is far from being the case, and that the radius of curvature decreases smoothly from the straight base to a region of maximum curvature some way below the tip (*cf.* X *H*). The values adopted for *r* and *l* are therefore of necessity arbitrary.

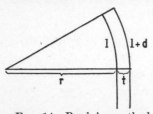

FIG. 14. Purdy's method of measuring the difference in growth between the two sides of a curved coleoptile. Explanation in text. (From Purdy, *Kgl. Danske Videnskab. Selskab., Biol. Medd. 3:* 3–29, 1921.)

If the test is carried out as above, the optimum time for photographing is about 90 minutes after application of the agar block (*cf.* Figure 20); after this time the curvature is no longer proportional to the concentration of hormone in the agar, because the curvatures produced by low concentrations decrease or remain stationary, while larger ones continue to increase.

C. 3. *Preparation of the Agar*

A good quality of agar is well washed and made up to a 3 per cent gel. To prepare the blocks containing auxin for the test, the agar may be either first cut into sheets and these soaked in the test solution or it may be melted and mixed with an equal volume of the test solution. The preparation of agar sheets of uniform thickness for the former method requires some precautions. The most satisfactory procedure is to cut a block of agar about 40 × 20 × 20 mm. and to surround this on 3 of its long sides with paraffin (see Figure 15). The agar is then cut in a microtome using a safety razor blade, and the resulting book of sheets (1 or 1.5 mm. thick) preserved in 60 per cent alcohol. Before use, these must be washed free of alcohol (1 hour). They are then cut into rectangles, with a special cutter, and these are placed in the test solution for at least 1 hour; sufficient solution must be present to ensure that the concentration is not changed appreciably by addition of the agar. For the second method, usually ½ cc. of the melted agar is mixed with ½ cc. of the test solution, and ½ cc. of the resulting mixture quickly poured into a shallow circular mould with removable base whose dimensions, 10.3 mm. radius × 1.5 mm. deep, are such that it is

exactly filled by ½ cc. After cooling, the resulting disk of agar is
cut into rectangles with the same cutter as above. With either method
the rectangles are finally divided into 12 equal blocks by means of
other special cutters (see Figure 11).

The sizes of blocks adopted vary in different laboratories
between 2 and 10 cmm. To avoid too much volume change
by drying out, etc., it is advisable to use blocks of volume
not less than 4 cmm., the volume changes being propor-
tionately less the larger the block. It has been shown
(Thimann and Bonner, 1932) that the curvature is primarily proportional to the
concentration of auxin in the
block and that the rate at
which the auxin enters the
plant is proportional to its
concentration in the block at
any moment; since part of
the auxin passes out of the
block during the test, the
change of concentration in
the block so caused is small

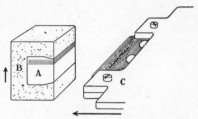

Fig. 15. Method of cutting thin
sheets of agar of uniform thickness. The
agar, A, is embedded on 3 sides in paraffin, B, and sliced on a microtome with a
safety razor blade. (From Went, 1928.)

if the blocks are large. Thimann and Bonner (1932) have
measured the amount of auxin which passes into the plant
during 110 minutes' contact, and from the data have calculated the curvatures which would be produced by different
sizes of blocks containing the same auxin concentration (see
Table III). The calculations were found to agree closely
with the curvatures observed.

The discrepancy between Went's conclusion (1927), that
with 0.9 cmm. blocks the curvatures are proportional to the
absolute *amount* of auxin in the blocks, and the conclusions
of van der Weij (1931) and Thimann and Bonner (1932)
that the curvatures are proportional to the auxin *concentration* in the block, is directly explained by Table III. In
Went's experiments 86 per cent of the auxin from the block
entered the plant; with larger blocks only 15–30 per cent
will pass into the plant.

TABLE III

VOL. OF BLOCK, MM.[3]	CURVATURE AS PER CENT OF CURVATURE WITH LARGEST BLOCK	PER CENT OF THE AUXIN APPLIED WHICH ENTERS THE PLANT
10.7	100	15.0
5.35	91.5	27.9
2.68	79.0	46.7
1.34	59.8	72.9
1.07	53.9	80.5
0.89	47.9	85.9

C. 4. Technical Modifications

A number of modifications of this technique have been used at various times and for different purposes. Only a few will be mentioned. The original method was to decapitate only once, at 5 mm. from the tip, and apply the agar blocks after waiting 40 minutes. The sensitivity of such plants is lower by 2 to 3 times than that of plants treated as above. Heyn (1935) recommends 3 decapitations, spaced 2 hours apart, the total length removed being still about 5 mm. The sensitivity of such plants is slightly increased. Van der Weij (1931) was the first to prove that increasing the time between first decapitation and putting on of the agar blocks increased the sensitivity of test plants. Subsequently this was also found by Brecht (1936) and in our own experiments $(u$ [1]$)$. Skoog (1937) has introduced the use of de-seeded plants, at about 30–36 hours after planting. The plants, no longer held in place by the socket, are held in the guides by wrapping cotton around the young coleoptiles (see Figure 16). The curvatures produced in such plants continue to increase for at least 6 hours without the regression due to regeneration, and this method is therefore able to detect much smaller amounts of growth hormone. The sensitivity of this method appears to be about the same as that of Söding's *Cephalaria* test method (see below).

Laibach and Kornmann (1933, 1933a) have applied auxin in agar blocks to the outside of intact *Avena* coleoptiles and

[1] The symbol u, which will be used throughout the text, refers to unpublished experiments.

found that curvature is produced. Apparently higher concentrations are needed than in the normal *Avena* test but the experiment provides an interesting demonstration that auxin may enter through the epidermis. The same fact has been utilized in a still further modification (Laibach, 1933*a*, 1935; Brecht, 1936) in which auxin is dissolved in

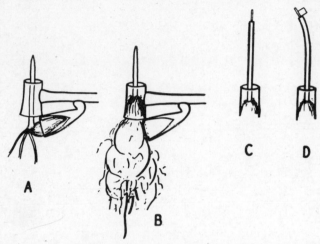

FIG. 16. De-seeding of *Avena*. A, normal seedling in glass holder; B, same with seed removed and coleoptile held in guide with cotton wool; C, decapitation; D, curvature. (From Skoog, *J. gen. Physiol. 20*: 311–334, 1937.)

lanoline (Laibach's method), and this paste applied externally to intact or decapitated coleoptiles.

If about 4 mg. of such paste be smeared over a length of 1 cm. of one side of the coleoptile, a curvature results which increases up to 24 hours, and is within limits proportional to the concentration of active substance in the paste. However, the lowest concentration which produces curvature appears to be about 10 times that which produces the same curvature when agar is used (see also Jost and Reiss, 1936). The method might be useful for the standardization of such pastes, but unfortunately it is highly non-specific, because acetic acid and other acids incorporated in the paste also give rise to curvatures. In the application of lanoline-auxin-paste to plants in general great care should be taken to control the results with plain pastes, because Schilling (1915) has shown that treatment of twigs or leaves with vaseline, paraffin, cocoa-butter, etc., gives rise to various kinds of outgrowths, and even root formation may be induced in this way.

Söding (1936) has found that seedlings of *Cephalaria* are very sensitive to low concentrations of auxin. His tests are carried out in diffuse light. If the concentration of hormone is very low, the *Cephalaria* test will show good curvatures where the (daylight) *Avena* test shows none.

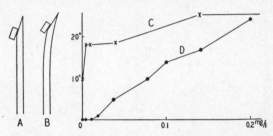

Fig. 17. *Cephalaria* test of Söding. A, decapitated hypocotyls with agar block applied; B, after 5 hours; curve C, relation between concentration of indole-acetic acid in mg. per liter and curvature of *Cephalaria;* curve D, the same for *Avena.* (From Söding, *Jahrb. wiss. Bot. 82:* 534–554, 1936.)

The seedlings are decapitated, the stem being cut through very obliquely, and the block of agar is placed upon the lower half of the cut surface (see Figure 17). The curvature is measured after 5 hours. As may be seen, the sensitivity at low concentrations is much higher than with *Avena* but the maximum curvature obtainable is about the same.

C. 5. *Evaluation of Results*

The *Avena* coleoptiles, prepared in the way described, are of great physiological uniformity, as is shown by plotting the variability of the curvatures given by a large number of identically treated plants. Most of the experimental faults will tend to reduce rather than increase the curvature so that in a faulty test the variability curve will be skew towards the lower values (see Figure 18). If, in a test of 12 or more plants giving a fairly symmetrical distribution, one or two values fall far off the distribution curve, they are generally neglected. If the values are too scattered, the experiment should be repeated with more uniform plants. As a rule, the mean of 12 good plants is taken.

As measure of the variation among the test plants the standard deviation of the mean [1] is best used, and this

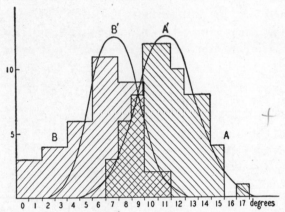

Fig. 18. Distribution of individual curvatures in the *Avena* test. Abscissa, curvature groups; ordinate, number of plants in each group. Diagram A, perfect test, agreeing with the variability curve A'; diagram B, imperfect test, skew with relation to ideal variability curve B'. (After Went, 1928.)

obviates the necessity of detailing the individual curvatures.

The possible causes for this variation between individual plants are many. Variations in thickness play no part (Went, 1928). Differences in actual age of the plants are of course excluded because all have been planted at the same time. Variations in the length of the cut tip do occur, but are of minor importance if they do not exceed a few millimeters. The following table shows the relative auxin curvatures of plants from which different lengths of tip have been cut off (Table IV).

---

[1] Standard deviation of the mean = $\sqrt{\dfrac{\Sigma \triangle^2}{n(n-1)}}$, where $\triangle$ is the difference between the individual observation and the mean, $\Sigma \triangle^2$ the sum of the squares of these, and n is the number of observations.

TABLE IV

Length of tip cut off, mm.	2	4	6	10	14
Curvature after 100 min., deg.	10.1	10.0	8.3	5.3	5.1

The age and length of the plant at the time of its use are of great importance in determining the resulting curvature. As a matter of convenience plants shorter than 15 mm. cannot easily be used, although their sensitivity is high. Between 15 and 30 mm. above the guides of the holders, there is little variation in sensitivity. In older plants, however, the sensitivity falls off rapidly, due to the so-called "aging" studied by du Buy (1933; see V A).

In testing impure preparations, it is an advantage of the *Avena* test that it is very little affected by the presence of salts, sugars, amino-acids, etc., all of which are substances ordinarily influencing growth. This is because, through the rapid transport of auxin from the cut surface to the reacting zones, a rigid selection occurs. Thus $M/1000$ $CuSO_4$ in the agar, a concentration which is ordinarily highly toxic to plants, has no effect on the curvature. Ni and Mn salts in the same concentration are equally without effect, although all these metals reduce or inhibit the auxin curvatures of *immersed* plant parts such as pea stems (*u; cf.* also IX B).

The effect of pH depends upon whether the auxin solution is buffered or not. Nielsen (1930) found that between 2.4 and 9.6 the pH of the agar mixture (unbuffered) does not affect the curvature. Dolk and Thimann (1932), however, showed that auxin solutions buffered at pH 7 give much smaller curvatures than at pH 5 (*cf.* VIII F). Kögl and Haagen Smit (1931) also advise the acidification of solutions before testing, but Jost and Reiss (1936) found no change in activity on adding varying amounts of acetic acid to pure auxin solutions, doubtless because these are not buffered.

If the tests are properly carried out, the curvatures obtained will be linearly proportional to the concentration of the active substance, within well-defined limits (see

Figure 19). Below the upper limit, whose position differs for different active substances, the activity of a substance can therefore be quantitatively expressed. The amount of a substance necessary to produce a given curvature under standard conditions is taken as a unit.

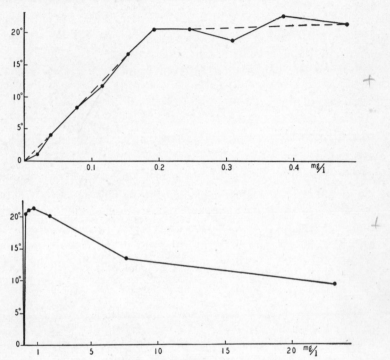

FIG. 19. Relation between auxin concentration (in mg. indole-3-acetic acid per liter) and curvature. Two decapitations 3 hours apart, agar blocks 10 mm³, 24° C., 85% relative humidity. The scale of the abscissae of the upper curve is 50 times that of the lower. Each point the mean of 30–50 plants.

The "*Avena*-Einheit" (AE) of Kögl and Haagen Smit (1931) is that amount of substance which when applied in a 2 cmm. block of agar causes 10° curvature. The "plant unit" (p.u.) of Dolk and Thimann (1932) is that amount of substance which when applied in a 10 cmm. block causes 1° curvature. These workers also define as "1 unit per cc." that concentration of solution which when mixed with an equal volume of 3 per cent agar and made into 10 cmm. blocks gives 1° curvature. Under the conditions then used (40–60 minutes between decapitation and application of block) 1 AE = 2.5 p.u. However, under the conditions described in section C 2 (3 hours between decapitation and application) 1 AE = about 1.5 p.u. The Wuchsstoff-Einheit (WAE) of Boysen Jensen (1933a) is defined as that amount of substance which, when dissolved in 50 cc. of water and mixed with an equal volume of 3 per cent agar, gives a d-value of 1 mm.

Now that it has been shown that one of the auxins is indole-3-acetic acid, which is readily available in pure form, the importance of such units has largely disappeared, and all activities may be expressed in comparison with the effect of indole-acetic acid. However, for the better understanding of data given in the literature, the following comparisons are tabulated (Table V). It should be noted that, weight for weight, auxin a is about twice as active as indole-3-acetic acid, or mol for mol about 3.75 times as active (Kögl, Haagen Smit, and Erxleben, 1934).

C. 6. *Positive Curvatures*

The curvature produced by auxin is a negative curvature, *i.e.* away from the side with the agar block, the active substance having caused an increase of growth on the side to which it is applied. Stark (1921) and Nielsen (1924) never obtained such negative curvatures by the application of blocks containing plant extracts. Seubert (1925) found also that the majority of substances dissolved in agar caused positive curvatures. This was considered as evidence of the existence of growth-retarding substances which were identified by Stark with wound-substances. Seubert even found that the same substance appears to be stimulating or inhibiting according to its concentration; thus, high concentrations of saliva or malt extract caused negative, low concentrations positive curvatures.

The absence of growth-promoting activity in plant extracts has been explained by Thimann (1934); it is due to the destruction of the auxin by enzymes set free on crushing the material. The production of positive curvatures, however, is something other than the mere absence of negative curvatures, and its mechanism has been elucidated by

TABLE V

Workers	Block Size	Weight Needed to Give 10° Curvature in mg.	Amount Entering Plant		Unit as Proposed (Defined in Text)	Weight of Unit in mg.
			In Per Cent of Amount in Block	In mg.		
Kögl and Haagen Smit (1931)	2 cmm.	$4\text{--}10 \times 10^{-8}$	58	$2.4\text{--}6 \times 10^{-8}$	AE	$4\text{--}10 \times 10^{-8}$
Dolk and Thimann (1932)	10.7 cmm.	$16\text{--}33 \times 10^{-8}$	15	$2.4\text{--}5 \times 10^{-8}$	p.u.	$1.6\text{--}3.3 \times 10^{-8}$
					unit/cc.	$320\text{--}660 \times 10^{-8}$
Boysen Jensen (1933)	3 cmm.	$ca\ 5 \times 10^{-8}$	43	$ca\ 2.1 \times 10^{-8}$	WAE	0.0052
Juel (1936)	4 cmm.		35	$ca\ 1.7 \times 10^{-8}$		

43

Gorter (1927). She found that whenever an extract causes negative curvature, it does so within 2½ hours after application of the agar. Within this time she never observed positive curvatures. More than 3 hours after decapitation and application of the block, however, pure agar or agar containing inactive extracts caused positive curvature, *i.e.* towards the applied block. This she explained by the onset of regeneration, which takes place about 2½ hours after decapitation (Dolk, 1926; Zollikofer, 1928; Li, 1930). If a block of pure agar be applied symmetrically to the top of a decapitated coleoptile, then formation of auxin in the regenerated tip is greatly inhibited (Skoog, 1937). This has the result that when pure agar is placed on one side of a decapitated coleoptile, the new production of auxin 2½ hours after decapitation will be greater on the side without the block than on the side with it, and this will cause a curvature towards the block (see Figure 20). Hence if agar with a high auxin concentration is applied to one side, the auxin supplied by it will exceed the auxin produced by regeneration, and the negative curvature will continue to increase after regeneration. With low applied auxin concentration, however, or with very small agar blocks, the negative curvature which first develops may change after regeneration into a positive curvature. In such cases the positive curvatures are not due to any growth-retarding substance.

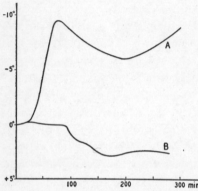

Fig. 20. The course of curvatures after application of auxin in agar (curve A) and plain agar (curve B). Blocks applied at time O, plants being decapitated 45 minutes earlier. Note development of positive curvature in B 85 minutes after application of plain agar, *i.e.* 130 minutes after decapitation. This corresponds to the regeneration time.

Whether there really are substances, other than toxic

compounds, which retard the growth of such organs as the coleoptile, is not clear. Tryptamine (see VII E) may give slight positive curvatures within 2 hours after application (Skoog, 1937), but within 6 hours these become strongly negative, doubtless due to transformation of the amine into indole-acetic acid. Czaja (1934) found that tannic acid, or plant tissues rich in tannins, cause positive curvatures, which seem to be due to shrinkage of the cells. Meyer (1936) obtained positive curvature with lanoline mixed with certain plant extracts. In lower concentrations the paste caused normal negative curvatures, so that apparently increasing the concentration brought the toxic or osmotically active substances up to a concentration at which their effect more than offset the growth-promotion effect. If agar blocks with low auxin concentration are applied to *Avena* coleoptile stumps *immediately* after the (first) decapitation, small positive curvatures may appear, but these change to negative curvatures after about 1 hour (u). Very high auxin concentrations will retard coleoptile growth (Bonner, 1933) but not under the conditions of the *Avena* test. Under ordinary test conditions the above cases are exceptions, and we may conclude that all substances active in the *Avena* test have growth-promoting effect. The growth-inhibiting action of auxins on roots and buds is a phenomenon of quite another type.

C. 7. *The Maximum Angle*

It will be seen that above a certain concentration the curvatures obtained in 90–110 minutes do not increase at all. This limiting curvature or "maximum angle" varies between 15° and 35°, according to experimental conditions. The zone of transition between the two arms of the curve of Figure 19 is exceedingly short. This type of curve indicates that two independent factors are here limiting the growth, providing an excellent example of Blackman's "limiting factors" (1905). On the left-hand arm the limiting factor is auxin, on the right-hand arm auxin is in excess, and a second factor, the "food factor," becomes limiting.

The maximum angle is a measure of the maximum *rate* at which curvature takes place, and is not determined by the maximum *amount* of curvature which the plant can undergo. After the 90–110 minute period in which the

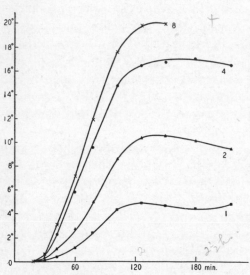

curvature is measured, the maximum angle continues to increase, although at a different rate (u). The reduction in the rate of increase, which is even more pronounced for curvatures below the maximum (see Figure 21) is due to three factors: *1*, the influence of gravity, which causes a geotropic curvature in the opposite direction (this may be seen by comparing plant 1 with plants

FIG. 21. Change of auxin curvatures with time. In these plants the blocks were applied immediately after decapitation, at time 0. Concentrations of indole-acetic acid: 1, 2, 4, and 8 × 0.07 mg. per liter respectively. Ordinate, curvature in degrees. Each curve the mean of 6 plants.

2 and 3 in Figure 2 of du Buy and Nuernbergk [1930]); *2*, the lateral transport of auxin from the block across the plant, detectable by a growth acceleration on the far side of the plant (du Buy and Nuernbergk, 1930; Laibach and Kornmann, 1933*a*); [it seems that this acceleration does not occur immediately on applying the auxin, but, as Nuernbergk (1933) has shown, there is a period after decapitation in which, presumably on account of the wounding, lateral transport is inhibited: this period appears to be of the order of 90 minutes (u)]; *3*, the effect of regeneration. This phenomenon,

as already mentioned, consists of the new production of auxin from the uppermost cells of the stump. No observable morphological change is associated with it. At 25° the time between decapitation and the beginning of regeneration is close to 150 minutes, as has been shown directly by straight growth measurements (see Figure 7). As stated above, the presence of a block of agar delays the onset of regeneration considerably, so that plants bearing a block of agar on one side will, 150 minutes after decapitation, regenerate more auxin upon the opposite side and hence will tend to curve towards the block. In *Avena* curvature tests, therefore, when auxin is in the block, this one-sided regeneration will have the effect of tending to reduce the auxin curvature.

To avoid the effects of the factors described under 2 and 3, which operate to reduce the auxin curvatures obtained, it is an advantage to decapitate the plants shortly before application of the block. This is the reason for the second decapitation 3 hours after the first, recommended above.

When very high concentrations of auxin, such as 0.01 mg. indole-acetic acid per cc. are used, the curvature obtained is less than the maximum angle (u). Figure 19 (p. 41) shows the broad range of concentrations over which the maximum angle is approximately constant, and its decrease at very high concentrations. To explain this we have only to consider that if auxin sufficient to cause maximal growth on the far side reaches that side by leakage, especially across the cut surface (Laibach and Kornmann, 1933a), no curvature can result. This can only occur if the concentration of auxin applied is very high. Evidently, also, all intermediate stages between the normal maximum angle and no curvature at all can result from suitable auxin concentrations. It is a characteristic of such "supramaximal" angles that the individual curvatures are extremely irregular, as can be seen from the photograph (Figure 22). This irregularity is doubtless due to variations in the moisture film at the cut surface.

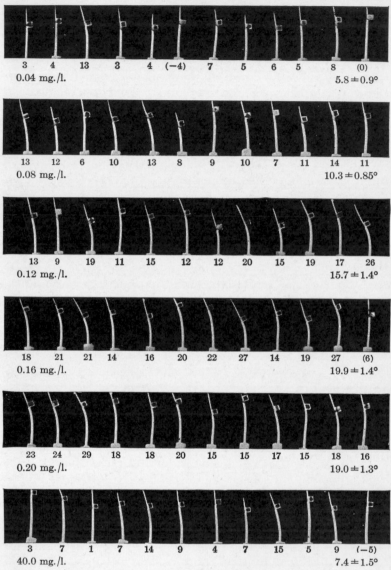

FIG. 22. Shadow prints of a series of *Avena* tests, 110 minutes after application of the agar blocks. Concentrations in mg. indole-3-acetic acid per liter; curvatures in degrees. The values in brackets are too low due to excessive guttation, and not included in means. Row 5 gives the same angle as row 4, which is therefore the maximum for the day; row 6 shows a supramaximum (200 × maximum concentration) and is characteristically irregular.

C. 8. *Variability of the Test*

The value of the maximum angle depends (*a*) on the cultural conditions, being greater for plants grown in earth than in water, and (*b*) on unknown factors which, although the plants are grown and used under constant conditions, cause its value to vary from day to day. In a series of *Avena* tests for quantitative determination of auxin it is always desirable to determine the maximum angle for the day, for the linear relation between concentration and curvature only holds for smaller angles.

Not only the maximum angle, but also the sensitivity, *i.e.* the mean curvature for a given concentration of auxin, varies from day to day and even from hour to hour. This phenomenon was first studied at Utrecht by Kögl and Haagen Smit (Kögl, 1933; Kögl, Haagen Smit, and van Hulssen, 1936). They found in general that the maximum sensitivity occurred in the early hours of the morning and the minimum in the late afternoon; the variation was several hundred per cent. At Copenhagen, Juel (1936) has found, working under a somewhat different set of constant conditions, that the variation from day to day is not more than 35 per cent. This does not necessarily conflict with the Utrecht workers' results, for if the tests are carried out always at the same time of day, the variation in sensitivity may be relatively small. This is particularly true at the time of maximum sensitivity, for there the curve is relatively flat and the sensitivity reached is the same on different days (*u*).

Figure 23 shows an example of sensitivity and maximum angle variations found at Pasadena. Curves A and B, determined on plants identically prepared (3 decapitations 2 hours apart), show that the sensitivity (Curve A) varies parallel to the maximum angle (Curve B). Curve C shows the variation in sensitivity for plants prepared in a different way (2 decapitations 40 minutes apart). It will be seen that the absolute variations are about the same for curves A and C, but since the angles are smaller on Curve C, the percentage variation is greater. Hence the long period between first decapitation and application of the block not only increases the sensitivity, but also greatly reduces the relative variability, so troublesome in Kögl's experiments. It may also be noted that even the greatest variations obtained at Pasadena are much less than those observed at

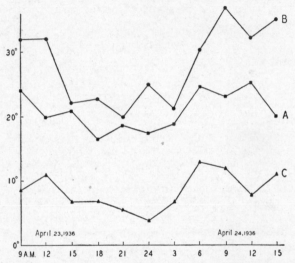

Fig. 23. Diurnal variation in sensitivity to auxin. Plants of uniform age (77 hours from soaking) tested every 3 hours from 9 A.M., April 23, to 3 P.M., April 24. Abscissa, time at beginning of test; ordinate, curvature. Curves A and B, 3 decapitations at 2-hour intervals; curve C, 2 decapitations 40 minutes apart. Indole-3-acetic acid for curves A and C, 0.13 mg. per liter; for curve B, 0.26 mg. per liter.

Utrecht, so that the variability is evidently different in different places. Kögl (1933) concluded that the variability is related to variations in the electrical field and ionization of the air. However, there are reasons for believing that other factors, such as light, are also involved (Kögl, Haagen Smit, and van Hulssen, 1936). While the ultimate cause of the variation is thus not known, it is probable that the immediate cause is variation in the auxin content of the plants.

Since the pure auxins have become available, the disadvantage of the variability is largely offset by "calibrating" the plants, whenever required, with an auxin solution of known concentration. For this purpose a dilute indole-acetic acid solution (0.1 γ per cc.), sterilized and kept sterile, retains its activity very satisfactorily.

D. Other Methods of Auxin Determination

1. *Straight Growth*

It goes without saying that all determinations of growth-promoting activity should be based on actual growth produced.[1] The convenience of curvature methods rests upon two facts: (1), the residual growth, after decapitation, is the same on both sides of the plant and thus is automatically eliminated from the measurements—no controls are necessary; and (2), only one measurement need be made; there is no "Zero reading," for the plants are chosen to be straight. Besides this, the curvature magnifies the amount of growth occurring and thus makes it easy to measure.

Since the absolute changes in length caused by auxin application are rather small—of the order of a few mm. at most—their measurement requires magnifications from 10 to 100 times. The most generally used instrument for this purpose is the horizontal microscope (described by Metzner, 1928, p. 133). The lengths of the plants, which must be placed on rigid supports, are measured periodically in red light with this instrument. The same end can be attained by photographing the plants automatically with a lapse-time moving-picture camera, and subsequently enlarging and measuring the pictures; this is especially convenient for long period measurements (see, for instance, Nuernbergk and du Buy, 1932). Both of these methods have been used in measurements of the distribution of growth over different zones of the plant. For the photography, small marks (tin foil, paraffin paper, sand particles, etc.) are affixed to the side of the plant; with the horizontal microscope, dots or fine lines made with india ink are sufficient. Other methods of growth measurement such as the interferometer (Meissner,

---

[1] Correspondingly, the term "growth-substances" should be restricted to substances which are actually shown to increase growth, a precaution which has been neglected by Hitchcock and Zimmerman (1935), and Zimmerman and Wilcoxon (1935).

1932; Laibach, 1932; Laibach and Kornmann, 1933) and the auxanometer of Koningsberger (1922) are also capable of application to auxin problems.

Quantitative measurements of the effect of auxin on straight growth of coleoptiles have been made by Nielsen (1930) and more extensively by Thimann and Bonner (1933). They decapitated the plants, pulled out the leaf completely, and placed blocks of agar containing auxin symmetrically on the cut surface. Correction had to be made for the growth of control plants treated with plain agar. Thimann and Bonner found that the extra growth caused by the auxin was proportional to the concentration in the block up to a limit, above which it increased less and less rapidly with increasing concentration (see Figure 24). Thus 29 plant units produce 2.66 mm. of coleoptile growth at 25°. At 15°, however, the proportionality factor is

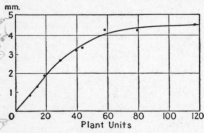

FIG. 24. Relation between auxin applied and straight growth produced, in decapitated *Avena* coleoptiles. The ordinate is the increase in growth over that of untreated controls. (After Thimann and Bonner, *Proc. Roy. Soc. B. 113*: 126–149, 1933.)

different. This places the *Avena* test, based on curvatures, on a firm foundation of actual growth increase. It also provides independent confirmation of the view that a second factor limits growth when auxin is in excess (but *cf.* VIII *E*).

If quite short cylindrical sections of coleoptiles are placed in auxin solutions they also respond by an increase in growth, which is approximately proportional, within limits, to the logarithm of the concentration of the auxin (Bonner, 1933). This makes possible a simple auxin determination by straight growth measurements under the microscope, eliminating the necessity for humidity control. The sections, usually 3–5 mm. long, are cut off from plants of about 30 mm. length. Only sections cut at the same distance from the tip are strictly comparable with one another. The response of sections cut from near the tip is greatest, but their residual growth (growth in water) is also greatest, on which account the results are sometimes variable. The response of basal sections is small, but since the residual growth is also small they too provide reliable results. For convenience in measuring, Bonner placed the sections upon glass rods; these are immersed in a shallow layer of the solution to be tested and their lengths measured, at once and after some definite period of time (6–24 hours), with the ocular scale of a dissecting microscope. In any method based on immersion, the penetration of the active substance into the tissues is greatly facilitated, since a large area of epidermis as well as two cut surfaces are in contact with the solution. Substances whose transport within the plant is very slow may therefore cause better growth response than in the normal *Avena* test. Even substances which are inactive in the *Avena* test may be found by this method to possess growth-promoting activity (Thimann, 1935*b*, Haagen Smit and Went, 1935; see VIII *G*). The same considerations apply to the pea test (see below). Jost and Reiss (1936) have described a similar method, using 20 mm. long coleoptile sections, dipping with their apical cut end in water or the solutions to be tested.

A quite different method for measuring straight growth has been developed by Cholodny (1930); it is based on the water uptake which is a necessary accompaniment of growth. This is determined by means of a micropotometer, which consists of a fine capillary tube filled with water, to the end of which the base of the isolated coleoptile is sealed. The coleoptile is immersed in running water of constant temperature, to prevent transpiration, so that the water which it absorbs is only used for growth, and this is determined by movement of the meniscus in the capillary tube. Cholodny has used this ingenious and sensitive method in the correlation of growth with phototropism (see X *G*).

D. 2. *The Pea Test*

It appears to be a general property of elongating organs, particularly stems, that if split longitudinally in the growing zone, the two halves curve outwards in water and inwards in auxin solution. The outward curvature is due to tissue tension, the epidermal cells being normally under tension and the pith cells under pressure. The inward curvature is a differential growth phenomenon of complex nature

FIG. 25. Curvature of split stems of etiolated pea seedlings in auxin solutions. Concentrations, left to right: 6.45, 2.15, 0.645, 0.215, 0.0645 and 0 mg. indole-3-acetic acid per liter. Photographed after 12 hours in solutions.

(see *e.g.* Jost and Reiss, 1936). Such curvatures in pea stems can be used as a convenient quantitative test for auxin (Went, 1934). Many other stems, coleoptiles, etc., react in a similar way.

Peas,—a pure line should be used [1] —are soaked in water for 6 hours and planted in moist sand in darkness. At the age of 7 days, when they have reached a length of 10–12 cm., the plants have developed two nodes, each bearing a scale, and one, at the top, bearing a leaf. Those plants are selected in which the internode between this leaf and the

[1] *Alaska* is very good.

terminal bud has reached less than 5 mm. in length. The top is cut off at 5 mm. below the terminal bud and the stem is split centrally lengthwise with a sharp safety razor blade, for a distance of about 3 cm. The split section is then cut off a few mm. below the split, and washed for an hour in water. Serial dilutions of the substance to be tested are prepared, volumes of about 20 cc. being convenient, and poured into Petri dishes. These solutions should not be more acid than pH 4, since then acid curvatures, in the opposite (outward) direction, may interfere with the auxin curvatures. A number of such sections (5–8) are transferred to these solutions, in which they are left for 6–24 hours in darkness. At the end of 6 hours the curvature is completed and remains stationary, the appearance being as in Figure 25. The angles of

curvature are then measured with a suitable protractor either directly on the plants or on a shadowgraph. This angle is that between the tangents to the extreme curved tip and at the point A (Figure 26) where the direction of curvature changes. The curvatures obtained are, within about a 10° range, independent of temperature. The plants may be prepared in diffuse white light without affecting the curvatures. A curious feature of these curvatures is that they are inhibited by heavy metals in concentrations which do not appear to be otherwise toxic. Thus M/4000 solutions of

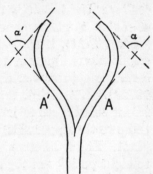

Fig. 26. Method of measuring curvature of split stem of *Pisum*.

Cu salts, M/1000 of Ni, or M/100 of Mn or Zn inhibit curvature practically completely, although the stems remain apparently healthy (*u*).

When the curvature is plotted against the logarithm of the concentration, a straight line is obtained within certain concentration limits (see Figure 45). The slope of this line will be, in general, different for different compounds and from it activities can be conveniently compared by the relationships:

$$\alpha = K \log \frac{C}{C_0}$$

where α is the mean observed curvature,
        C the concentration, in moles per liter,
        C_0 the concentration at which the curvature is zero, and

K the slope of the line. This varies somewhat from
day to day.

In theory two values of α suffice to characterize the line, but
since the curve deviates from a straight line at its upper
and lower ends, a larger series of values is desirable.

It is worth noting that in the *Avena* test there is no evidence for any "threshold" concentration C_0, and the calculation of activities is based upon this fact; the activity,
in "units" per milligram, is really a measurement of K.

D. 3. *Epinastic Responses*

Since Uyldert (1931) has shown that the epinasty of
stems is a phenomenon of asymmetrical growth due to
auxin (X *M*), it follows that a test could be based on the
application of auxin to petioles and measurement of the
resulting epinasty. This has been done by Hitchcock (1935,
1935*a*). His technique was to make serial dilutions of different substances in lanoline (Laibach's method) and apply
these to the upper side of the base of the petiole of a tobacco
plant. Eight different pastes were applied at the same time
to eight petioles of the same plant! The change in the angle
between stem and petiole was used as measure of the activity. This method must be used with great caution, since
Hitchcock himself has shown (1935*a*) that a substance
applied to one petiole may cause curvature of the petiole
below. In addition, a number of simple acids such as pyruvic,
malonic, and benzoic cause the same response, so that the
test is not specific. (*Cf.* also X *M*.)

D. 4. *Other Methods*

The fact that auxin is involved in a large number of
processes other than simple cell elongation makes possible
a number of means of assaying it. The inhibiting effect of
auxin on the growth of roots has been used as a test method
for auxin assay (IX *B*). The formation of roots on cuttings
(XI *B*), the inhibition of lateral bud development (Chapter
XII), and the production of swellings on stems and hypocotyls (XIII *C*) have also been used.

CHAPTER IV

FORMATION AND OCCURRENCE OF AUXINS

A. The Formation of Auxin in the Plant

We have seen that in *Avena* the auxin produced in the tip is one of the principal factors controlling growth. The question therefore arises, how far can the findings on *Avena* be applied to the general phenomenon of growth in the plant kingdom? Although auxin has been found in the green alga *Valonia* (van der Weij, 1933, 1933*b*), and in fungi (see IV *E*, VII *C*), our knowledge of those growth correlations in lower plants which may be controlled by special substances is too limited to allow any comparison with higher plants. Our first consideration must therefore be, how general is the production and occurrence of auxins, and in what parts of the plant are they produced?

First of all it must be pointed out that there are a number of chemically different auxins, whose physiological action is, except for quantitative differences, the same. We shall make no attempt to distinguish between these here. In those few plants which have been examined there is, however, evidence that the auxin present is auxin *a* (see VII *D*).

There are two main methods for obtaining auxin from plant parts. The first, and most used, is that of allowing auxin to diffuse out into water or an aqueous gel. For this agar is generally used. The method was first applied by Went to *Avena* coleoptile tips, but has subsequently proved itself of general applicability to almost all auxin-producing organs. In some cases the auxin so obtained may be inactivated by enzymes diffusing out of the cut cells. That such inactivation is a usual consequence of crushing tissues was first shown by Thimann (1934) and later by the experiments of van Overbeek (1935), Kornmann (1935), Fiedler (1936), and Larsen (1936). The inactivation at cut surfaces may be decreased by first placing the auxin-producing plant parts on wet filter paper before transferring them to the agar.

The second method is to extract the plant tissue directly with a solvent (Thimann, 1934; Boysen Jensen, 1936a). For this purpose, water, alcohol, ether, and chloroform have been used. Extraction with water, however, usually leads to inactivation, almost certainly by oxidizing enzymes (Thimann, 1934). Chloroform is the most suitable solvent, but it must be carefully freed from traces of peroxide or chlorine; this is done by freshly redistilling chloroform of anesthetic quality, adding about 0.5 per cent alcohol and preserving in the dark. Ether, if used, should also be made peroxide-free by distilling from a mixture of $FeSO_4$ and CaO (method of Garbarini, 1909).

The first evidence for actual production of auxin in the plant was given by Paál's experiment (1919) with coleoptile tips of *Coix*. The same procedure, namely, the causing of curvature by placing the tip one-sidedly upon the stump, was carried out on *Avena* by Nielsen (1924), and on hypo-cotyls of the dicotyledon *Helianthus*—using the plumula as tip—by Beyer (1925). Proof that auxin is produced in coleoptile tips of *Zea Mays* was also given by Cholodny (1926). The clearest evidence was, however, given by the straight growth measurements of Söding. His work on *Avena* (1923, 1925) has been previously discussed (III *B*). In 1926 he extended these experiments to flower stalks of *Cardamine*, *Cephalaria*, and some composites, showing that the auxin-producing organ was in these cases the flower or inflorescence. This was confirmed for *Bellis* by Uyldert (1927, 1931) who also proved that the effect of applying the inflorescence could be duplicated by agar on which *Avena* coleoptile tips had stood. Gradmann (1928) showed that auxin can be obtained from the tip of *Convolvulus* stems, but only to a lesser extent from zones immediately below the tip. Koning (1933) could only obtain small amounts of auxin from buds of *Ipomoea*, but sections of the stem yielded somewhat more.

The production of auxin in the tip of the *Avena* coleoptile may be considered in more detail. Went (1928) showed that only the extreme tip, less than 0.7 mm. in length, produces auxin. In fact if the auxin is collected at a point 10 mm. or more below the tip, the amount obtained may be very much less, because auxin is used up in growth, or destroyed, during its downward movement (*cf. e.g.* van Overbeek, 1936). Nagao (1936) found the same thing for *Avena* roots.

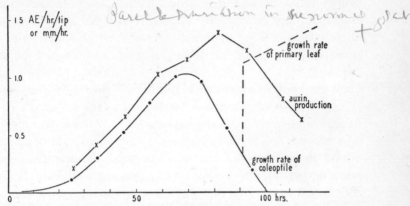

Fig. 27. Auxin production (crosses) in AE per hour per tip, and growth rate (circles), in mm. per hour, in *Avena* coleoptiles at different ages. Abscissa, age in hours from soaking. Each point the mean of 30–50 plants.

When cut off and placed on agar, the coleoptile tip continues to produce auxin for many hours (van der Weij, 1931), providing it is kept at temperatures below 30°. The production finally drops to zero, however, probably on account of exhaustion of the auxin precursor (*cf.* IV *B*). Very young coleoptiles produce little auxin; the auxin production closely follows the increase in growth rate and continues at a high level even when the growth rate of the coleoptile decreases again. This has been found both in *Zea Mays* (van Overbeek, *u*) and in *Avena* (*u*); see Figure 27. These results contrast with those of du Buy and Nuernbergk (1932) and du Buy (1933), who state that coleoptile tips from short plants produce no auxin at all, and that auxin production is afterwards constant over a period of 4 days. Their findings, however, appear to be based on insufficient experimental data.

As to the effect of external factors, du Buy (1933) found that at low as well as high temperatures auxin production is reduced, the optimum being around 25°. Gravity, irrespective of its direction of action, has no effect on auxin production (Went, 1926; Dolk, 1930; Pfaeltzer, 1934). The effect of light, both as regards wave-length and intensity, has given very variable results, some of which are conflicting; a systematic study would be very desirable (*cf.* Went, 1928; du Buy, 1933). The effect of light on auxin production in more fully grown plants is somewhat better understood (see below).

Some knowledge about auxin production may be derived from growth measurements. Thus, the experiments of Oosterhuis (1931) indicate that in *Asparagus* the growth of the stem is largely controlled by the terminal and axillary buds; these, therefore, are presumably the auxin-producing centers. Similarly, Uyldert (1931) showed that, in *Tradescantia*, the apex, consisting of the bud and one leaf, promotes the growth of the lower internodes, and hence she regarded the apex as an auxin-producing center.

In *Helianthus* seedlings, Fliry (1932) found that auxin was formed in the plumula, but not in the cotyledons. The lack of production in the cotyledons agrees with the findings of Beyer (1925). Navez (1933a) found that the cotyledons and plumula of *Lupinus* seedlings also produce auxin, and further that seedlings grown in light produce about twice as much as those grown in the dark. In the seedlings of *Lepidium* and *Raphanus* van Overbeek (1932, 1933) showed that there is auxin production both in the plumula and the cotyledons, but that production in the cotyledons soon falls off unless the plants are exposed to light. Dijkman (1934) obtained auxin from all parts of *Lupinus* seedlings grown in the dark, and concluded, in disagreement with the work just mentioned, that there was no special auxin-producing center in these plants.

The formation of auxin in woody plants was first demonstrated by van der Weij (1933a), who obtained auxin by diffusion from the young leaves of *Eleagnus*. However, he could obtain no auxin in this way from terminal buds of young sprouting twigs. Czaja (1934), on the other hand, obtained auxin readily by diffusion from sprouting buds of a number of trees and shrubs, including *Populus*, *Salix*, *Quercus*, and especially *Aesculus*. W. Zimmermann (1936), also using the diffusion method, has studied auxin production by buds in some detail, and finds their behavior to be closely similar to that of buds of herbaceous plants studied by Thimann and Skoog (see below). Production is greatest in the terminal bud, and the more basal the lateral buds the smaller is their production. In general he found a strict correlation between the rate of growth of a shoot and the amount of auxin produced in its terminal bud, and thus concludes that in trees development is largely dependent on auxin production.

As to roots, the first evidence for auxin production in the root tip came from the observation that root tips, like coleoptile tips, could restore the geotropic sensitivity of root stumps to which they were applied. However, it was not until the experiments of Hawker (1932) and Boysen Jensen (1933a) that direct evidence of the presence of auxin in root tips was obtained. They placed root tips on gelatin (Hawker) or agar containing 10 per cent dextrose (Boysen Jensen) and the resulting blocks were then able to cause auxin curvatures on *Avena* coleoptiles. The same result was obtained by Thimann (1934) by the extraction of root tips with chloroform (see Figure 30). The question as to whether this auxin is actually produced in the root tip or not is discussed in IX *C*.

A more complete survey of the auxin production in the entire plant in light was made by Thimann and Skoog (1933, 1934) on *Vicia Faba* (see Figure 28). The main center of auxin production was found to be the terminal bud with its embryonic leaves, but all the young leaves also produce auxin to a lesser extent. The older leaves produce little or none. When the plant is about 40 cm. in height, production by its terminal bud ceases. The dormant axillary buds produce practically no auxin until, following decapitation, they start to develop; their auxin production then rapidly increases. In the dark, auxin production soon ceases but its utilization continues, with the result that the auxin, which at first is present in considerable quantities in the stems, rapidly becomes exhausted from them. The production of auxin by the leaves of *Nicotiana* was studied by Avery (1935), who showed that the maximum amount was produced by young leaves of about 20 sq. cm. area, the production rate thereafter steadily decreasing with age. Production takes place in the blade only in light, and the auxin is accumulated in the veins. In the leaves of *Ipomoea* Koning (1933) found the largest auxin production to coincide with the period of most rapid growth, and the same is true for the developing buds of *Aesculus* and *Malus* (Avery, Burkholder, and Creighton, 1937).

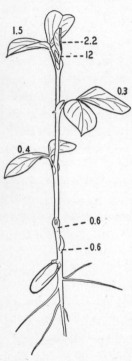

Fig. 28. Auxin production in *Vicia Faba*. Young plants, grown in light. The figures represent the amount of auxin diffusing from the various leaves and buds in AE per hour. (Data of Thimann and Skoog, 1934.)

Laibach and Meyer (1935) have published data on the total auxin content of *Zea Mays* and *Helianthus* plants during their whole life cycle. The results, which were obtained by alcohol extraction, are open to objection on account of the probable loss of auxin by enzymic inactivation. They seem to show that auxin is absent from *Zea Mays*, and almost absent from *Helianthus*, during the period of most rapid development.

The presence of auxin in the pollinia of several orchids and the pollen of *Hibiscus* was shown by Laibach (1932a);

it appears to be principally in the fatty substance between the pollen grains. The extracts from a number of different pollens were analyzed for their auxin content by Thimann and Went (1934). The activities found were very variable, *Hicoria* being the highest. *Sequoia* pollen was also shown by Thimann (1934) to be rich in auxin.

On the presence of auxin in seeds there is some difference of opinion. Cholodny (1935) found that auxin was absent from *Avena* seeds, but appeared as soon as the seed had taken up some water.[1] From then on the amount rapidly increased and then decreased again, completely disappearing in 48 hours. The auxin production was found to be in the endosperm and not in the embryo, which, in fact, appeared to absorb it. Pohl (1935, 1936) has also found that if *Avena* seeds are punctured and placed in water, auxin diffuses out into the water. Application of an e.m.f. across the seed increased the diffusion into the water, and the auxin accumulated at the anode. The growth rate of shoots from seeds so treated was greatly reduced (*cf.* below).

Kögl, Erxleben, and Haagen Smit (1934), using water extraction, found great variation in the auxin content of *Hordeum* seeds; in the ungerminated seeds the amounts were extremely small, but during the germination of most varieties the amounts increased up to the 5th day, the highest value reached being 0.42 mg. per kg. They found, however, that maize germ oil, which is prepared from ungerminated *Zea Mays* seeds, is rich in auxins, and they were able to isolate two of the pure substances from a sample of maize oil which contained about 0.7 mg. per kg. The authors' own experiments have shown that some samples of wheat germ, wheat germ oil, corn meal, and rice polishings often contain considerable amounts of auxin, up to 4 mg. per kg. being found (*cf.* Thimann, 1934).

On the other hand, the data of Laibach and Meyer (1935) cited above, show that the auxin content both of *Zea Mays*

[1] On account of its possible rôle in germination he suggested the name "Blastanin," but since the activity was determined on *Avena* it falls under the definition of auxin.

and of *Helianthus* decreases steadily during germination from a relatively high value in the husked seeds almost to zero. These observations disagree so completely with all those above that they must be regarded as doubtful.

B. THE AUXIN PRECURSOR

The rôle of the seed in the formation of auxin in the other parts of the young *Avena* seedling has been partly elucidated by Skoog (1937). If the seed is removed, auxin production in the coleoptile tip decreases steadily, and if the plants are decapitated about 12 hours later, regeneration of auxin production in the stump does not occur. The plants, however, as shown by their sensitivity to applied auxin, remain normal. The auxin secreted by

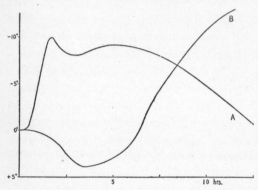

FIG. 29. Change of curvature of *Avena* coleoptiles with time. Curve A, indole-3-acetic acid, 0.1 mg. per liter, in agar; curve B, indole-ethylamine, 1 mg. per liter. After a preliminary positive curvature (cf. Figure 20), curve B shows a strong negative curvature due to transformation of indole-ethylamine into indole-acetic or indole-pyruvic acid.

the coleoptile tip does not come directly from the seed, as has been claimed by Pohl (1935, 1936), because if so, it should be possible to intercept it by removing the coleoptile and placing an agar block upon the stump. Skoog could obtain no auxin in this way, even with very young plants. This was shown by the failure of such blocks to produce any curvature on *Avena* within two hours. If, however, the blocks are left on the test coleoptiles for 2 to 6 hours after application, they give rise to distinct auxin curvature; this indicates that some substance (*precursor*) is being converted into auxin within the tissues of the test plant (see Figure 29).[1] For such tests, de-

[1] This may explain the observations of Beyer (1928a) who found that cylinders from 3 mm. below the tip of the coleoptile, if placed one-sidedly upon the stump,

seeded plants, which do not show any regeneration, were used. The evidence is therefore strong that a precursor, present in the seed, moves up into the coleoptile tip and is there converted into auxin. Some of it is doubtless also converted into auxin in the seed itself.

It will be seen that few general conclusions can be drawn as to auxin production during the early seedling stages. Ungerminated seeds certainly contain some auxin, but the amounts found are extremely variable, partly due to difficulties of extraction, and partly due to variation in the extent of wetting, which according to Cholodny (1935) causes rapid auxin formation.

This rapid formation of free auxin is presumably from the precursor. It may be suggested that this precursor is an ester, the esters of auxin a being themselves inactive. This would explain the results of Pohl (1936), who found that if *Avena* seeds were cut open and electrolyzed (*cf.* p. 63), the subsequent growth of the coleoptile was reduced. If now the electrolyzed seeds were soaked in a solution of auxin a the subsequent growth of the coleoptile was more nearly normal, but soaking in a solution of indole-acetic acid did not have this effect. The auxin a, if the above view is correct, would be esterified and the ester carried to the tip of the young coleoptile. The esters of indole-acetic acid, being readily hydrolyzed in the plant (*cf.* VII E) could not be so transported on account of the polarity of the coleoptile. This suggestion is also supported by the work of Kögl, Erxleben, and Haagen Smit (1934), who obtained considerable yields of auxin after the saponification of various oils prepared from seeds.

As to the auxin in the seedling, probably much of the variation between the results of different authors is due to inactivation during the extraction (see below). In general, the production of auxin takes place in the apical parts of all organs which are actively elongating, such as terminal buds

cause no curvatures within the first three hours but then produce definite negative curvatures.

on growing stems, young leaves on growing petioles, inflorescences or flowers on growing flower-stalks, and coleoptile tips. Now we know that in young seedlings the last stage in the production of auxins, *i.e.* the transformation of the precursor into the active form, can take place in darkness (Skoog, 1937). Since we must conclude, from the general agreement between the experiments on plants other than seedlings, that auxin production in such plants takes place *only* as a result of the action of light, it follows that *light is necessary for the formation of the auxin precursor*. Light is, of course, necessary for the formation of all organic substances in the plant, through its part in producing carbohydrate; this carbohydrate may afterwards undergo changes to other substances, such as fats and proteins, but without the intervention of light. Now the fact that auxin production in *Lupinus* and *Raphanus* seedlings may become very low in darkness, while the cotyledons are still full of carbohydrate and other reserves, shows that the effect of light on the formation of the precursor cannot be simply through the photosynthetic production of carbohydrate. There must, on the other hand, be a definite light-sensitive reaction involved in the formation of the precursor. Along completely different lines, Gregory (1928) came to a similar conclusion with regard to the effect of light on leaf growth; although leaf growth is directly dependent on light its Q_{10} is different from the Q_{10} of photosynthesis, and hence he concludes that "a master photochemical reaction, independent of carbon assimilation, leads to the formation of a substance directly involved in leaf expansion." Whether auxin itself plays any part in leaf expansion has not yet, however, been shown. There is evidence that it is connected with the elongation of the veins, but the mesophyll is not influenced at all by auxin application.

The exceptions to the formation of auxin as a result of the action of light are all provided by seedlings. In these, as we have seen, it is almost certainly formed from an inactive precursor which is stored in the seed. It is important to note that for the growth of seedlings, which have to begin their lives in darkness, not only carbohydrates and other nutrients, but also auxin, is thus stored in a readily available form.

It should be added that auxin production is not in general due to meristematic activity or to the presence of embryonic cells, as is proven by its production in coleoptile tips and in leaves. (A very clear case is that of the saprophytic tropical orchids *Gastrodia* and *Didymoplexis*, whose ovaries strongly promote the elongation of their pedicels, but only *after* the growth of the ovary and embryos is complete [*u*].) The exact significance of its production in growing regions is discussed in IV *C*. Goodwin's finding (1937) that, weight for weight, auxin production is the greatest in the very youngest leaves of the bud is of interest in this connection.

On the other hand, there is a distinct correlation between the *position* of an organ and its auxin production; only the most apical regions form auxin, and the more terminal their position the greater their production.

C. DISTRIBUTION OF AUXIN IN THE PLANT

Besides its presence in the producing zones, auxin is also distributed throughout other parts of the plant. Söding showed (1929) by straight growth measurements that auxin was present in small amounts in sections of green *Avena* coleoptiles immediately below the tip, but that further down than 2.5–5 mm. from the tip no growth-promoting effect was detectable.

Determinations of the auxin content of different zones of the etiolated coleoptile and roots of *Avena*, using the method of extraction with chloroform, were made by Thimann (1934). The results, summarized in Figure 30, show that auxin is present everywhere in the seedling, but that its concentration falls off rapidly with increasing distance from coleoptile tip and root tip. His finding auxin throughout the plant, where earlier workers found none (Stark, 1921;

Nielsen, 1924; Went, 1928; Söding, 1929) is at least in part due to the fact that the chloroform method determines the total auxin present at the moment of extraction, while the diffusion method is successful only if there is continued production.

It should be noted that Thimann's results bring for the first time evidence that the auxin in the plant is present in at least two different forms: the free moving auxin, which can be collected by the diffusion method, and the bound auxin, which is obtained, together with the free auxin, by extraction of the tissues (see also VIII *F* and Boysen Jensen, 1936*a*).

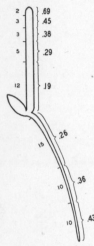

FIG. 30. Auxin distribution in *Avena* seedling. Right-hand figures, auxin in plant units per mm. (or AE per 2.5 mm.) of coleoptile or root; left-hand figures, lengths of the extracted sections. (From Thimann, *J. gen. Physiol. 18:* 23–34, 1934.)

Recently, however, the presence of auxin in the lower parts of the coleoptile has been confirmed by the diffusion method, this being made possible by the development of more sensitive tests. Thus, Söding (1935*a*) using his *Cephalaria* test, detected auxin diffusing from lower parts of green coleoptiles in amounts approximating 25 per cent of that obtainable from the tip. However, the fact that he also obtained, by diffusion from the lower zones, auxin in amounts sufficient to be detectable on *Avena*, which no previous workers have been able to do, suggests that his green coleoptiles are richer in auxin than etiolated ones. By using the de-seeded *Avena* test, which gives increased sensitivity (*cf.* III *C* 4) Skoog has obtained auxin from the lower zones of truly etiolated coleoptiles by diffusion. The yield was less than 5 per cent of that from the tips. Small amounts of auxin could also be obtained by diffusion from the primary leaf. Dollfuss (1936) has obtained small amounts of auxin by diffusion from the zone 2–4 mm. below the tip of *Sorghum* coleoptiles.

Dijkman (1934) found that by placing sections from young *Lupinus* hypocotyls on agar, about the same amounts of auxin were obtained from the upper, middle, and lower zones. In older plants, the auxin concentration decreased towards the base.

Avery (1935) found that in tobacco leaves, the veins contain auxin although presumably they do not produce it; the auxin appears to accumulate in the veins towards the base of the leaf.

It is clear from what results are so far available that auxin is present almost throughout the plant, although in highest amounts near to where it is produced or stored.

To account for the presence of auxin far below the growing regions (in which it is known to be used up in the growing process), Söding (1936a) assumes that although cells need auxin for their growth, they also form it during growth, and even give it off. The arrival of auxin at one end of a cell would stimulate the other end to form some auxin.[1] Thus auxin formation would be a typical response to stimulus, and Söding concludes: auxin is not only the *cause*, but also the *result* of growth. However, in none of the very numerous experiments on transport has more auxin ever been collected from the basal portions than had been administered apically. In a few cases the original auxin content of the tissues has added to the amount found, but this can be determined from blank transport experiments, in which no auxin is applied. Further, we have seen in IV A that in darkness the auxin content of a plant (other than a seedling) continually decreases, so that there is, *in toto*, no new formation although there is growth. If it is further remembered that auxin production is not by any means limited to growing parts, it will be clear that Söding's assumption is unjustified.

The facts can more usefully be looked at in the reverse direction. Naturally if a region of the plant begins to produce auxin it will also begin to use that auxin for growth, providing

[1] *Cf.* Stanley's suggestion (1936) for the movement of the virus protein.

it is capable of growth. We must therefore envisage the plant as furnished with certain spots or areas, each of which, by virtue of precursor storage or supply, or presence of the proper enzyme system, can produce auxin for a time. Generally the production ceases after a while, but in the meantime if these spots or areas are, like buds, capable of growth, they will grow. Since, however, a very little auxin can bring about a great deal of growth (10^{-6} mg. can produce about half a centimeter of coleoptile, as shown in III D 1), it follows that many of these centers will produce auxin more rapidly than they can use it up, and thus auxin will diffuse out of them into other parts. Auxin, then, is not produced as a result of growth, but, rather, the auxin which enters our experimental agar blocks is the excess over that which has been used in growth. Auxin production is thus the primary, and growth the secondary, phenomenon. A similar conclusion was reached by W. Zimmermann (1936).

D. Auxin in Animal Material

The experiments of Seubert (1925) showed that auxin may be present in considerable concentrations in saliva and pepsin, both animal secretions. Systematic examination of animal excretions and tissues was made by Kögl and Haagen Smit (1931) and Kögl, Haagen Smit, and Erxleben (1933, 1933a); in the dog, most tissues contain very small amounts, the kidneys, the urine, and the colon and its contents having the most; human urine, however, was found to be extremely rich in auxin and was in fact used for the isolation of pure auxins (see VII B). Maschmann (1932) and Maschmann and Laibach (1932, 1933) found the liver and kidneys of the mouse and hen to be higher in auxin than other tissues. According to Maschmann (1932) and to Kögl, Haagen Smit, and Tönnis (1933) the auxin content of human carcinomas is higher than that of the surrounding tissue. The authors' own experiments did not show any particularly high auxin content in rapidly growing mouse carcinomas (u). There is no reason to ascribe any physiological significance to the auxin present in carcinomas, or in animal tissues in general. Fischer found no effect of auxins on the growth of animal tissue cultures (see Kögl, Haagen Smit, and Tönnis, 1933); this, however, is not conclusive proof of the ineffectiveness of auxin, since the embryonic fluid which is used for tissue cultures is relatively rich in auxin (u). The fact that the large quantity of auxin in the urine is derived partly from the food and partly from the action of bacteria in the intestine also does not support the view that auxin plays any part in animal growth.

Robinson and Woodside (1937) have followed the auxin formation in the hen's egg during its development. The auxin, which is principally in the embryo, increases parallel to the increase in weight of the embryo for the first 7 days; thereafter it increases rapidly to reach a maximum of 40,000 plant units, or about 1 γ of auxin, at about 14 days. Finally it decreases again. Although the parallelism between the auxin content and the growth is suggestive, there are no direct experiments to show that the growth is in any way due to the auxin.

Navez and Kropp (1934) and Kropp and Crozier (1934) found that extracts of crustacean eye-stalks contain an auxin. In view of the facts above it is not surprising to find auxin in lower as well as in higher animals, but here again there is no reason to ascribe any physiological significance to it. The attempt of Navez and Kropp to associate the auxin with the chromatophore activator also present in the extracts seems quite unwarranted, since auxin itself had no effect on the chromatophores.

E. PRODUCTION OF AUXIN BY MICROÖRGANISMS

Nielsen (1930) was the first to show that an auxin, which he named "Rhizopin," is produced in the growth of fungi. Subsequently he (1931, 1932), Boysen Jensen (1931, 1931a, 1932), Kögl and Haagen Smit (1931), Dolk and Thimann (1932), and Thimann and Dolk (1933) showed that numerous fungi and bacteria are able to produce auxin in culture. Certain amino-acids are particularly favorable for the production of auxin (Boysen Jensen, 1932), but the most important, particularly as a constituent of peptones, is tryptophane (Thimann, 1935a). The yield of auxin produced by *Rhizopus* under standard conditions on peptone media is proportional to the amount of aëration which the culture received (Bonner, 1932; Thimann and Dolk, 1933); this has been explained as due to the oxidative deamination of tryptophane to indole-acetic acid (Thimann, 1935). The presence of carbohydrate with the peptone facilitates the production of auxin. The bulk of the auxin is produced after the growth of the fungus (*Rhizopus suinus*) has ceased, and its concentration, after reaching a maximum, decreases again on account of destruction. Auxin production by yeast cultures follows similar lines, most of the auxin appearing after growth has ceased (Robinson, *u*). However, with yeast the yield of auxin appears to vary inversely with the amount of growth. The auxin does not appear to play any rôle in the growth of either of these fungi. Auxin production by pathogenic microörganisms may be of great importance in plant diseases (*cf.* IX *C* and XIII *C*).

CHAPTER V

THE RELATION BETWEEN AUXIN
AND GROWTH

In order to be able to explain the normal growth of the plant in terms of auxin, we must first be able to demonstrate that in every case auxin is formed above the region where growth in length occurs. That this is true was shown in Chapter IV. The second prerequisite is that there shall be a direct relation between the quantity of auxin applied and the growth obtained. Such direct proportionality has been shown to hold in whatever plants have been studied in sufficient detail. The best cases are those of the curvature and straight growth of *Avena* resulting from the application of auxin in agar (see III *C* 5). Similar proof was given for *Raphanus* hypocotyls by van Overbeek (1933) and for *Lupinus* hypocotyls by Dijkman (1934); in these, as in *Avena*, both curvature and straight growth appear to be strictly proportional to the applied auxin up to a clearly defined limit. It goes without saying that such proportionality holds only if all other conditions are constant, especially the physiological age of the reacting cells. The phenomenon of aging will be further discussed below.

A. Auxin and the Growth of Coleoptiles

In itself the direct proportionality between auxin applied and growth resulting is not rigid proof that auxin is indispensable for growth. The proof is only complete if it can be shown, firstly, that when the plant is freed from its auxin its growth ceases, and, secondly, that on subsequent application of auxin growth is resumed. Since auxin is a hormone and is produced only in certain regions, which may be separate from the reacting zones, we should be able to free the growing zones from auxin by removal of the producing region. This is, however, extremely difficult for reasŏns which will become apparent later. Nevertheless, Dolk (1930, mentioned by Went, 1928) practically succeeded in doing this by decapitating *Avena* coleoptiles, waiting two hours and then decapitating again, when growth came practically to a standstill (see Figure 31). If at this point auxin in agar was applied, growth was at

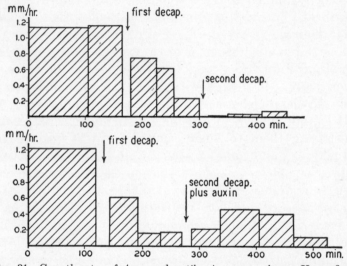

Fig. 31. Growth rates of *Avena* coleoptiles, in mm. per hour. Upper figure, two decapitations; lower figure, auxin applied after second decapitation. (From Dolk, *Diss.*, Utrecht, 1930.)

once resumed. The conclusion is that "Ohne Wuchsstoff kein Wachstum," *without auxin no growth*. It is perhaps necessary to mention that the reverse of this statement, namely "where there is no growth, there is no auxin," or even "where auxin, there growth" (Fitting, 1936), is by no means necessarily true.

A variant of this experiment was carried out by Went (1928). Continuous growth measurements were made on basal zones of *Avena* coleoptiles, and when they were found to have just stopped elongating, they were treated with auxin; as a result growth was restored, although slowly (*cf.* Figure 32).

Beyer (1928*a*) was unable to confirm the fundamental experiment of Dolk, finding instead that after two decapitations growth still continued but at a lesser rate. He used, however, very short plants, in which there is an excess of auxin present (*u*); this means that a much longer period without any regeneration would have been needed to deplete the plant of its auxin and to stop growth.

Evidence similar to the above has been obtained from the growth of immersed sections of *Avena* coleoptiles (Bonner, 1933; Thimann, 1935*b*). These grow at a rather slow rate and correspondingly their growth continues, at a gradually decreasing rate, for a long time; they show, however, no regeneration. If treated with acid their growth is temporarily accelerated by activation of the auxin present (see VIII *F*), but subsequently it falls virtually to zero; on then transferring them to auxin solution growth begins again and may be quite considerable.

It is satisfactory to note that on such a fundamental point comparable evidence is available with another plant and by another method. Cholodny (1926) showed that if the central cylinder of *Lupinus* hypocotyls were bored out, care being taken to remove all the phloem, the growth rate falls to 30 per cent of the normal. If now the tips of *Zea Mays* coleoptiles were inserted into the hollow, the growth was greatly accelerated (see Figure 47). With one tip the growth rate became 70 per cent, with 4 to 6 tips 90 to 100 per cent of the normal. Moissejewa (1928) varied the experiment by inserting gelatin upon which *Zea Mays* coleoptile tips had stood, with similar results.

It is thus satisfactorily proven that cell elongation is dependent upon, and controlled by, the presence of auxin.

One of the complicating factors in the analysis of plant growth in terms of auxin is the fact that the further we go from the auxin-producing zone the less sensitive do the cells become to applied auxin. This phenomenon is termed "aging." It is produced, as has been shown by du Buy (1933), by the continued decrease in auxin supply to those cells. The longer a man has been without exercise the less he is able to exercise, and correspondingly the longer a cell has been without auxin, the less it can respond to applied auxin. The loss of sensitivity may be clearly seen from Table IV (p. 40), which shows that if the apical zones are removed, the curvature obtained is less; this is because the basal zones curve less, for a given concentration of auxin, than do the upper zones. Du Buy showed that the same phenomenon namely decreased sensitivity to auxin, occurs

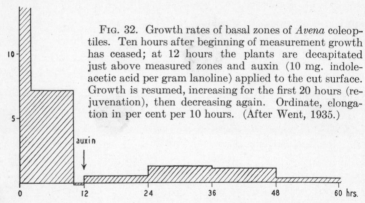

Fig. 32. Growth rates of basal zones of *Avena* coleoptiles. Ten hours after beginning of measurement growth has ceased; at 12 hours the plants are decapitated just above measured zones and auxin (10 mg. indoleacetic acid per gram lanoline) applied to the cut surface. Growth is resumed, increasing for the first 20 hours (rejuvenation), then decreasing again. Ordinate, elongation in per cent per 10 hours. (After Went, 1935.)

in old coleoptiles (more than 100 hours from planting). In plants of the same age, physiological aging may be produced by decapitating, and preventing auxin regeneration by redecapitating after suitable intervals. The first effect of this treatment is to increase the response to applied auxin (see III C 4) because the auxin content of the plant becomes very low, but subsequently, if the lack of auxin continues, the plants become less and less sensitive,—they are "aged." Apparently this aging is due to the thickening of the cell walls, which continues independent of elongation. Du Buy found that aged plants show a decreased extensibility, as measured by their bending under applied lateral tension, which would explain their decreased response to auxin. That aging is due to thickening of the walls is confirmed by the behavior of de-seeded plants from which the materials for wall thickening are removed, and which show correspondingly

less aging (Skoog, 1937). Went has shown (1935) that if a
sufficient auxin supply be maintained no aging occurs for
a long time. Indeed, the opposite effect, namely *rejuvenation*, is observed if high concentrations of auxin are applied
to greatly aged regions of the coleoptile; the growth rate
increases slightly at first and then more in the next period,
so that the sensitivity is actually increasing with time (see
Figure 32).

Since the auxin content decreases steadily from tip to
base in the coleoptile, it follows that each zone has a different auxin content and a
different physiological age.
It is therefore essential to
consider each zone sepa-
rately, before an integral
picture of the growth of the
whole can be obtained.
Measurements of the growth
of marked zones were first
carried out by Rothert
(1894) who found that in
young coleoptiles, up to
15 mm. long, the growth
rate was greatest at the
base, while in older coleoptiles there was a maximum
growth rate in the middle,
some 6–9 mm. below the tip.

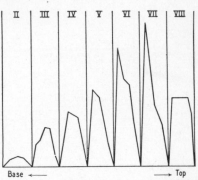

FIG. 33. Distribution of growth in
the internodes of a rapidly elongating
shoot of *Polygonum sachalinense*. Initial length of all internodes taken as
equal. The numbers give the number
of the internode from the base; vertical
lines represent nodes. Ordinate, final
length of each zone. (From van Burkom, *Diss.*, Utrecht, 1913.)

His observations have been confirmed by Went (see below).
The type of growth exemplified by coleoptiles 20 mm. or
more long, with a maximum growth rate near the middle,
is of common occurrence in plants. Hence any explanation
arrived at for *Avena* should be capable of application to the
many other cases known. Thus, Figure 33 illustrates the
growth rates of zones of successive internodes of *Polygonum*
(Van Burkom, 1913); it may be seen that the distribution
of growth rates in each internode, and also the distribution

of growth rates of internodes over the whole stem, is similar to that in *Avena*. Went has explained this growth distribution, in *Avena*, by the interaction of two factors: *1*, auxin, coming from the tip, and *2*, a food factor or complex of factors, coming from the base (Went, 1928, 1935). The auxin content would thus decrease with distance from the tip,

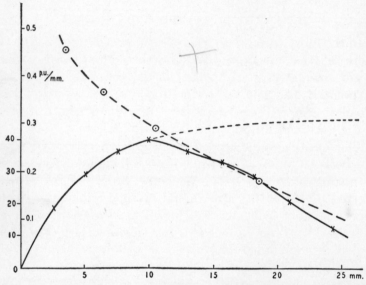

FIG. 34. Distribution of growth rate (crosses) and auxin concentration (circles) over the length of a coleoptile of *Avena sativa*. Abscissa, distance from tip of coleoptile in mm.; ordinates (outer figures), increase in length in per cent of original length per 8 hours, (inner figures), auxin present (by extraction) in plant units per mm. length. The auxin curve continues upward at the left to reach a very high point for the region close to the tip. Thin broken curve to right represents distribution of hypothetical food factor. (After Thimann, 1934.)

and the food factor with distance from the base, because both are used up during the actual process of growth.

That the auxin concentration within the coleoptile does actually fall off with increasing distance from the tip, and that there is no maximum in the middle to correspond to the maximum in growth rate, was shown by Thimann (1934) with his chloroform extraction method. Figure 34 combines the curve for distribution of growth rate with part of the curve for auxin content and shows that three zones are distinguishable: one, the most apical, in which growth is independent of the auxin concentration; a second in which growth is proportional to the auxin; and a third, most basal, in which the growth is slightly less than would be expected from the auxin content, due to aging.

B. The Rôle of the Food Factor

In the most apical zone where auxin does not limit growth, there is good evidence that growth is limited by a food factor or factors. To avoid misunderstanding it should be pointed out that the term "food factor" is used in its broadest sense. There is evidence that, like auxin, it is more of the nature of a hormone than of a nutrient.

The limiting influence of auxin and the effect of aging can both be removed by applying very high concentrations of auxin; if this is done, then the limitation of growth exerted by the food factor should become apparent. In the experiments of Went (1935), high concentrations of auxin, in paste form, were applied to the tips of intact coleoptiles at five different stages of growth, i.e. at five different physiological ages. The final lengths of the upper 15 mm. of the treated coleoptiles after 22 hours were 248, 246, 253, 251, and 244 per cent, and of the controls 192 and 198 per cent, of the original lengths. Hence in these zones the growth increase was *the same* irrespective of the age at which the excess auxin was applied, and hence their growth must be limited by some factor other than auxin or aging. If, on the other hand, the plants are de-seeded some time before auxin is applied, this would reduce the amount of the food factor present, and the excess auxin could then not bring about so much increased growth. To test this view, normal and de-seeded plants were compared. To half of each group excess auxin was applied. After 22 hours the de-seeded controls had increased 21.0 per cent and those treated with auxin 30.4 per cent; on the other hand, the intact controls had increased 37.7 per cent and the intact plants treated with auxin 101.3 per cent. The auxin thus produced only a 9 per cent increase in the de-seeded against a 63 per cent increase in the intact plants, so that growth of the de-seeded plants was being almost entirely limited by the food factor.

A simple demonstration that growth of the upper part of a coleoptile is limited by a factor other than auxin may be given by applying auxin paste of low concentration to one side of the extreme tip of an intact coleoptile. The first visible curvature appears 6–10 mm. below the tip, showing that the upper part of the plant does not respond to the applied auxin; this must be because auxin is here in excess and the food factor is therefore limiting (u).

C. The Limitation of Size in the Plant

In the preceding pages certain cases have been discussed in which auxin is not the factor limiting growth. Laibach and Kornmann (1933a), who were the first to apply auxin to intact *Avena* coleoptiles, obtained with it only a temporary increase in growth rate, the treated plants being very soon caught up again by the controls. They therefore drew the same conclusion as had Cholodny (1931a), that auxin "appreciably accelerates the rate of development and (correspondingly) shortens the duration of the life cycle of each cell." In other words, if we hasten the growth rate by applying auxin we also hasten the onset of maturity. This view is the opposite of that of Went (1928), that "the mature state of a cell is only conditional; cells do not attain any absolute final length, but their cessation of growth is the result of a complex of circumstances." There are no facts, nor any *a priori* reasons, for assuming that growth is an autonomic function of a young plant cell, and that the action of auxin is only to accelerate this primary growth. In this monograph we have subscribed to the simpler view that auxin is one of the many factors necessary for the ordinary growth process, and "without auxin no growth."

It is important, also, that in some cases excess auxin, applied to intact plants, has definitely caused growth

beyond the normal. Went (1935) found that in *Avena* application of strong auxin paste to the extreme tip of the
coleoptiles made them reach a length of 66–72 mm., while
controls reached only 45–54 mm. Schlenker and Mittmann
(1936) and van Overbeek (*u*) obtained an increase both in
growth rate and in final length by treating dwarf plants
with auxin (*cf.* also Loehwing and Bauguess, 1936). Since
in some plants auxin is not the limiting factor in growth,
while in others the application of high auxin concentrations
to the growing region causes swellings which—secondarily—
inhibit further growth in length (see Chapter XIII), it is
not always possible to increase the final length by auxin
application. But this in no way invalidates the thesis that
the ultimate size of many plants is limited by the auxin
which they form, and not by any inherent "morphological"
factor.

D. APPLICATIONS OF THE TWO-FACTOR SCHEME

It is clear that the two-factor scheme of growth, developed
above, may be applied to a number of different types of
growth. Thus Bünning (1927) found in *Secale* coleoptiles
that the growing zone was limited to only 4 mm. in the
center of the 24 mm. length. Incision above this growing
zone gave positive curvatures below the incision, which
may be taken as showing that the auxin supply from above
was being intercepted. Incision below this zone gave positive
curvatures above the incision, showing that the supply of
the food factor from below was now being intercepted.
The existence of this narrow growing zone must be ascribed
to the rate of supply of these two factors being relatively
slow compared to their rate of combination. We have been
unable to confirm Bünning's findings on *Secale* coleoptiles
(*u*), but the same considerations apply to mesocotyls of
Zea Mays grown in darkness (see Figure 35, a). The opposite case is given by the coleoptile of light-grown *Zea
Mays*, in which the growing zone is a very long region (Figure 35, c). In this part of the plant the rate of supply of the

two factors must be relatively fast as compared with their rate of combination, and hence neither is limiting over a considerable zone. *Avena* grown in red light is intermediate between these two (Figure 35, b). Another variation of

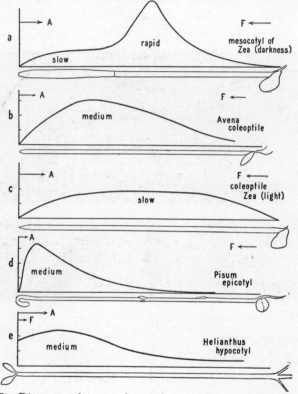

FIG. 35. Diagrams of types of growth in seedlings. Ordinates, relative growth rates; abscissae, zones of the shoot. Relative amount, and direction of movement, of auxin, A, and food factor, F, indicated by length and direction of arrows; their rate of combination indicated by rapid, medium, or slow.

this growth type is that in which the growth is almost entirely apical, as in *Pisum* seedlings (Figure 35, d). This is comparable with the *Zea* mesocotyl, but the growing zone is shifted to the tip, doubtless on account of the very low auxin supply, only small amounts of auxin being obtainable from apical buds of *Pisum* by diffusion (*u*).

The growth of the mesocotyl of grasses merits special

consideration. Elongation of the mesocotyl has been encountered as a technical difficulty by almost everyone who has worked with *Avena*, the very long curved mesocotyls making it impossible to obtain straight plants. This can be prevented by exposing the germinating seeds to light (Beyer, 1927) or to heat (du Buy and Nuernbergk, 1929, 1929a, 1930) (see Figure 36). The mesocotyl length of

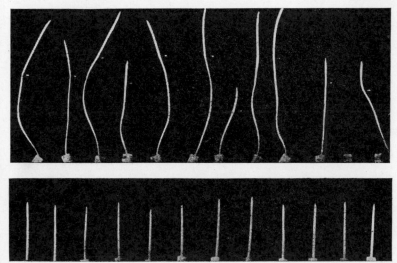

Fig. 36. Upper row, *Avena* seedlings grown in darkness: white dots indicate node between mesocotyl and coleoptile; lower row, grown in yellow light. (From van Overbeek, 1936.)

4-day old *Avena* seedlings may reach 60 mm. if grown in darkness, but is only 2 mm. if occasionally exposed to red or yellow light during growth.

An explanation of this phenomenon has been given by van Overbeek (1936), according to whom it depends on a decrease in the amount of auxin produced by the tip on exposure to red or yellow light, or to high temperature. Thus the coleoptile tips of *Zea Mays* plants which had been kept for 45 minutes at 48°, and whose mesocotyls were correspondingly greatly inhibited, gave off less auxin than those of control plants. If this auxin deficiency was removed by smearing 0.02 per cent auxin paste on the tip of the coleoptile after the heat treatment, growth of the mesocotyl was resumed. In the controls, the mesocotyls reached 48.5 mm., in the heat-treated plants 20.7 mm., and in the heat-treated plants treated with extra auxin, 48.2 mm. In addition to this effect, it is possible that the mesocotyl cells are more sensitive than coleoptile cells to applied auxin, at any rate in darkness. The growth of the mesocotyl is thus entirely dependent on the auxin which reaches it from the base of the coleoptile.

By differences in the relative rates of supply of the auxin and the food factor the known morphological types of seedlings of the grasses can be similarly explained. Those types with short coleoptile and long mesocotyl (*Setaria* type) presumably have relatively high auxin supply and low food factor supply; those with long coleoptile and short mesocotyl (*Avena* type) the reverse.

Du Buy and Nuernbergk (1932) have attempted to group the known cases of growth distribution into four main growth types. Their type 1 is the *Avena* coleoptile (b in Figure 35), having a relatively long growing zone. Type 2 is the *Helianthus* seedling and presumably the hypocotyls of all dicotyledons. In plants of this type the growth is largely apical and does not stop for some time on removal of the plumula and cotyledons. There is also no regeneration of auxin production. In accordance with the view developed above, however, the characteristic of this type is that *both* the auxin *and* most of the food factor are provided from above, *i.e.* from the cotyledons (Figure 35, e). In *Helianthus* and *Lupinus* the auxin is present in excess, as shown by the fact that it is readily obtainable by diffusion out of all parts of the hypocotyl. Correspondingly, the addition of auxin has a relatively small effect because the principal limitation is provided by the food factor. A different explanation for this type of growth has been adopted by Dijkman (1934), du Buy and Nuernbergk (1932), and Jost and Reiss (1936). According to these workers, in *Lupinus* (or *Helianthus*) auxin is formed over the whole length of the hypocotyl. Dijkman, however, found that the degree to which such hypocotyls will grow out after decapitation depends on their initial length, which fits in better with the above view of a flooding with auxin in the earlier stages of growth. Production of auxin all over the hypocotyl would be at variance with everything known for other etiolated plants, and does not explain the experiments below. Fliry (1932) found that the addition of auxin and sugar, or replacement of the tip, gave better growth of decapitated hypocotyls than auxin alone, which confirms the above view that food factors are limiting in these seedlings (see Table VI).

TABLE VI

GROWTH INCREMENTS, IN *mm.* PER 20 HOURS, OF DECAPITATED *Helianthus* HYPOCOTYLS WITH VARIOUS APPLICATIONS. AFTER FLIRY (1932). MEAN OF 10–14 PLANTS IN EACH GROUP

EXPERIMENT No.	CONTROL	AUXIN	SUGAR	TIP REPLACED	AUXIN AND SUGAR
29	2.9	6.7		10.4	
55	3.0		4.7		
61	2.5		6.3		
85 and 93	2.9	4.2			8.0

In Type 3 of du Buy and Nuernbergk the growth is still more restricted to the apex, as in etiolated *Pisum sativum* stems (*cf.* Figure 35, d). Since the growing zone is so limited, tropistic curvatures do not travel very far down the stem. This type is, in our view, quite unrelated to the hypocotyl type (Figure 35, e) but is merely an extreme case of a and b with low rate of auxin production. Correspondingly little or no auxin can be obtained from such stems by diffusion.

Type 4 is exemplified by roots, the growth there also being principally apical. As the function of auxin in the growth of roots is not yet clear, they need not be considered in this two-factor scheme.

An early application of the two-factor scheme was made by Dolk (1930) in his attempt to explain the migration of curvatures down the *Avena* coleoptile, and the autonomic straightening of the curved zones ("autotropism"). If an unequal distribution of auxin between the two sides of the plant has been brought about by gravity or other means, then the side with the more auxin grows rapidly (convex side) and thus temporarily reduces the supply of food factor. When the auxin distribution becomes equal again, the side which has grown less (concave side) is better supplied with food factor and hence reacts more to the auxin. It thus becomes slightly convex, and this results in a straightening.

Weber (1931) has raised a number of objections to the two-factor theory, based on experiments on geotropic curvature of *Hordeum*. The growth measurements which he presents, however, are scarcely accurate enough to allow detailed conclusions to be drawn.

It may be concluded that this scheme of the limitation of growth either by auxin or by the food factor provides an acceptable theory for the growth of a great many objects.

E. Auxin Inactivation and Dwarf Growth

One of the most marked chemical properties of the auxins is their extreme sensitivity to oxidative destruction. They are readily destroyed also by plant enzymes, probably by the peroxidase or oxidase system, as we have seen (Chapter IV *A*). That auxin disappears within the plant tissue was shown by the analyses of Bonner and Thimann (1935) on coleoptiles previously treated with auxin. If low concentrations were applied the amount of auxin disappearing was proportional to the resulting growth, but when high concentrations were used there was a rapid disappearance of the excess auxin without any accompanying growth.

A phenomenon similar to this was found by van Overbeek (1935) in dwarf forms of *Zea Mays*. These differ by only one gene from the normal type, and their growth rates, especially of the mesocotyl and stem, are greatly reduced. In *nana*, one of the dwarf races, the seedlings were found to produce less auxin than the normals and also to respond less to applied auxin. Since their relative auxin production and their sensitivity to applied auxin were the same, namely 55 per cent of the normal, van Overbeek concluded that both these effects were due to an increased power of inactivating auxin. This was proved directly by measurements of the auxin inactivation; when mesocotyl sections were placed on agar containing auxin, the *nana* inactivated about twice as much auxin as the normal. This power affects particularly the growing zones distant from the auxin-producing center, so that although the coleoptile may reach normal size, the mesocotyl scarcely elongates at all. If the normal plants were warmed to 48° for 30 minutes, the rate of auxin inactivation was increased, and correspondingly the growth rate decreased. In dwarf races more extreme than *nana*, having both coleoptile and mesocotyl greatly reduced in length, a correspondingly still smaller production of auxin has been found (van Overbeek, *u*).

Lehmann (1936), Hinderer (1936), and Graze and Schlenker (1936) have investigated auxin production in the stem tips, and auxin content in the ripe anthers, of a number of *Epilobium* strains and their hybrids. That the small *Epilobium* hybrids are prevented from growing simply by lack of auxin was directly shown by applying auxin to them, when very good growth resulted (Schlenker and Mittmann, 1936). The aim of this group of workers was to account for the differences in length of the reciprocal hybrids in terms of auxin production by them and by their parents. While they find a gross correspondence, the exceptions make it clear that other factors are also involved. Of these, we suggest that the sensitivity to auxin is the most important. If sensitivity be assumed to be determined by the genes, and auxin production by the cytoplasm, then a qualitative agreement between the observed and predicted values is obtained.

These first attempts are doubtless the beginning of the application of our knowledge about auxins to problems in plant genetics. Auxin is one of the principal internal factors controlling growth and the only one which as yet can be experimentally investigated. Since the action of the genes is through their control of internal factors, the intermediate stages between growth genes and their effect can now be approached through auxin.

F. Radiation and Its Effects on Auxin

It has often been observed that short wave-length radiations have a markedly inhibiting effect on plant growth (see Duggar, 1936, Chapters XXII, XXVI, and XXIX). In regard to x-rays, the relation between this and their effect on auxin has been investigated by Skoog (1935). He found that the direct effect of hard x-radiation was on the auxin itself, which is readily inactivated, both *in vitro* and *in vivo*. The inactivation is almost certainly by oxidation. Neither the sensitivity to auxin, nor its rate of transport, was changed after the irradiation of *Pisum, Avena,* and *Helianthus* seedlings, but their auxin production was greatly decreased. For short periods after irradiation the diminished growth could be accounted for by the auxin destruction. Thereafter, a secondary effect of the x-rays on the auxin-producing system became evident in *Pisum.*

Ultra-violet light also inhibits growth, and correspondingly Laibach and Maschmann (1933) found that unfiltered ultra-violet inactivates auxin solutions almost completely. According to Koningsberger (1936), ultra-violet of wavelengths between 230 and 330 mμ inactivates auxin *a* lactone solutions with great rapidity.

Bright light also has a dwarfing effect on many plants. This is due to the effect of light in decreasing sensitivity to auxin. The experiments of van Overbeek (1933) with *Raphanus* hypocotyls, and of Thimann and Skoog (1934) with *Vicia Faba* stems, have shown that in light a given amount of auxin produces much less elongation than in darkness. Whether this reduced sensitivity is due to increased destruction of auxin in light is not clear. Van Overbeek (1933) was not able to show (by transport experiments) any destruction of the free-moving auxin in *Raphanus* hypocotyls. However, he later found (*cf.* X G) that in light *Avena* coleoptiles react differently to auxin *a* and to indole-acetic acid, and explains this by a greater destruction of auxin *a* in the plant in light. On the other hand, in the experiments of Thimann and Skoog (1934), *Vicia Faba* stems, supplied, not with auxin *a* but with indole-acetic acid, showed the characteristic decrease of sensitivity to auxin in light. It is therefore probable that, while light inactivation of auxin *a* may occur, there is also a direct effect of light on sensitivity of cells to auxin.

CHAPTER VI

AUXIN TRANSPORT AND POLARITY

A. AUXIN TRANSPORT IN GENERAL

The *Avena* test method for measuring the concentration of auxin in agar blocks makes use of the ready transport of auxin within the coleoptile. Practically every auxin experiment reveals how easily the plant allows the rapid movement of auxin from one place to another. On this transportability of auxin depends its function as a hormone or correlation carrier.

The rate of auxin transport in the plant is far greater than that of diffusion, and, as will be seen later, van der Weij (1932) has shown that many properties of the transport process rule out the possibility of its being a diffusion phenomenon. In the intact coleoptile the rate of auxin transport is of the order of 15 mm. per hour, in the cut coleoptile slightly less,—10–12 mm. per hour. The rate also differs for different auxins, auxin *a* being transported about 10 per cent faster than indole-acetic acid (*u; cf.* VIII *G*).

As to the path of transport of auxin, few data are available, and, as is always the case in the absence of good data, conflicting views are held. It is generally assumed that in the *Avena* coleoptile transport takes place through all parts of the parenchyma, and not primarily through the vascular bundles. If the latter were the case, no well oriented curvatures towards light or gravity could be expected, because there are only 2 bundles present. Further, if an agar block containing auxin is placed on the cut surface of a coleoptile stump, a curvature is obtained whether the agar covers a vascular bundle or not. Van der Weij (1932) states that the curvature is stronger when it does not, but Laibach and Kornmann (1933*a*) find the reverse (*cf.* also Snow, VI *C*). In our own experiments (*u*), no important difference between the transport of auxin along the broad and narrow sides of the coleoptile could be found [1]; the discrepant results of Laibach and Kornmann may perhaps be explained by their use of too low a humidity, which causes pronounced drying of the tissue outside the vascular bundles. At all events, transport can take place through the parenchyma, the cells of which are strongly elongated in the direction of transport. Lateral transport of auxin across the coleoptile must be slight; if it were not, curvature could not so easily be produced by applying auxin to one side. Direct evidence that the movement of auxin follows the direction of elongation of the parenchyma is provided by some experiments of Tammes (1931). He found that when a permanent torsion is brought about in the upper part of an *Avena* coleoptile, the phototropic or geotropic stimulus is no longer transmitted longitudinally, but follows the direction of the twisted cells. The displacement of the plane of phototropic curvature out of the direction of the light was proportional to the amount of torsion imposed on the upper part of the coleoptile.

The path of transport of auxin in other organs may be different from that in the coleoptile. In the *Nicotiana* leaf auxin moves almost exclusively through the vascular bundles, or at least through the veins (Avery, 1935). Similar results have been obtained in *Malva* leaves (*u*). Correspondingly, Cooper (1936) showed that in *Citrus* stems the movement is through the phloem, where it follows the same rules as the translocation of carbohydrates. On the other hand, Hitchcock and Zimmerman (1936) found that auxin may be transported with the transpiration stream; this, as will be shown in section *D*, only occurs when excessively high auxin concentrations are applied.

B. POLARITY IN GENERAL

The earliest investigators of correlation found that such correlations as were studied, particularly shoot and root

---

[1] The bundles are on the narrow side—see Chapter III.

formation, were of a polar nature. The original concept of polarity in the plant was defined as a tendency to produce regenerates of different nature in apical and basal parts, the apical ends tending to give rise to shoots, the basal ends to roots. In the words of van der Lek (1925), "polarity shows itself as a persistent contrast between basal and apical pole in regard to organ formation." That this difference is inherent in the plant itself, and little subject to modification by external factors, was made clear especially by Vöchting (1878, 1884, 1892, 1908), who compared the polarity of the plant very aptly to that of a magnet. At first Sachs (1880) disagreed with the idea of inherent polarity, believing that the polarity had been established by the continued effect of gravity. Vöchting, however, replied to this criticism by showing, amongst other things, that twigs of weeping willow, which had been for a long time inverted with respect to gravity, maintained their normal polarity with respect to root and shoot formation. In this connection an interesting recent study of polarity in bud formation (Schwanitz, 1935) has shown that such a polarity becomes established in rhizomes, which are maintained horizontal after removal from the plant. At about the time of Sachs and Vöchting similar phenomena in regard to regeneration of organs were being investigated in zoölogy, and the same general state of affairs was found to exist in both animals and plants. Thus it was natural that theories which were current in the zoölogical field came to be applied to polarity in plants. These theories, including those of fields, axial gradients (later modified to metabolic gradients), and food concentrations, were scarcely more than restatements of the observed facts.

With the development of plant physiology, the idea of polarity appeared again in connection with a new phenomenon, the polar transmission of phototropic stimulus. Both Darwin (1880) and Rothert (1894) showed that if the tip of the plant be illuminated from one side, then not only the tip, but also the base, bends towards the light. The reverse, however, does not occur (Rothert, 1894; van der Wolk, 1911);

(an apparent exception was described by Von Guttenberg [1913], but this was afterwards contradicted). Hence the phototropic stimulus is conducted only from the apex towards the base.

C. Polarity of Auxin Transport

The experiments of Boysen Jensen (1910, 1911, 1913) showed that the conduction of the phototropic stimulus may take place across a cut surface and therefore involves a

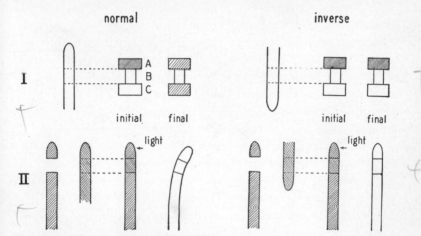

Fig. 37. Polar transport of auxin in the *Avena* coleoptile. I. Agar block, A, containing auxin, is placed on coleoptile section, B, resting on plain agar block, C. Degree of shading indicates auxin content of agar. Left side, normal transport; right side, section inverted—no transport. (After Went, 1935*b*.) II. Transmission of phototropic stimulus through introduced section of coleoptile.   Left side, stimulus passes normally placed section; right side, does not pass inverted section. (After Beyer, 1928*a*.)

diffusion process.   The polarity of its movement led Paál (1919) to suggest that the transport of the growth substance in the coleoptile might itself be polar.   The truth of Paál's suggestion was proven by the experiments of Went (1928). Since small amounts of auxin can be quantitatively analyzed by the curvature technique, its movement through plant tissues may be accurately followed.   Went's technique was as follows: on a number of sections of coleoptile (B in Figure 37, I) was placed a block of agar (A) upon which a number of coleoptile tips had previously stood, and which therefore contained auxin. The concentration of auxin in a control block prepared in the same way was determined directly by the *Avena* test. Underneath the coleoptile sections was placed a block of plain agar (C) and after they had been in contact with it for some time, this, and also the top block, were again analyzed by the *Avena* test. Thus the original and final concentrations in the donating block, A, and also the final concentration in the receiving block, C, were known, and hence the amount which had been transported was found. Some auxin also was consumed, or inactivated, during the experiment, but this had little effect on the result. The principal conclusion was that transport took place *only* from the apical to the basal end of the section, and not inversely. It should be added that these experiments were carried out with physiological concentrations of auxin.

A confirmation of the fact that movement of the phototropic stimulus within the coleoptile is strictly polar was given by Beyer (1928*a*), whose experiments were an extension of those of Boysen Jensen. Between the tip and the base of an *Avena* seedling he interposed a cylinder of coleoptile which in one group of experiments was in the normal position, in the other group inverted (see Figure 37, II). If the tip was now illuminated, the stimulus was transmitted to the base, causing curvature there, but only through the normally inserted section.

Since it was now clear that the polar transmission of stimulus is due to the polar transport of auxin, the nature of this transport was subjected to an intensive investigation by van der Weij (1932, 1934). His technique was essentially that described above, and qualitatively he confirmed the strict basipetal (apex-to-base) polarity of the transport (Figure 38 C). If there is any acropetal transport it is excessively slight (*cf.* Snow, p. 97). As regards the quantitative aspects, he found it necessary to distinguish between the velocity, in mm. per hour, and the "intensity" or capacity of the auxin transport, in units per section per hour. The velocity is about 10–12 mm. per hour in *Avena* sections at 25°, and is almost completely independent of temperature (Figure 38 A). The capacity, or amount transported per unit time, however, depends on temperature, increasing rapidly from 0° to reach an optimum at 35–40°.

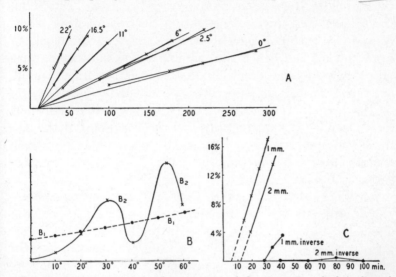

Fig. 38. A, auxin transported as per cent of the amount applied (ordinate) through 2 mm. sections of *Avena* coleoptiles as a function of time (abscissa) and temperature. Since all curves cross the x axis at about 10 minutes, the transport velocity is unaffected by temperature. B, amounts of auxin transported (ordinate) at different temperatures (abscissa); curve B_1 pure diffusion, curve B_2 transport through coleoptile sections. C, auxin transported through 1 mm. and 2 mm. coleoptile sections: crosses, from apex to base; circles, inverse. (All from van der Weij, *Rec. trav. bot. néerl. 29*: 379–496, 1932.)

Between 0° and 30° the Q_{10} is close to 3, *i.e.* that of a chemical process (see Figure 38 B). Further, at physiological temperatures the capacity is independent of the length of the section. Since the capacity of true diffusion falls off with the square of the distance, the transport process must be fundamentally different from that of diffusion. Under van der Weij's conditions, the concentration of auxin in the receiving block became equal to that in the donating block in 1–2 hours,—a rate of transport many times that which diffusion could cause. At 0°, however, the character of the process changes, the capacity becoming partly determined by the length of the section, although its direction is still polar ("polar diffusion"). With increasing concentration of auxin in the donating block the absolute amount transported through a given section increases, but not quite in proportion, so that the percentage transported decreases.

He later found (1934) that the polarity of the transport is so strict as to be completely independent of an external auxin gradient, auxin being actually carried from a lower to a higher concentration (see Table VII). The increase in

TABLE VII

Auxin Transport through 1 *mm*. Coleoptile Cylinders. Concentration 100 = 14.6° ± 0.5°. (After van der Weij, 1934)

Auxin concentration at the beginning of transport experiment				
In upper agar block	100	100	100	100
" lower " "	0	100	200	300
Auxin concentrations after 5½ hours' transport at 23° C.				
In upper agar block	14	14	12	14
" lower " "	87	193	284	378
Decrease in upper block	86	86	88	86
Increase in lower block	87	93	84	78

auxin concentration in the receiving block may be seen to equal exactly the decrease in auxin in the donating block. The best simile for the transport is that of objects along a moving band; the band goes at constant speed, so that the number of objects arriving at the end per unit time is independent of the length (capacity independent of length of section); the time required for the first object to reach the end is proportional to the length of the band (velocity constant); if not removed from the end the objects continue to pile up (transport against the gradient).

If the coleoptile sections are placed in low concentrations of ether vapor, the polarity is suspended and the transport becomes essentially a diffusion, the capacity becoming inversely proportional to the length of the section. This may be compared with the transport at 0°, which also approaches that of diffusion, but which, by contrast, maintains its polarity. If the ether concentration used is just high enough to make polarity disappear it will reappear on re-aëration ("reversible narcosis").

That the polar transport of auxin is as strict in the intact plant as in cut sections follows from a number of considerations. The strictly basipetal translocation of tropistic stimulus mentioned above is a good example. The polarity of root formation (XI B) and of cambial stimulation (XIII B) are others. The experiments of Laibach and Kornmann (1933a) also confirm it. They applied small agar blocks containing auxin to the outside of intact coleoptiles at different distances from the tip. The resulting curvatures were always below, never above, the block. However, Snow (1936) finds that if relatively high concentrations of auxin in lanoline are applied to the outside of coleoptiles, curvatures occur above the paste; this result is most marked if the paste is applied to the narrow side (cf. above), and is very slight and slow in beginning if applied to the broad side. It is thus largely due to transport upwards in the transpiration stream.

The same polarity of transport appears to hold in other tissues, such as *Elaeagnus* stems (van der Weij, 1933a), *Raphanus* hypocotyls (van Overbeek, 1933), *Vicia Faba* stems (Thimann and Skoog, 1934), *Lupinus* hypocotyls (Dijkman, 1934), *Coleus* stems and growing petioles (Mai, 1934; Gouwentak and Hellinga, 1935), *Nicotiana* leaf-veins (Avery, 1935), *Pisum* stems (*u*), and *Salix* stems (Michener, *u*); apparently, however, it does not hold in roots (see IX C).

Earlier workers on geotropism have found that plants which are inverted after being placed horizontally give greater geotropic curvatures than those which are placed upright after the same geotropic stimulation ("geotonic effect"). Since the geotropic reaction is now explained in

terms of the lateral transport of auxin (see X C), it might
be thought that this "geotonic effect" is due to the action
of gravity on the longitudinal transport of auxin. Pfaeltzer
(1934), however, was unable to find any indication of an
effect of gravity, acting in the longitudinal axis of the plant,
on auxin transport. Its polarity is therefore completely
independent of gravity.

The effect of light on the transport has been studied by
du Buy (1933). In 1926 Went had concluded, from the
effect of light on auxin curvatures, that light temporarily
decreases the rate of auxin transport, and a temporary decrease in curvature for half an hour after illumination was
confirmed by van Overbeek (1936a). The exact explanation
of this phenomenon is, however, difficult in the present
state of our knowledge. The experiments of du Buy were
measurements of the effect of lateral or terminal illumination on the amount of auxin transported through coleoptile
sections. His data, however, are scarcely sufficient to support the rather far-reaching conclusions which he draws
from them, and one can only say with certainty that light
appears to have no effect on auxin transport. The earlier
experiments of van Overbeek (1933) on *Raphanus* hypocotyls also failed to show any effect of light on the transport,
and the same conclusion may be drawn from Boysen Jensen's
experiments (1933) with *Avena*.

We may therefore conclude that the polarity of auxin
transport is determined by some property inherent in the
living cells, and difficult to influence from without.

D. OTHER VIEWS ON THE TRANSPORT OF AUXIN

Recently Czaja (1931, 1935a) has suggested that the
polarity is not the cause of, but is due to, the movement of
auxin. Thus he believes that the apex-to-base gradient of
auxin, caused by its production at the apex, is the cause of
the polarity in the plant. If high concentrations of auxin
be applied to the side of the plant the gradient from outside
inwards is at right angles to the longitudinal gradient and

this is considered to cause the growth inhibition observed (see Chapter XIII). The inhibition of the growth of roots by auxin he also interprets in terms of two gradients (see IX *D*). There are two major objections to this view. In the first place it is in opposition to the experiments on transport, especially those of van der Weij (VI *C*). In these, the direction of transport is shown to be totally unaffected by auxin gradients applied from without. Even if the polarity is suspended by narcotization, then, on removal of the ether, it is re-established in the original apex-to-base direction, irrespective of whether this is with or against the applied auxin concentrations. Czaja's view as applied to roots has also been directly disproved by experiment (see IX *D*). In the second place, opposing streams of auxin are inconceivable, for an auxin stream has no inertia, by which it might retain its direction, and therefore the cell cannot distinguish an auxin molecule which has entered it from above from one which has entered from below. Two such streams in opposite directions would merely amount to a more equal auxin distribution throughout.

Hitchcock and Zimmerman (1935, 1936) have denied that the transport of auxin is polar at all. They found that when very high concentrations of auxins were applied to the roots of intact plants, some of it was absorbed and moved upwards, presumably in the transpiration stream. In the first place, it is very doubtful whether it is justifiable to apply the results of experiments at such unphysiologically high auxin concentrations to the processes of the normal plant (see also p. 101.) In the second place, it has, of course, been known for a great many years that any substance, even though it be toxic, when it is once in the vessels will be carried with the transpiration stream. The auxins would not be expected to be exceptions to this. Snow (1936) has studied the acropetal (base-to-apex) movement of auxin in coleoptiles and hypocotyls, and concludes that the bulk of it takes place in the conducting strands (*cf.* p. 97). The extensive experiments discussed above, and those on auxin

correlations in Chapters XI, XII, and XIII show that the
normal transport of auxin is through living tissues and it is
this transport which is polar. Hitchcock and Zimmerman
have completely failed to grasp the importance of the relation between the polarity of auxin transport and the already
well-established polarity of growth, organ formation, and
transmission of stimulus.

Laibach and Fischnich (1936) have shown that if a *Coleus*
leaf be split so that the lower part of the blade be connected
to the midrib only through laminal tissue above it, auxin
applied to this lower part will still reach the midrib and thus
the petiole; its path of transport must therefore be at first
acropetal in the leaf-blade. They thus oppose Avery's (1935)
conclusion that auxin transport in the leaf is a strictly polar
phenomenon. However, in Avery's experiments the polarity
was determined in leaves with veins, while in Laibach and
Fischnich's work the veins were cut, so that the possibility
remains that auxin transport in the larger veins is polar,
but in small veins and mesophyll not. Here, too, it must
be emphasized that the lack of polarity is only detected
when unphysiologically high auxin concentrations are used.

Both Cholodny (1935) and Pohl (1935, 1936) claim that
auxin moves from the seed upwards into the coleoptile,
especially in the early stages of germination. As we know
from Skoog's experiments (1937), this, however, is not
auxin, but an auxin precursor, which is converted into auxin
in the coleoptile tip, and also, probably, is convertible into
auxin in the seed itself (*cf.* IV *B*). It is impossible to obtain
the slightest amount of auxin from the apical cut surface
of a coleoptile or mesocotyl stump when connected with the
seed, even in the earliest stages of germination (*u*). Further,
Thimann (1936*a*) has shown that application of indole-
acetic acid to the scutellum of de-seeded plants does not
accelerate the growth of the coleoptile.

Many of the conflicting conclusions regarding polarity of
auxin transport are brought into line by the assumption
that auxin transport in the shoot is perfectly polar as long

as the auxin is present or applied in a concentration similar to that normally obtaining in the plant, but that when the applied concentration exceeds the normal by a factor of 100 times or so, the polarity disappears. An exactly similar conclusion is reached in Chapter XI in regard to root formation, which is completely polar so long as auxin is applied in concentrations of the same order of magnitude as those in the plant, but which becomes non-polar when concentrations 100 to 1000 times the normal are used. No conclusions can therefore be drawn from the indiscriminate application of auxin paste of high concentrations, and no good reason has yet been given for doubting the polarity of normal auxin transport in the plant.

E. POSSIBLE MECHANISMS OF AUXIN TRANSPORT

We have seen that auxin transport is not a process of diffusion, both on account of its characteristics (especially the velocity) and of its polarity. No satisfactory explanation has yet been given for the transport.

To account for the high velocity of transmission of the phototropic stimulus, Brauner (1922) invoked the theory of de Vries (1885) according to which the streaming protoplasm carries with it organic materials, which are thus carried more rapidly than they could diffuse. Went (1928) transferred this view to the transport of auxin in the coleoptile. Van der Weij (1932), however, opposed it because of the independence of the transport velocity on temperature. Bottelier, however (1934, 1935), has shown that between 17° and 35° C. there is no appreciable change in the streaming velocity in *Avena* at the age generally used. He has discovered a remarkable parallelism between the effect of light on the streaming velocity and the well-known light-growth reaction; both are proportional to the total energy and both show the same variation with wave-length of the light. Further, the amount of streaming protoplasm in the coleoptile shows a daily and yearly variation which in many ways parallels the variation in sensitivity to auxin discussed in III *C* 8.

There is thus sufficient parallelism to suggest that protoplasmic streaming could account for the high velocity and capacity of auxin transport, though it cannot, of course, account for the polarity. The latter might perhaps be limited to the passage from cell to cell. Alternatively, the relation may not be causal, but both transport and streaming may be dependent on the same underlying cause.

Although the transport of auxin is not readily comparable with that of other organic substances in plants, it may be mentioned, firstly, that Kok (1931, 1932) failed to find any influence of protoplasmic streaming on the transport of lithium or of caffeine. In the second place, if the transport of auxin were comparable with that of fluorescein within the tissues, then the above theory would be almost certainly discredited by the observations of Schumacher (1936). Among a number of interesting experiments made with the fluorescence microscope, he has observed that in hair-cells of *Cucurbita* the fluorescein moves strictly polarly towards the tip of the hairs. At the same time the protoplasm was observed to be in vigorous rotation, and the movement of the fluorescein continued independent of it. The dye appeared to move through the cross walls as readily as in the cells, and he suggests that the movement takes place in some way along the wall itself. In this connection Mangham (1917), Van den Honert (1932), and Söllner (1933) have suggested a mechanism for the transport of organic substances which fits in very well with the observations and might explain some aspects of auxin transport.

If at an interface between two liquids, such as ether and water, a third substance which is absorbed at this interface be added, it will move along the interface with a velocity of up to 3 cm. per second. If the arrangement is such that this third substance reacts at the other end of the interface, considerable amounts of it may be so transported (see Figure 39). Van den Honert achieved this result by using potassium oleate as the third substance, and allowing it to react with HCl at the other end of the interface. This scheme would allow for transport with high capacity and velocity, being many hundred times faster than diffusion. However, at the moment there seems no acceptable way of associating it with any polarity of movement.

All these schemes, though they may explain the type of movement observed, are without any bearing on the essential problem, namely that of the polarity. Directed movement of a substance in solution can only be due to (1) a pressure gradient, (2) a concentration gradient, or (3) an electric potential gradient. Types (1) and (2) can be discarded because no pressure gradient exists, and because transport takes place independent of, or even against, concentration gradients. Potential gradients could only cause the movement of ions, and so far all the auxins known are ionizable substances.

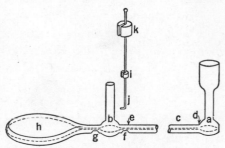

Fig. 39. Model to show rapid transport of surface-active substances along an interface. Horizontal tube ab, 100 cm. long from d to e, is half filled with very dilute acid and half with ether, and chlorphenol red is added. When a little potassium oleate solution is added at a the indicator changes to purple, the color change moving rapidly along to b, where it can be titrated with acid, using the stirrer kij. Thus there is mass movement of potassium ions along the interface. (From van den Honert, *Proc. Kon. Akad. Wetensch.* Amsterdam *35:* 1104–1111, 1932.)

Went (1932) has tried to base a theory of polarity upon these considerations and upon some experiments with dyes. It was found that acid dyes moved in plant tissues more rapidly toward the base than toward the apex, while basic dyes moved in the reverse direction. This shows that direction of movement is determined not merely by chemical constitution, but rather by the dissociating groups. Correspondingly, of the numerous measurements of electric potentials in plants which have been made in the past, the majority show that the apex of the shoot is negative to the base, a potential in the right direction for transport of an anion, such as of auxin, towards the base. However, in such measurements it is never quite clear what kind of potential is being measured. Ramshorn (1934) has opposed the above theory on the ground that in his experiments the growing region was always positive to its surroundings. The measurements of Clark (1935), however, show that the apex of *Avena* is negative to the base. The potentials observed, while they show interesting parallelism with the light-growth reaction, show no parallelism with auxin transport, and the external application to *Avena* sections of a potential opposite to the inherent one was found to have no effect on the direction of auxin transport in the section (Clark, 1937). So far, then, there is no direct evidence to support an electrical theory of the transport, or, indeed, any other theory. This is regrettable because polarity is of great theoretical importance for the explanation both of growth and of correlations. Morphological polarity is essentially only a descriptive term, but it may become analytically approachable through the phenomenon of polar transport of a morphogenetic substance.

CHAPTER VII

THE CHEMISTRY OF THE AUXINS

A. EARLY WORK

The first indication that growth-promoting substances occur in quantity outside the plant was given by the experiments of Seubert (1925) who found that malt extract, saliva, diastase, and pepsin contained a substance active in causing negative *Avena* curvatures. On boiling these preparations for 15 minutes most of the activity remained, but in spite of this she concluded it was connected with the enzymic activity. Gorter (1927) also found growth-promoting activity in numerous enzyme preparations. Went (1928) in his experiments on the auxin secreted by the coleoptile tip showed, however, that it is stable to boiling as well as to light. He also determined its molecular weight (see section *D*).

Nielsen (1928) then found that the medium on which *Rhizopus suinus* or *Absidia ramosa*, two pathogenic fungi, had grown, was rich in a substance active in producing *Avena* curvatures. He made a preliminary study of the purification of the substance from *Rhizopus* cultures. At first he believed it was only produced on solid media, but this was later shown by Bonner (1932) to be due to the necessity of aërating the cultures. Nielsen (1930) found the substance to be soluble in ether but readily inactivated by the traces of peroxide normally present. By extracting with purified ether he obtained a syrup of which $1/60 \, \gamma$ [1] caused a definite curvature in *Avena*. Dolk and Thimann (1932), using liquid *Rhizopus* culture medium, then found that the substance is extracted by ether only from acid solution, *i.e.* it is itself an acid. By shaking out into ether and analyzing extract and residue for auxin, its partition

[1] One γ = 0.001 milligram.

coefficient between ether and water was found to be 9.4; using this value and shaking into ether from solutions buffered at different pH, the dissociation constant could be determined. It was 1.8×10^{-5} or pK = 4.75, *i.e.* about the same acid strength as acetic acid (for dissociation curve see Figure 43, p. 131). The substance is destroyed by warm acid but stable to warm alkali. Its extreme sensitivity to oxidizing agents was taken to indicate presence of one or more double bonds. Simultaneously and independently Kögl and Haagen Smit (1931) made preliminary purifications of the auxins formed by cultures of *Rhizopus reflexus*, yeast, and *b. coli*. These products also behaved as acids.

B. The Isolation of Auxins *a* and *b*

At the same time Kögl and Haagen Smit (1931) found an active substance to be present in large quantities in human urine. The bicarbonate-soluble fraction of the ether extract of urine was extracted with petroleum ether, and purified by partition between benzene and aqueous alcohol; it was then precipitated with lead acetate from weakly alkaline 70 per cent alcohol, treated with $Ca(OH)_2$ to precipitate a colored impurity, and finally heated with acid methanol. This, instead of giving an ester, produced what turned out to be a lactone. The product was distilled *in vacuo* (0.1 mm.), when the bulk of the active substance distilled at 125°–130°C., and yielded crystals of the acid $C_{18}H_{32}O_5$ ("auxin *a*"). Both acid and lactone were of about the same activity (approximately 50,000,000 AE per mg.). The method of purification is summarized in Table VIII, which is taken from Kögl, Haagen Smit, and Erxleben (1933). The extent of purification from evaporated urine was about 20,000 to 50,000 times.

Another active substance was subsequently isolated from malt and from corn germ oil by a very similar purification method (Kögl, Erxleben, and Haagen Smit, 1934). This substance, $C_{18}H_{30}O_4$, is isomeric with the lactone, but is an acid and was named auxin *b*. It had the same activity as auxin *a*. In a series of brilliant researches the constitutional

TABLE VIII

Purification of Auxin *a* from Urine
(Adapted from Kögl, Haagen Smit, and Erxleben, 1933)

TREATMENT	ACTIVE FRACTION Urine Concentrate (from 150 liters) (contains about 15000×10^6 AE)	WT. (GRAMS)	INACTIVE FRACTION
Acidify and extract with ether	↓		
	Ether extract	87	Residue
Fractionate with NaHCO₃	↓		
	Acid fraction	45	Neutral fraction
Extract with petroleum ether	↓		
	Residue		Petroleum extract
Extract with hot ligroin	↓		
	Residue	19.7	Ligroin extract
Dissolve in aqueous alcohol and extract with benzene	↓		
	Benzene layer		Aqueous alcohol layer
Extract with water and then with 50 per cent methanol	↓		
	Aqueous and methanol extracts		Benzene layer
Evaporate methanol and extract with ether	↓		
	Ether extract	5.5	Aqueous layer
Dissolve in aqueous alcohol and fractionate by lead salt formation	↓		
	Filtrate and (sometimes) ppt. from alkaline solution		Ppt. from neutral solution and (sometimes) ppt. from alkaline solution
Acidify and extract with ether	↓		
	Ether extract	3.2	Residue
Dissolve in aqueous alcohol and add KOH and Ca(CH₃COO)₂	↓		
	Filtrate	2.25	Ppt. (colored)
Heat with 1.5 per cent HCl in methanol	↓		
	Neutral fraction	1.2	Acid fraction
Distil *in vacuo*	↓		
	Middle fractions (125°–135°)	0.18	First fractions and residue
	↓		
	Crude crystallisate (contains 560–840 $\times 10^6$ AE) (*i.e.* yield 3–6 per cent)	0.04	
Recrystallize from alcohol-ligroin or aqueous acetone	↙ ↘		

Auxin *a* (m. 196°)   Auxin *a* lactone (m. 173°)

formulae of these two closely related compounds has been elucidated, although the whole amount of active crystals available was only 700 mg. (Kögl, Erxleben, and Haagen Smit, 1933; Kögl and Erxleben, 1934, 1935).

First the acid and lactone were shown to have but one double bond, and the acid to have one COOH group. After addition of hydrogen at the double bond, the number of H atoms in the molecule is still two short of saturation, and hence there must be one ring in the molecule. In auxin a the remaining three oxygen atoms were found to be in hydroxyl groups, while in auxin b one hydroxyl and one keto-group could be identified. Oxidative degradation of both auxin a and b gave rise to a C_{13} dicarboxylic acid which contained no hydroxyl groups. Similar oxidation of the hydrogenated derivative, which is biologically inactive, yielded a neutral C_{13} ketone. The oxidation has therefore carried away all the hydroxyl groups, together with a chain of 5 C atoms. From the difference between the two oxidations it is also clear that the double bond was not in the side chain which was removed. Further reasoning indicated that this side chain contained the three hydroxyl groups and the COOH group, and established their relative positions; hence the oxidations must be formulated as follows, substance I being auxin a, and II dihydro-auxin a:

$$\underset{\text{CH}}{\overset{\text{C.CHOH.CH}_2\text{.CHOH.CHOH.COOH}}{\Big\|}} \quad \text{I} \qquad \longrightarrow \qquad \underset{\text{COOH}}{\overset{\text{COOH}}{\Big<}} \quad \text{III}$$

$$\underset{\text{CH}_2}{\overset{\text{CH.CHOH.CH}_2\text{.CHOH.CHOH.COOH}}{\Big|}} \quad \text{II} \qquad \longrightarrow \qquad \underset{\text{CH}_2}{\overset{\text{CO}}{\Big|}} \quad \text{IV}$$

$$\underset{\text{CH}}{\overset{\text{C.CHOH.CH}_2\text{.COCH}_2\text{.COOH.}}{\Big\|}} \quad \text{V}$$

Since auxin b loses CO_2 on heating to give a neutral ketone, it must have its keto-group in the β-position and therefore be formulated as V. The relation between these two compounds, auxin a and b, or auxentriolic and auxenolonic acids, is thus similar to the relation between the two female sex hormones, theelol (trihydroxyoestrin) and theelin (keto-hydroxyoestrin). The structure of the C_{13} residue was worked out by breakdown experiments (Kögl and Erxleben, 1934), while finally the synthesis of a dicarboxylic acid identical with the oxidation product III, ("auxin-glutaric acid") (Kögl and Erxleben, 1935) confirmed the following formulae for auxin a and b:

$$C_2H_5-\overset{\overset{\displaystyle CH_3}{|}}{CH}-CH\underset{\underset{\displaystyle CH_2}{\diagdown}}{-}C-CHOH.CH_2.CHOH.CHOH.COOH$$

$$C_2H_5-\underset{\underset{\displaystyle CH_3}{|}}{CH}-CH-CH$$

auxin a, auxentriolic acid

$$C_2H_5-\overset{\overset{\displaystyle CH_3}{|}}{CH}-CH\underset{\underset{\displaystyle CH_2}{\diagdown}}{-}C-CHOH.CH_2.COCH_2.COOH$$

$$C_2H_5-\underset{\underset{\displaystyle CH_3}{|}}{CH}-CH-CH$$

auxin b, auxenolonic acid

A remarkable property of both auxin a and b is their spontaneous inactivation. This, which occurs in the solid crystalline state, involves no oxidation because it may take place *in vacuo* and in the dark, being complete in 1–2 months (Kögl, Erxleben, and Haagen Smit, 1933). Analysis of the inactive product ("pseudo-auxin") showed no change in composition or molecular weight, so that the change must be one of isomerization. Study of the ultra-violet spectra (Koningsberger, 1936; Kögl, 1936a) has shown that it consists of a shift of the double bond from the ring to the side-chain, the δ—OH group shifting to the ring; this produces an asymmetric C atom, which explains the formation of two optically isomeric "pseudo-auxins" from auxin a:

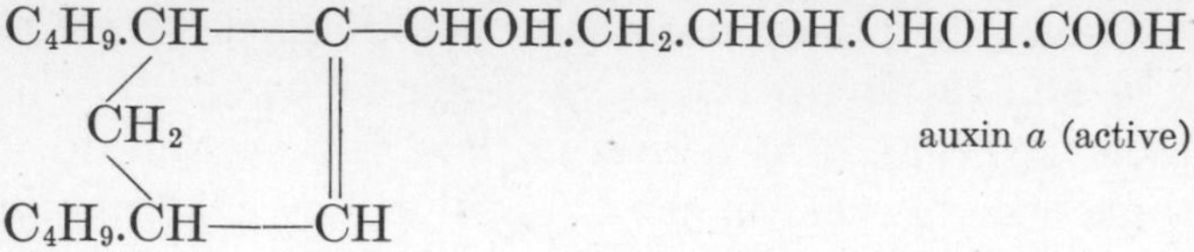

$$C_4H_9.CH\underline{\quad\quad}C\underline{\quad}CHOH.CH_2.CHOH.CHOH.COOH$$

$$\begin{array}{c} \diagdown \\ CH_2 \\ \diagdown \\ C_4H_9.CH\underline{\quad\quad}CH \end{array}$$

auxin a (active)

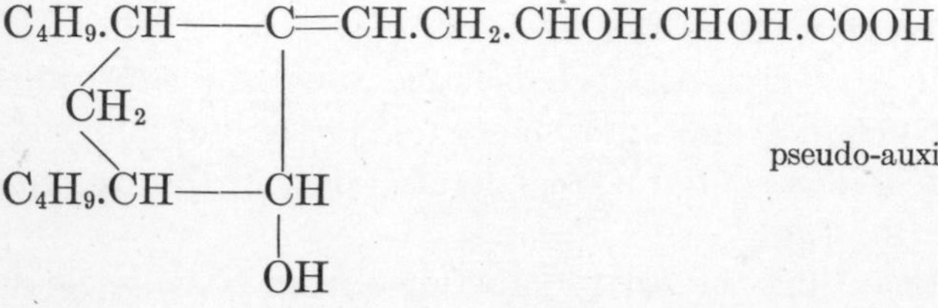

$$C_4H_9.CH\underline{\quad\quad}C{=}CH.CH_2.CHOH.CHOH.COOH$$

$$\begin{array}{c} \diagdown \\ CH_2 \\ \diagdown \\ C_4H_9.CH\underline{\quad\quad}CH \\ | \\ OH \end{array}$$

pseudo-auxin a (inactive)

Whether this change has any physiological significance remains to be seen. In the case of the lactone, in which the change is accompanied by loss of H_2O, and introduction of a second double bond in the side-chain, the same change may be brought about by ultra-violet irradiation.

C. DISCOVERY OF INDOLE-3-ACETIC ACID AS AN AUXIN

Subsequently another active substance was found. This was the result of the development of a charcoal absorption method for removing the active substance from urine, which led to the working up of still larger volumes (Kögl, Haagen Smit, and Erxleben, 1934). Under these conditions it appeared that the bulk of the activity in the charcoal eluate could not be purified by the methods previously found satisfactory. The active substance was largely destroyed on attempting to lactonize, and other methods involving only precipitation and solution were therefore substituted in the later stages. These led readily to the separation of another active substance which turned out to be identical with indole-3-acetic acid (usually called hetero-auxin),

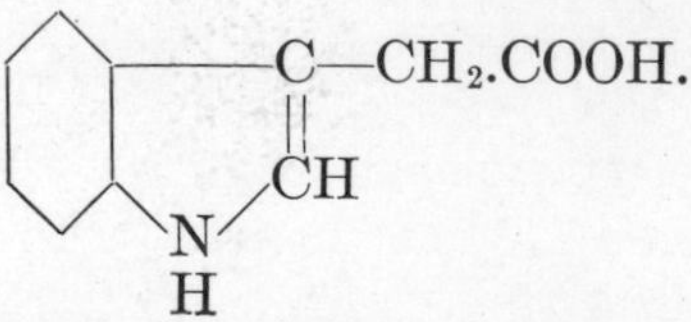

This substance had been isolated from fermentations in 1885 by E. and H. Salkowski, and was shown by them to be also present in urine. The activity of indole-3-acetic acid is of the same order as that of the C_{18} compounds auxin a and b and is not due to an impurity, because the synthetic product has the same activity.

Kögl and Kostermans (1934) isolated the same substance from yeast plasmolysate and showed that the indole-acetic acid obtained represented a considerable part of the original activity of the yeast.

At the same time the active substance from *Rhizopus* cultures, originally called by Nielsen "Rhizopin," was worked up in a somewhat different way by Thimann (1935). He was able to carry out a large number of purification stages without any loss in activity. The impossibility of lactonization, together with the sensitivity of the substance to acid previously found (Dolk and Thimann, 1932), made it probable that it was identical with indole-acetic acid rather than with auxin a or b. After purification, first by shaking out at different controlled pH, and then by extraction with various solvents, the free acid was distilled in very high vacuum (10^{-4} mm.) in a special still, and the minute amount of crystalline material finally obtained gave all the reactions characteristic of indole-acetic acid. Comparison with a synthetic sample confirmed the identity.

The mode of formation of indole-acetic acid by these microörganisms is almost certainly by the oxidative deamination of tryptophane. Thus the yield of auxin is determined by the amount of tryptophane present in the peptone used for culture (Thimann, 1935). It is also proportional, in a given culture, to the extent of aëration (Thimann and Dolk, 1933), which is explained by the entry of oxygen into the reaction:

$$\text{(indole)}\;C\!-\!CH_2.CO.COOH$$
$$\overset{CH}{\underset{N,H}{}} \quad + NH_3 \qquad \xrightarrow{\frac{1}{2}O_2}$$

$$\text{(indole)}\;C\!-\!CH_2.COOH$$
$$\overset{CH}{\underset{N,H}{}} \quad + CO_2$$

The study of Frieber (1922) on the color reactions for indole derivatives given by cultures of various bacteria makes it probable that numerous bacteria, growing on peptone media, produce indole-acetic acid. The identification of the auxins of yeast and *Rhizopus* with indole-acetic acid gives us good reason to believe that the auxin found in cultures of bacteria (Boysen Jensen, 1931) and certain other fungi (Nielsen, 1931) is also indole-acetic acid. This agrees also with the molecular weight determinations below. Boysen Jensen (1932) however, has shown that *Aspergillus niger* produces an auxin from histidine, lysine, leucine, tyrosine, phenylalanine, and tryptophane, but not from glycine, alanine, or arginine. These facts are difficult to interpret unless chemically different substances, active on *Avena*, are derived from these different amino-acids. However, it is well-known that the synthetic activities of fungi are very great.

So far as is known, the indole-acetic acid produced by fungi has no effect on their growth. Nielsen (1931a) showed that if the auxin-containing ether extract of medium on which *Rhizopus* had grown were added to fresh medium, it did not stimulate the growth of *Aspergillus niger*. The auxin does, indeed, disappear from the medium in which it is produced after some time, but there is no reason to suppose its destruction is correlated with the growth of the fungus (Thimann and Dolk, 1933). There is, however, a substance or group of substances, produced by *Rhizopus*, which does stimulate the growth of *Aspergillus;* this action has been shown by Nielsen and Hartelius (1932) to reside in the ether-insoluble fraction, and it is entirely unconnected with auxin. The active substance has been termed Wuchsstoff B (not to be confused with auxin *b*). This and much other evidence shows that the auxins in general have little or nothing to do with the substances stimulating growth of fungi, yeasts, and bacteria, about which there is a large literature.

D. IDENTITY OF THE NATIVE PLANT GROWTH HORMONE

Now that it has been shown that such chemically different compounds, all active on *Avena*, are widely distributed in nature, it becomes of interest to know which of these is the native growth hormone in the various higher plants. While the final proof can only be given by isolations, Kögl, Haagen Smit, and Erxleben (1934) have given good evidence by indirect methods that the active substance of the *Avena* coleoptile is auxin *a*. Firstly, the molecular weight may be determined by the diffusion method, using agar blocks which are assayed on *Avena* before and after diffusion; from the results the diffusion constant, D, is directly calculated, and since $D\sqrt{M} = ca.$ 7.0 (Öholm, 1912) the molecular weight, M, is thus obtained. In Went's experiments (1928) this molecular weight was found to be 376 for the auxin coming from *Avena*, and Kögl, Haagen Smit, and Erxleben obtained the same value for pure auxin *a* by this method (actual mol. wt. $C_{18}H_{32}O_5 = 328$). The auxins from *Zea Mays* coleoptiles, the regenerated tip of *Avena* coleoptiles, and the root tip of *Vicia Faba* all give about the same value (Heyn, 1936). On the other hand the auxin from *Aspergillus* gave 169, from *Rhizopus* 176 and 190, and from yeast 193 (Kostermans, 1935). These, together with Heyn's value for the auxin from *Phycomyces*, are all close to 175, the theoretical value for indole-acetic acid. Secondly, the sensitivity to pH provides a differentiation of another type; indole derivatives in general are destroyed by warm acid, but not by alkali; auxin *a* is destroyed by alkali but not by acid; auxin *b* is destroyed by both. The auxin of coleoptiles is sensitive to alkali, and that from fungi to acid. The facts, therefore, are consistent with the view that the auxin of coleoptiles is auxin *a*. It is, indeed, probable that other higher plants contain the same auxin.[1]

E. ACTIVITY OF COMPOUNDS RELATED TO INDOLE-ACETIC ACID

Since the discovery of the activity of indole-3-acetic acid, a large number of other substances, more or less active as auxins, have been recognized. Kögl and Kostermans (1935) prepared a large number of derivatives of indole-3-acetic acid and tested them by the *Avena* curvature method. They regarded substances with an activity 0.04 per cent of that of indole-3-acetic acid, or less, as inactive. Later, some of these substances have been retested by *Avena* curvature and other methods, and their small activities determined (see VIII *G*). Kögl and Kostermans first considered the importance of the carboxyl group, and therefore prepared a series of esters. It was found that the activity decreased with increasing size of the esterifying radical thus:

		ACTIVITY IN AE PER MG.
INDOLE-3-ACETIC ACID:	Free acid	$25.\ 10^6$
	Methyl ester	$10.\ 10^6$
	Ethyl ester	$3.\ 10^6$
	n-Propyl ester	$1.\ 10^6$
	Iso-Propyl ester	$0.1.\ 10^6$

It seems likely that the esters are hydrolyzed in the plant, so that they owe their activity to the acid produced from

[1] It should be remembered that Stark and Drechsel (1922) believed that the "phototropic hormones," which have now been identified with auxin, were different in different species. They found that when coleoptile tips of one species of grass were placed on decapitated stumps of another species, the number of stumps which reacted was smaller the greater the systematic difference between the species of the tip and the stump. Not only has this view never been confirmed, but the entire weight of evidence has always supported the complete non-specificity of the auxins. Recently Söding (1936) has reported that apparent differences in activity of auxins from different plant sources were due merely to quantitative variations in amount. There is therefore nothing against the view that the same auxin occurs throughout all the higher plants.

them.   The decreasing activities may be ascribed to decreasing rates of enzymic hydrolysis.   The double bond
appears to be essential for activity, for the 2-3-dihydro-
derivative,[1] like the dihydro-derivatives of auxin *a* and *b*,
is inactive.   Introduction of an alkyl group into the 1- or
5-position of the nucleus always reduced the activity, sometimes completely.   Methylation of the N atom reduced
the activity more than methylation elsewhere,[2] and the
ethyl group reduces the activity more than methyl.   Introduction of methoxyl in any position completely removes
all activity (*u*).   The activity of all active substances is
listed in Table XII, pp. 137ff.

The length of the acid side chain also greatly affects
the activity; indole-3-carboxylic acid is completely inactive,
as is also indole-2-carboxylic acid.   Indole-3-propionic acid
has only very slight activity, but indole-3-isopropionic acid
was almost comparable with indole-acetic acid.   Of other
derivatives indole-lactic acid was found inactive, while
indole-pyruvic acid had low activity.

Commercial tryptophane (indole-3-alanine) has slight
auxin activity, but this is lost on recrystallization and is
therefore due to impurities.   However, the behavior of
tryptophane is interesting from another standpoint.   If
applied to *Avena*, curvatures are produced after a lapse of
two hours or so.   It also accelerates the growth of coleoptiles
when applied to the base (*u*).   Tryptamine, indole-3-ethyl-
amine, behaves in the same way (Skoog, 1937).   The latter
substance, while it does not contain an acid group, could
doubtless be oxidized to indole-acetic acid, via indole-3-
acetaldehyde.   Tryptophane, as we have seen, may be con-

[1] Numbering of the ring-atoms of indole-compounds is as follows:

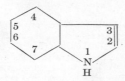

[2] This does not hold for activity on straight growth of *Avena*.

verted to indole-3-acetic acid by fungi and bacteria, and the same conversion by the plant is therefore extremely probable. Tryptophane and tryptamine are of special interest as constituting models of the auxin precursor in the coleoptile: they are substances which, inactive in themselves, are readily converted to the active form by plant enzymes. It may also be pointed out that tryptamine is a base and therefore, according to the electrical polarity theory outlined in VI E, would travel upwards in the plant.

Not only variations in the side chain, but variations in the nucleus itself, may be effected without wholly losing the activity. Thus, Thimann (1935b) has shown that indene-3-acetic acid, which contains a carbon atom instead of the nitrogen of the indole, has moderate activity on Avena. Cumaryl-acetic, on the other hand, with oxygen instead of the nitrogen atom, was inactive in producing curvature (cf. VIII G).

Zimmerman and Wilcoxon (1935), Zimmerman, Hitchcock, and Wilcoxon (1936), and Manske and Leitch (1936) tested several substances for their activity in causing epinasty on Nicotiana. Their results are therefore not comparable with the above, and will be considered again in VIII G. Haagen Smit and Went (1935) have tested a large number of compounds by different methods; this work will also be dealt with in VIII G. They have also listed a number of substances which are completely inactive in all test methods. Glover (1936) reported—erroneously (u)—that skatole had growth-promoting activity on Avena.

In connection with the activity of esters, it is of interest that the esters of auxin a are inactive. There is good evidence that auxin a occurs in a number of natural products in the inactive ester form. Thus Kögl, Erxleben, and Haagen Smit (1934) were able to obtain considerable activity from Arachis oil and some other vegetable oils by hydrolyzing the oils with a lipase preparation or with sodium ethylate. Some oils, such as corn germ oil, contain auxin in free form, as we have seen. Auxin esters in edible fats and oils may well be the source of the auxin *a* in the urine, as has been made very probable by feeding experiments: it was found that the auxin content of the urine increased greatly after ingestion of salad oil or butter, but not after ingestion of pure protein, sugar, or hydrogenated *cocos* fat (Kögl, Haagen Smit, and Erxleben, 1933*a*). The possibility that the auxin precursor in the plant is an ester of auxin *a* was discussed in IV *B* (p. 65).

CHAPTER VIII

THE MECHANISM OF THE ACTION

The development of the field has been so recent that it is perhaps only to be expected that the inner mechanism of the action of auxin on the growth process should be as yet little understood. Nevertheless there are a number of factors which make a successful attack more probable in this than in any other comparable case. In the first place, the active substances are relatively simple and their constitutions are completely known. In the second place, the process they affect, at least in so far as cell enlargement is concerned, is directly open to physiological analysis, and the action, compared to that of some other hormones (see Chapter XIV), is very direct. Finally, the cells on which the auxins act are of the least differentiated and simplest type.

There are two possible methods of approach to such a problem, and both have been to some extent exploited. One is to attempt to unravel the chain of physiological processes which ultimately results in growth. This we may call the physiological approach. The other, which has been opened up by the fact that a number of different substances have growth-promoting action, consists in an attempt to identify those properties of the molecule which give it its activity. This we shall term the chemical approach; in its later stages it becomes interrelated with the physiological analysis. To adopt Emil Fischer's simile of the key in the lock—already used by Kögl—one may call the auxin the key which opens the lock to allow growth, and it is clear that the opening process may be studied either by analyzing the lock (physiological approach) or by analyzing the key (chemical approach). Both methods will be discussed in this chapter.

118

I. THE PHYSIOLOGICAL APPROACH

A. DEFINITIONS

We shall restrict the term "growth" to *irreversible increase in volume*. The phenomena involved can be separated, following Sachs, into four growth stages:

1. *Organization, i.e.* the formation of organ primordia—the determination of their number and place, (but not the determination of their exact nature);
2. *Differentiation*, which consists both of the determination of the nature of the organ and of the laying down of most of its cells;
3. *Elongation, i.e.* enlargement of the cells formed by differentiation, taking place largely by water uptake;
4. *Maturation*, or chemical changes occurring in the completed organ.

The first two stages are essentially morphogenetic and correspond to the zoölogist's use of the term *growth*, especially because in animals (with certain exceptions) cell enlargement plays a relatively minor rôle. The third stage, elongation, often intergrades to some extent with the second—that is, it may be accompanied by increase in cell number. For our purposes the complication which cell multiplication introduces will be omitted. In nuclear division and the subsequent formation of a primary cross-wall no elongation, that is, no *growth* in the sense of irreversible increase in volume, is involved. All four stages may be influenced by auxin, but at this point we shall restrict ourselves to a consideration of the third stage, in which the action is probably most direct, and shall return to the effects on the other stages in later chapters.

B. NATURE OF GROWTH

Increases in cell volume may be due to water uptake, or increase in dry weight, or both. Usually water uptake is the major factor; cell wall formation accompanies it and is responsible for most of the increase in dry weight, while actual formation of new protoplasm, in the stage of growth we are concerned with, may or may not take place.

The tendency of the cell to take up water, which may be defined as the Suction Force, is given by the difference between the osmotic pressure of the cell contents and the pressure exerted on them by the walls (Ursprung and Blum, 1924). The tendency to take up water can be increased either by increasing the osmotic pressure of the cell contents or by decreasing the counter-pressure exerted by the wall. (The *rate* at which water is taken up can be increased temporarily by increasing the permeability for water, but this does not affect the ultimate dynamic equilibrium.) That growth itself is probably not due to an increase in osmotic pressure is shown by the observation of Ursprung and Blum (1924) that there is no increase in osmotic pressure in rapidly growing tissue. Nevertheless Czaja (1935*a*) has suggested that auxin acts by changing the osmotic value of the cell. Auxin, being an acid, is supposed to change the charge on the cell membrane from negative to positive; this would cause negative osmosis, and thus increase the turgor. As sole support for this theory, Czaja cites some experiments on plasmoptysis (bursting) of root-hairs in 4 per cent sucrose solution, in which indole-acetic acid gave a somewhat greater effect than HCl at the same pH. In the absence of further experimental support and in view of the observations of Ursprung and Blum, the theory does not seem to justify further comment.

While there is thus no direct relation between growth and osmotic pressure, investigations directed at the cell wall have shown that there is a close relation between growth and certain changes in its properties. During the last 50 years a considerable literature has grown up around the cell wall, which we cannot attempt to review here. The reader may be referred to Frey-Wyssling (1935, section I), or Anderson (1935). Briefly, it may be said that irreversible extension of the wall could be brought about by plastic stretching alone, by active intussusception, that is by the laying in of new particles between the old ones of the wall, or thirdly by the deposition of new material while the old wall is held in an elastically stretched state. Combinations of these processes may also be envisaged.

C. EFFECT OF AUXIN ON THE CELL WALL

Direct measurements on the effect of auxin upon the stretching properties of the cell walls have been made by Heyn (1930, 1931, 1931a, 1932, 1932a, 1933, 1934, 1934b) and by Söding (1931, 1932a, 1934), with similar techniques and essentially the same results. Such experiments can only usefully be made on plasmolyzed material, because turgid cells show very little stretching, as was shown by Söding (1931). The essential technique is to make two marks on the plasmolyzed coleoptile or other object, suspend it in front of a horizontal microscope, and determine the distance between the marks before and after various loads have been attached to its lower end. Part of the elongation produced by such loads will be reversible; the reversible stretching is a measure of the *elasticity* and the irreversible stretching gives the *plasticity*. However, according to Buck (1935), there is no difference in principle between these; any sufficiently great and prolonged elastic stretching goes finally over into irreversible, plastic extension.

The first finding was that after decapitation both the elastic (see also Horreus de Haas, 1929) and the plastic extensibility of the coleoptile decrease. That this decrease is connected with the decrease in auxin content of the plant is indicated by the fact that after regeneration both elasticity and, more especially, plasticity increase again. The changes in plasticity follow very closely the changes in growth rate, while the elasticity continues to decrease for a number of hours after regeneration has occurred, and only rises much later. Figure 40, plotted from Heyn's data (1932), shows a typical group of experiments. Similarly, if auxin is applied, the plasticity is greatly and the elasticity slightly increased. Heyn concludes that the changes in growth rate are *due* to changes in plasticity, while the elasticity changes only as a *result* of growth. Increased plasticity allows increased elongation, the actual force causing elongation being the turgor.

The elasticity can be independently measured by plasmolyzing the plants after they have undergone auxin curvatures (Söding), the decrease in curvature giving that part of it which was purely elastic. Correspondingly, normal

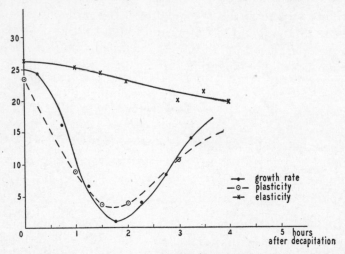

Fig. 40. Changes in growth rate (dots), plasticity (circles), and elasticity (crosses) of an *Avena* coleoptile after decapitation. Ordinates, arbitrary units. (Data of Heyn, 1932.)

plants can be plasmolyzed, when the decrease in length gives that part of the straight growth which was purely elastic (Heyn, 1931a). Further, though turgid coleoptiles show little stretching, they show appreciable bending if they are supported horizontally at one end and riders are placed on the other. Both of these techniques give results similar to the above; the auxin curvatures are almost entirely due to increase in plasticity.

The flower-stalks of a number of plants behave in essentially the same way (Söding, 1932b; Heyn, 1934b), but Söding found that while decapitation of these caused a decrease in growth it caused little change in plasticity. On this account he has concluded that changes in neither plasticity nor elasticity can be the primary cause of growth; growth, he considers, is therefore caused by active intussusception. Thus, according to Söding, growth must be accompanied by an increase in dry weight of the walls. However, other experiments indicate that this is not so. Heyn and van Overbeek (1931) found that the increase in plasticity and the increase in length caused by auxin take place also if the plants are kept at 4°. Bonner (1934a) therefore measured the dry weights of the walls of coleoptile sections in auxin and in water, and found that at 25° elongation was paralleled by an increase in weight, but at 2° there was considerable elongation but no increase in weight (see Table IX).

TABLE IX

(After Bonner, 1934a)

TREATMENT	FINAL LENGTH IN AUXIN AS PER CENT OF CONTROLS	FINAL WEIGHT IN AUXIN AS PER CENT OF CONTROLS
25° C.	115	116
2° C.	110	101
Fructose at 25° C.	128	142

He further found that, if placed in 1 per cent fructose solution, the increase in weight, i.e. the cell wall formation, exceeded the rate of growth. From these measurements the processes of wall thickening and elongation would appear to be independent, as Heyn concluded on other grounds. Thus the evidence is consistent with the view that auxin allows growth by increasing the plasticity of the wall, rather than that it causes active intussusception of wall material. The exceptions remain, but there are a number of possible explanations for them which will require further investigation. The work of Amlong on roots apparently provides definite contradiction (see IX D). Zollikofer (1935) has studied the curvatures of the flower-stalks of Tussilago and Papaver during the floral movements, of which unfortunately the auxin relations are not known. Her measurements, however, suggest that the nodding of the bud at first is largely due to differences in elastic stretching on the two sides, presumably caused by osmotic changes; the subsequent straightening is accompanied by increase of plasticity on the more rapidly growing side.

Friedrich (1936) has confirmed the findings of Warner (1928) and Metzner (1934) that upon geotropic stimulation the lower side of wilted *Helianthus* seedlings has a higher content of reducing sugars than the upper. Not only is it doubtful whether this difference is established as soon as is the growth difference, but also no such difference could be detected after application of indole-acetic acid. However, Friedrich ascribes this to the different behavior of this substance and the auxin *a* probably present in the plant (see VII *D*), and concludes that the difference in sugars is caused by the difference in auxin *a* content between the upper and lower sides. The increased sugar concentration is then considered to cause the increased rate of growth on the lower side. Unfortunately the evidence is as yet too weak to substantiate this suggestion.

D. STRUCTURE OF THE GROWING CELL WALL

To explain the changes in plasticity and elasticity during growth, attempts have been made to take the structure of the cell wall into account. Heyn (1933), on the basis of stretching measurements with the automatic load-extension apparatus of Denham and Lonsdale (1928), has concluded that the cell wall of *Avena* consists of at least 2 layers, the outer of which has much greater extensibility than the inner; on plasmolysis the inner layer becomes wrinkled. Thus, according to conditions, the properties of the wall should be determined mainly by one layer or the other; under natural conditions this is the inner, difficultly extensible, layer and hence the action of auxin would be mainly on this layer.

Analysis of the cell walls of growing *Avena* coleoptiles gives the following figures in per cent of the dry weight: cellulose 42 per cent, pectin 8 per cent, hemicellulose 38 per cent, protein 12 per cent (Thimann and Bonner, 1933). Since the dry weight is only one third of the fresh weight, cellulose constitutes only 14 per cent of the fresh cell walls. Nevertheless, it is structurally probably the most important constituent, and even the thin growing parenchyma walls have a well-developed continuous cellulose skeleton (Bonner, 1935). On this account, experimental study of the cell wall has been principally directed at the cellulose. The techniques used are based upon its crystalline structure, and are therefore those of x-ray photography and the polarizing microscope. The cellulose consists, at least partly, of submicroscopic crystalline aggregates or *micelles*, whose orientation determines the stretching properties of the wall. In the epidermis they are mostly arranged parallel to the long axis, an arrangement which Frey-Wyssling (1935) has called "fiber-like structure" (Figure 41 b) (Heyn, 1933*a*, 1934*a*; Bonner, 1935). The micelles themselves, being crystalline, do not stretch, and correspondingly it is found that the epidermis stretches very little when suspended in auxin solution (Bonner, 1934). In the growing parenchyma, however, the micelles are oriented more nearly perpendicular to the long axis—Frey-Wyssling's "tube-structure"—(Figure 41 d). Further, since they occupy only a small part of the volume of the cell wall but yet form a continuous skeleton, these micelles, which are probably smaller than those in the epidermis, must be attached to one another in some way. We thus have a network, the openings being rhomboidal, with the long axis of the rhomboid perpendicular to the long axis of the plant. Under tension these rhomboids will change shape, the long axis finally coming parallel to the direction of tension. However, in growing coleoptiles the orientation remains on the whole perpendicular to the long axis of the plant, as shown by the optical measurements of Bonner (1935), and therefore growth cannot be a *simple* stretching. Growth must therefore be accompanied by a sliding of the points of attachment and the laying down of new micelles between the old in the same direction (see

Figure 42). The conception of Söding that growth cannot be only plastic stretching and must involve also intussusception is thus supported.

X-ray analysis, however, has recently revealed the presence of a crystalline element other than cellulose which is

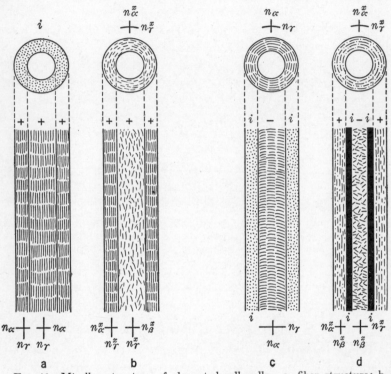

FIG. 41. Micellar structure of elongated cell-walls. a, fiber structure; b, fiber-like structure; c, ring structure; d, tube structure. (From Frey-Wyssling, *Protoplasma 25:* 261–300, 1936.)

also present during elongation in *Avena* and in the cotton-hair (Hess, Trogus, and Wergin, 1936). These workers claim that in the cotton-hair the large crystalline aggregates of cellulose which are responsible for the x-ray diffraction patterns are completely absent during the period of elongation, while in growing *Avena* coleoptiles they are largely confined to the epidermis. This, if substantiated, would indicate that the importance of the larger cellulose micelles in the growth process is probably slight, and would take much of the force out of the above arguments. It thus seems impossible at present to arrive at a definite conclusion

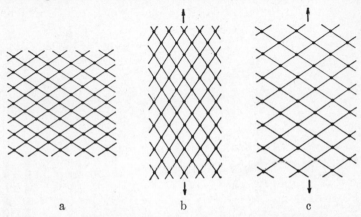

a   b   c

Fig. 42. Scheme of the micellar structure of the growing cell wall. a, original structure; b, the same after 50% stretching by artificial tension; c, the same after 50% elongation by growth—there is no change in orientation of micelles, as there is in b, but there is sliding of the points of attachment. New micelles will become inserted in the spaces. (From Frey-Wyssling, *Protoplasma* 25: 261–300, 1936.)

as to the constituent of the cell wall on which auxin exerts its ultimate effect.

E. The Intermediate Processes

While the ultimate effect of auxin is thus upon the cell wall, we have little information as to the way in which this effect is brought about. There is good evidence that there must be a number of intermediate stages. This is clearly indicated by comparison between the amount of auxin applied to the *Avena* coleoptile and the total amount of straight growth which it brings about (Thimann and Bonner, 1933). From determinations of the growth, the amount of auxin entering, and the analysis of the cell wall material, it was calculated that at 25° one molecule of auxin brings about the laying down of 3×10^5 hexose residues in the form of cellulose. Similar large ratios hold for pectin, hemicellulose, and protein. At 15° more auxin is required for the same amount of growth. These facts show that there is no direct stoichiometric relationship between the auxin entering and the cell wall constituents upon which it ultimately acts. There is not nearly enough auxin to form even a monomolecular film over the surface of the new cell wall which it produces, by which it might affect permeability. Thus auxin acts in some indirect way. This conclusion is supported by the fact that its action is connected with respiration (Bonner, 1933, 1933a, 1936a). Sections of coleoptiles in solution in nitrogen do not elongate appreciably when auxin is added. Further, the addition of KCN or phenyl-urethane, in concentrations which inhibit respiration, inhibits growth also; if the inhibition is partial it occurs to about the same extent for respiration as for growth. Thus growth does not involve a separate special oxygen uptake, but it is dependent on the presence of the respiration in general. Bonner's earlier view that auxin accelerates the respiration has been shown not to be true (Kögl, Haagen Smit, and van Hulssen, 1936; Bonner, 1936a), since his earlier experiments were carried out with only a partially purified auxin preparation.

Another attack has been directed towards following the fate of the auxin within the plant (Bonner and Thimann, 1935). Determinations of the total amount of auxin in *Avena* coleoptiles by the chloroform extraction method show that the value of 5.7 units per plant falls, 2 hours after decapitation, to 3.0 units, *i.e.* 2.7 units have disappeared. The growth which has taken place in this time is 0.79 mm., which, according to the straight growth measurements, would require the addition of 2.9 units. The growth resulting has therefore been strictly proportional to the amount of auxin which disappeared.

If, however, high concentrations of auxin are applied to the plant, then the growth which results uses up only a small part of the auxin, and most of the rest disappears. Similarly, if auxin be applied to cut-off coleoptiles without water supply, they do not grow but the auxin continues to dis-

TABLE X

THE GROWTH PROCESS

	1 $\longrightarrow$	2 $\longrightarrow$	3 $\longrightarrow$	4* $\longrightarrow$	5 $\longrightarrow$	6
Reaction:	auxin transported to the cell	uptake by cell; reversible addition product formed with some cell constituent "bound auxin" (see Table XI)	auxin inactivation	reaction inhibited by HCN	physical or chemical change in cell wall	stretching (e.g. by water uptake)
Growth is inhibited by:	lack of auxin, lack of oxygen	high pH		presence of HCN, lack of oxygen		lack of water

* Reaction 4 may possibly be on another chain of events which combines with these processes to produce reaction 5.

129

appear. In presence of HCN it also disappears, so that the inactivation must precede the HCN-inhibited process. Thus the inactivation of auxin—when it is present in low concentration and conditions are favorable—results in growth, but when excess auxin is present, or when conditions are unfavorable, most of the auxin disappears without resulting in growth. Thus one stage of the growth process is an inactivation of the auxin.

The various steps in growth so far known can be summarized as shown in Table X.

F. THE EFFECT OF ACID ON GROWTH

Strugger (1932, 1933, 1934) has suggested a mechanism for growth of an entirely different type. He considers the physical and colloidal properties of the protoplasm, especially viscosity and hydration, as the controlling factors. These will be dependent upon the pH, and correspondingly he finds that if hypocotyls be wounded on one side and immersed in buffer solutions they curve, the amount of curvature varying with the pH. Parallel with a two-peaked curve for the variation of protoplasm viscosity with pH, he finds a similar two-peaked curve for the variation of curvature (growth) with pH, the minimum for both growth and viscosity occurring at pH 5.1, which is considered to be "the isoelectric point of protoplasm." Bonner (1934) has shown, however, that for growth there is no such two-peaked curve: the growth caused by acid (see Figure 43) increases steadily toward higher acidities. If we allow for the fact that the pH within the tissues is not the same as the pH of the buffer, then the curve of acid growth against pH follows closely the pH dissociation curve of auxin (pK = 4.8). This suggests that only the free acid form of auxin has growth-promoting activity, and that the applied acid sets free the auxin acid from the salt form in which it is present (pH of sap = 6.1). That the applied acid is not in itself effective in producing growth is supported by the fact that 2 hours after decapitation, when the auxin content has fallen to about one half (see p. 128), the curvatures produced by acid are also reduced to about one half. It is still more clearly borne out by the experiments of Thimann (1935b). He immersed coleoptile sections in acid buffer, which caused temporary growth acceleration: when this had ceased, immersion in fresh acid had no effect because

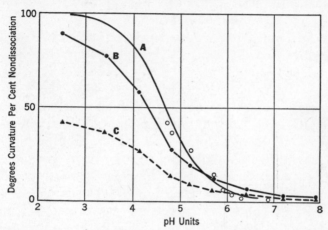

Fig. 43. Activity and dissociation of the weak acid, auxin. A, theoretical dissociation curve of auxin, pK = 4.75; B, acid curvatures (in degrees) obtained by peeling epidermis of *Avena* coleoptiles on one side and placing in acid buffers; C, same data plotted as per cent so as to meet curve A at pH 6.1. White circles are the data of C corrected to internal pH in the cells, showing close agreement with the dissociation curve A. (From Bonner, *Protoplasma 21:* 406–423, 1934.)

all the auxin in the sections had been used up, but immersion in auxin gave good growth.

Thus it is clear that the action of acid is *through its effect on the auxin in the plant,* and there is no evidence that the colloidal properties of protoplasm control growth in the way assumed by Strugger.

It has been shown in IV A that there is good evidence for the presence of at least 2 forms of auxin in the plant—one form free-moving, and obtainable in agar by the diffusion method, the other bound in some way in the cell, and obtainable only by extraction with solvents like chloroform. Boysen Jensen (1936a) has suggested that the freely moving auxin may be the free auxin acid discussed above, and the bound form its salt. This, however, is improbable, because, if so, the so-called acid curvatures should migrate downwards below the point of application of acid, which appears not to be the case. It is also remarkable that the immersion of coleoptiles in acid buffers, which sets free auxin acid and thus accelerates the growth rate, does not set free any auxin which can be redistributed under the influence of gravity (u). Table XI, which is partially hypothetical, combines these facts with those of Chapter VII into a composite scheme of the various possible states of auxin in the plant.

TABLE XI

STATES OF AUXIN IN THE PLANT

Auxin in plant	*inactive in Avena test*	(precursor, auxin-esters, storage form in seeds, easily transformed into auxin)	
	active in Avena test	*free moving*	(transport form, can be collected by diffusion method, redistributed by light or gravity) ("free auxin").
		inside cells (can be extracted by organic solvents only) ("bound auxin").	*auxin acid* (active in producing growth)
			auxin in salt form (not active in growth, reserve auxin in cells).

II. THE CHEMICAL APPROACH

G. PRIMARY AND SECONDARY ACTIVITY

We have seen in VII E that a number of different substances have been found to possess activity to a greater or lesser extent on *Avena*. This fact has been subjected to a physiological analysis by Thimann (1935). He compared the activity of the three substances indole-3-acetic acid, I; indene-3-acetic acid, II; and cumaryl-1-acetic acid, III:

I

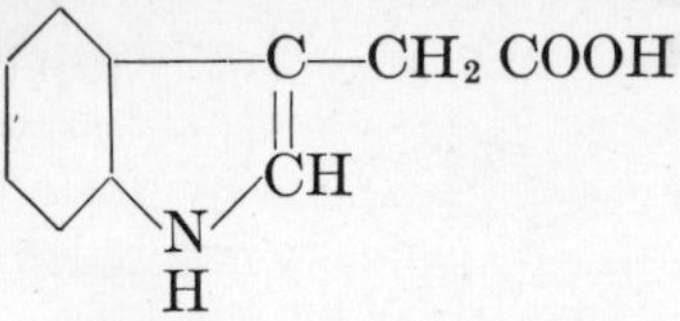

II

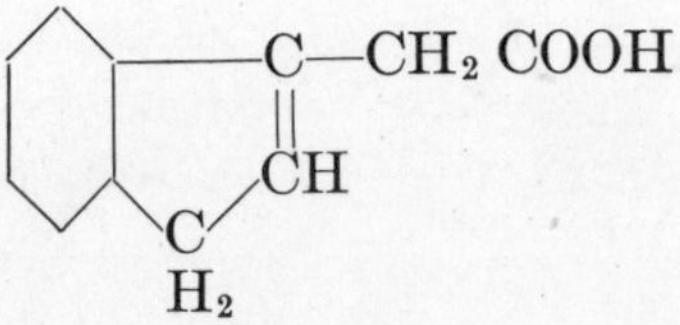

ch-coon (handwritten annotation)

III

no avena gives pea. (handwritten annotation)

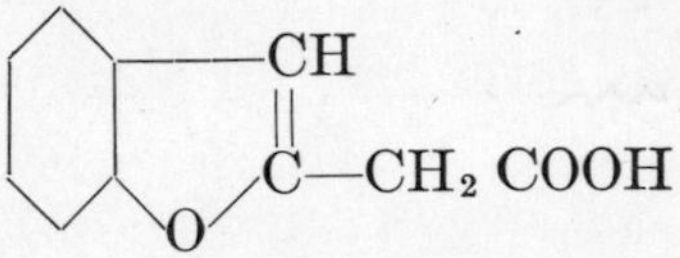

The substance III was found to have no activity in producing curvature in *Avena*, but on the other hand it possessed moderate activity in promoting straight growth of *Avena* sections and still more in producing pea stem curvatures. Hence a substance may be active in growth promotion without causing any curvature on *Avena*. A similar case, though less extreme, is presented by the indene derivative II, which has only small activity in *Avena* curvature, but has much greater activity in producing straight growth of *Avena* sections, while on pea stem curvatures its activity is up to $\frac{1}{4}$ of that of indole-acetic acid. There are, of course, different ways of explaining such action. One is that these substances act only by their effect on the pH, their acidity setting free the auxin in the plant as we have seen above. This, however, was ruled out for straight growth by first exposing the sections to acid till their auxin supply was practically used up and their growth had ceased, and then placing them either in a solution of the test substance or again in acid. The controls in acid now scarcely elongated at all, while those in solutions of I, II, or III elongated vigorously. Application of the acids in the form of their sodium salts was equally effective, so that this confirms that the substances do not act by their effect on the pH. We know in addition that the pea test is practically insensitive to acid (see III *D* 2).

Another observation led to the elucidation of the behavior of these substances. It was found that the curvatures on *Avena* produced by indene-3-acetic acid are restricted to a very short region, about 3–4 mm. from the point of appli-

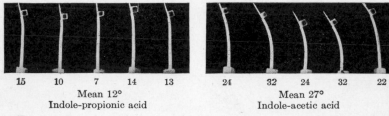

15	10	7	14	13		24	32	24	32	22

Mean 12°
Indole-propionic acid

Mean 27°
Indole-acetic acid

FIG. 44. Short curved zone caused by indole-3-propionic acid (93 mg. per liter) contrasted with long curved zone caused by indole-3-acetic acid (0.32 mg. per liter).

cation (see Figure 44, which shows a similar effect of indole-propionic acid). This suggested that the rate of transport of the substance limits its activity. Hence tests like those on *Avena* sections and *Pisum* stems, which are carried out by immersion of the test plant, would be expected to give higher activities. The inability of these two substances to be transported was confirmed by experiments on root formation and bud inhibition (see XI *C* and XII).

Thus the physiological activity of a substance depends not only on its direct effect, but also on its secondary properties which determine whether it will reach the place of action or not. To use again the simile of the key in the lock, the effectiveness of the key is determined not only by the wards but also by the grooves in the side of the key, which in themselves, of course, have nothing to do with the opening process. Still, the incorrect arrangement of the grooves may prevent an otherwise correctly shaped key from opening the lock. The importance of Thimann's discovery, then, lies in the fact that we are now able to study separately each property of the key, and are warned against ascribing the activity of a substance to those details in its chemical structure which only affect its secondary properties.

Is it possible now to test for one of these properties, especially for the primary one of growth promotion, without

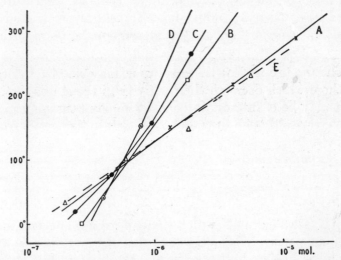

Fig. 45. Relation between auxin concentration and curvature in the pea test. A, indole-3-acetic acid; B, indole-3-propionic acid; C, indole-3-butyric acid; D, naphthalene-acetic acid; E, auxin a and b (obtained by extraction of corn meal).

being confused by the interference of others?   In other words, can we test for the wards of the key independently of the grooves? To some extent at least, we can, by using Went's pea test. We have seen that substances inactive, or of only small activity, on *Avena* may be highly active in causing pea stem curvatures. Such substances may be regarded as possessing *primary* growth-promoting activity. The relation between molar concentration and activity on pea stems has been compared for a number of substances which show widely varying activity in the *Avena* test (u). The result is that auxin a, indole-3-acetic, indole-3-propionic, indole-3-butyric, and α-naphthalene-acetic acids at low concentrations approach the same activity per mol (see Figure 45). This means that, irrespective of the secondary factors which operate to decrease the activity on *Avena*, the number of molecules of these substances necessary to produce a minimum growth effect is the same. The production of the primary growth effect is therefore, apparently, a chemical reaction involving stoichiometrical relationship between the active substance and the substrate inside the cell on which it acts. Substances which do not give the same molar ratio are presumably prevented from doing so by other secondary properties; these may or may not be the same as those which decrease their activity in the *Avena* test.

It may be of interest to consider some of these secondary properties, although they do not enter into the actual growth process. *1, Transport.* The rôle of transport has been discussed above and is clearly of considerable importance. The complex of factors involved cannot be further analyzed until we know more about the path of transport and the forces which cause it. *2, Permeability,* using the term in the broad sense, *i.e.* the ability of the substance to enter the cell and reach its point of action. Undoubtedly the solubility both in lipoids and in water plays an important part here. *3, The sensitivity of the substance to inactivation.* Thus, we know that auxin *b* is about twice as sensitive to H_2O_2 as is indole-acetic acid (Thimann and Went, 1934), and auxin *a* is more sensitive to the plant oxidases than indole-acetic acid (van Overbeek, 1936). On the other hand, indene-3-acetic acid is unattacked by H_2O_2 under the same conditions (Thimann, 1935). *4, A number of other factors, such as lateral transport, and the velocity of the actual growth-producing reaction, may also be of importance.

H. The Relation between Structure and Activity

A list of all the substances which show any kind of activity on *Avena* curvatures, straight growth of *Avena* sections, pea stem curvatures, and other processes, is given

TABLE XII

SUMMARY OF THE ACTIVITIES OF ALL SUBSTANCES FOR WHICH QUANTITATIVE DATA ARE AVAILABLE. ACTIVITY EXPRESSED AS PER CENT OF THAT OF INDOLE-3-ACETIC ACID THROUGHOUT

SUBSTANCE	TEST METHOD					
	Pisum Split Stem Curvature	Avena Straight Growth	Avena Curvature	Pisum Root Formation	Avena Root Inhibition	Other (see key, p. 139)
Auxin a (auxentriolic acid)	?100		ca 200	ca 400	ca 500	75C
Auxin a lactone			ca 150			ca 100A
Auxin b (auxenolonic acid)	?100		ca 200		ca 500	100
Indole-3-acetic acid	100	100	100	100	100	
Acids						
Indole-3-propionic	100		0.1	< 0.1	4	2B, 5D, E
" butyric	100		5			5D
" valeric	100		0.1			
" pyruvic	50		ca.1			E
" lactic			0			
" acrylic						E
" methylacetic	100		20			
" oximinopropionic						E
1-Methyl-Indole-3-acetic	30	20	0.15			
2-Methyl- "	20	5	0.5			
5-Methyl- "	100	20	6			
2-Ethyl- "	ca 0		0			
2-5-Dimethyl- "	20		0.2			
Indene-3-acetic	20	7	1	local, ca 100	active	14A
Cumarane-3-acetic	ca 15		0			
Cumarane-2-acetic	4	0.3	0	local, ca 50		4A

137

TABLE XII—*Continued*

SUMMARY OF THE ACTIVITIES OF ALL SUBSTANCES FOR WHICH QUANTITATIVE DATA ARE AVAILABLE. ACTIVITY EXPRESSED AS PER CENT OF THAT OF INDOLE-3-ACETIC ACID THROUGHOUT

SUBSTANCE	Test Method					
	Pisum Split Stem Curvature	Avena Straight Growth	Avena Curvature	Pisum Root Formation	Avena Root Inhibition	Other (see key, p. 139)
Phenyl-acetic	10	1	0.02			0.2B, 2.5D
Phenyl-propionic	2					
m-nitro-phenylacetic	5					
α-naphthalene-acetic	100		2.5			ca 1B, 50D
β- " "						ca 0.05B
Acenaphthene-acetic						ca 1B
Fluorene-acetic						ca 0.5B
Anthracene-acetic						ca 0.05B
Cis-Cinnamic (Allocinnamic)	100	20	0.06		20	
o-methoxy-cis-cinnamic	5	0.2	0			
α-phenyl-lactic (atrolactic)	0.5	0.5	0			
Isatinic	5	2	0.2			
Vulpinic	0.2					
Pulvinic	0.2					
o-amino-phenylglyoxylic	5					
Amino Acid						
Tryptophane (indole-3-amino-propionic acid)	delayed, 10	delayed	delayed	active		
Amine						
Tryptamine (indole-ethyl amine)			delayed, 10–100			

138

TABLE XII—Continued

Summary of the Activities of All Substances for Which Quantitative Data Are Available. Activity Expressed as Per Cent of That of Indole-3-Acetic Acid Throughout

Substance	Test Method					
	Pisum Split Stem Curvature	Avena Straight Growth	Avena Curvature	Pisum Root Formation	Avena Root Inhibition	Other (see key below)
Esters						
Indole-3-acetic Methyl ester			40			?ca 200D
" Ethyl "			12			
" n-Propyl "			4			
" isopropyl "		10	0.4			
2-methyl-indole-3-acetic Methyl ester	100	10	0			
Indole-3-propionic Methyl ester	50					12D
Indole-3-butyric " "						12D
Naphthalene-acetic " "						25D
" " Ethyl "						12D
Phenylacetic Methyl ester	5					1.25D
" Ethyl "						0.6D
" n-Butyl "						0.25D
" Isobutyl "	5					0.125D
Phenylpropionic Ethyl "	1					

Key to column 6:
A. Bud inhibition on Pisum (Thimann, 1935b).
B. Curvature of green Pisum stem in light (Zimmerman and Wilcoxon, 1935).
C. Callus formation on Populus twig (Rogenhofer, 1936).
D. Curvature of green Lycopersicum petiole in light (Zimmerman, Hitchcock, and Wilcoxon, 1936).
E. Activity reported equal to that of indole-propionic acid for various responses (Bauguess, 1935).

139

herewith. This table (Table XII) is founded on those of Kögl and Kostermans (1935) and Haagen Smit and Went (1935), with additions from various sources.

The conclusions to be drawn from this table are in some respects modified from those touched on in VII E. Tentatively we may say that:

The primary growth-promoting activity is connected with the presence of: 1, the double bond, or aromatic unsaturation; 2, a carboxyl group, free, or if esterified, readily hydrolyzable; 3, a ring system, either 5-membered (auxin a and b), aromatic (naphthyl or phenyl), or a combination of both (indole, indene, etc.); 4, a minimum distance of at least one C atom between the carboxyl group and the ring; 5, a very definite steric structure, since in the one case studied the cis-compound is active, the trans-compound not.

The chemical changes which do not directly influence the primary growth reaction, but modify the secondary properties of a growth-promoting substance, are:

1. length of the acid side-chain,
2. methyl substitution in the nucleus,
3. substitution in the side-chain,
4. the structure of the nucleus itself.

A more detailed discussion and a hypothesis relating structure to activity has been given by Went, Koepfli, and Thimann (1937).

Although this is only a beginning, we are already in a position to predict what substances should possess activity. Presumably an exact knowledge of the active grouping will help in determining the type of the reaction involved.

CHAPTER IX

THE GROWTH OF ROOTS

In the preceding chapters reference has been made only to the relation of auxin to shoots. In roots the relations are entirely different, although in many respects analogous.

A. The Effect of the Tip in Root Growth

Unlike shoots, in which decapitation almost invariably reduces the growth rate, decapitation of roots does not greatly influence the growth. In the 70's and 80's of last century a flood of literature appeared dealing with this subject. Every investigator used a different object, and opinions were about equally divided as to whether decapitation retarded growth or was without effect; Wiesner (1884), working with roots under water, even found an acceleration.

Probably on account of the disagreement, the whole question was shelved for almost half a century. It was Cholodny who in 1924 and subsequent years took up the problem again and showed that in fact, if precautions were taken to ensure that the roots received sufficient water, there was an acceleration after decapitation (Cholodny, 1926). He worked first with *Zea Mays* and later confirmed the effect with *Lupinus* (1926). The differences were in all cases small (ca. 12 per cent), but real. Later Bünning (1928) showed that the acceleration was limited to a few mm. of the growing zone only, and that if sections of tip longer than 1 mm. were removed the acceleration did not take place. The acceleration is preceded by a temporary decrease in growth rate, which is probably due to a loss of turgidity of the cells resulting from the wounding (Janse, 1929). Bünning found this acceleration in *Lupinus*, *Zea Mays*, and *Vicia Faba* roots, but not in *Pisum* roots. Gorter (1932) also found that *Pisum* roots show no change in growth rate after decapitation. It is thus clear that if the experiments are carried out carefully and not too much of the tip is removed, all of the roots studied—with the exception of those of *Pisum*—show a definite acceleration after decapitation (*cf.* also Cholodny, 1933).

In an attempt to explain this phenomenon, Cholodny (1926, 1931*a*) replaced the tip on maize roots and found that their growth was again retarded. Coleoptile tips had previously been found to behave in the same way (1924). Keeble, Nelson, and Snow (1931*a*) confirmed these results. Further, when the tip is removed, the root stump loses its sensitivity to gravity, as has been known since Darwin (1880), but if root or coleoptile tips are replaced on the stump Cholodny (1924) found that its geotropic sensitivity is largely regained. This suggests, as Cholodny (1926) pointed out, that both the root tip and the coleoptile tip secrete a substance retarding root growth, and that this substance enables the root to give a tropistic response by becoming more concentrated on one side than the other (*cf.* X *B*). From its production by coleoptile tips it might be supposed that this growth-retarding substance is identical with auxin.

B. The Effect of Auxin on Root Growth

The above possibility was strongly borne out by the experiments of Nielsen (1930), Navez (1933), and Boysen Jensen (1933*b*) (see also Keeble, Nelson, and Snow, 1930). They immersed roots of various plants in water and in different concentrations of *Rhizopus* culture medium (which contains indole-3-acetic acid, *cf.* VII *C*). The growth of the roots was very greatly retarded by the active culture medium. That this retardation is really due to the auxin and not to the other substances present was shown by Kögl, Haagen Smit, and Erxleben (1934*a*) by immersing *Avena* roots in solutions of auxin *a*, auxin *b*, and indole-3-acetic acid, when they were strongly retarded. The extent of inhibition is proportional to the concentration of auxin, and

the lowest active concentration is about that which gives
5° curvature on the *Avena* coleoptile (Lane, 1936; Meesters,
1936).   The inhibition is not due to pH, and is not comparable with that produced by toxic substances.   Since
indene-3-acetic acid exerts the same inhibiting effect (Thimann, 1935*b*), it is presumably a general property of growth
promoting substances to inhibit root elongation.   Root inhibition can even be used as a method for the assay of auxin,

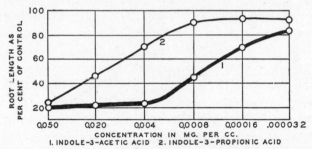

Fig. 46. Relation between auxin concentration and the inhibition of root
elongation in *Avena*.   The seeds were soaked 24 hours in water and then 24
hours in test solution.   The concentration of indole-propionic acid necessary
to cause a given inhibition is 25 times that of indole-acetic acid.   (From Lane,
Am. J. Bot. *23:* 532–535, 1936.)

for which it is both simple and sensitive, the inhibiting
concentrations of auxin being much lower than those of
ordinary toxic substances such as mercury and silver ions
(Lane, 1936).   The ratio of activities of indole-propionic and
indole-acetic acids, which in *Avena* coleoptile curvature is
0.2 per cent, in *Avena* root inhibition is about 4 per cent,
(see Figure 46).

Extremely low concentrations of auxin may produce
acceleration of root growth.   Thus Amlong (1936) finds that
if *Vicia Faba* roots are decapitated and 3 hours later, when
their auxin content will have somewhat decreased, are
treated with auxin solutions, then 10^{-9} mol. indole-acetic
acid causes slight but definite growth promotion.   Higher
concentrations still inhibited growth.   Fiedler (1936) obtained a similar result with isolated *Zea Mays* roots in culture medium without yeast extract; their auxin content was

then practically nil, and 2.10^{-9} mol. indole-acetic acid (0.1 γ per liter) caused about 30 per cent acceleration in growth, while higher concentrations only inhibited. Thimann (1936a) obtained a slight acceleration of the growth of *Pisum* roots when auxin was applied to the base of the stem. He ascribed this acceleration to the very low concentrations of auxin which reach the root under these conditions, together with the relatively small amount of auxin present in these roots. Further, if *Avena* roots are inhibited in auxin solutions and then transferred to water, their growth is accelerated beyond that of water-treated controls; this, presumably, is due to the rapid disappearance of auxin from the root, so that its concentration eventually reaches the accelerating level (u).

C. Auxin Production in the Root

In order to complete the picture it is necessary to have proof that root tips really do produce auxin, and this has been given by a number of workers. First, Cholodny (1928) showed that placing a root tip of *Zea Mays* on decapitated *Avena* coleoptiles would increase their photo- and geotropic responses. Then Hawker (1932) in experiments primarily directed to the study of geotropism, placed root tips of *Vicia Faba* on gelatin blocks and showed that if subsequently applied to one side of decapitated root stumps the blocks caused the stump to curve towards them, *i.e.* the stump was inhibited on the side to which the gelatin was applied. However, Boysen Jensen (1933a), who similarly placed root tips on agar and then tested this agar on *Avena* coleoptiles, could obtain no auxin in this way from *Zea Mays* root tips. He found, however, that the tips of very young *Zea Mays* roots (not longer than 5 mm.) would cause curvature of *Avena* coleoptiles if placed one-sidedly upon them, but the tips of older roots would not do so. Believing that the reason for this failure was the need for nutrient, he used agar containing 10 per cent dextrose, and this brought immediate success. Root tips of *Vicia Faba* gave a small amount of auxin to plain agar (as Hawker had found), but five times this amount with dextrose agar. With this method he showed that, in *Zea "caragua,"* the concentration of auxin decreases rapidly from the tip of the root towards the base, and subsequently (1933b) also confirmed Hawker's finding that more auxin diffuses out of the lower than the upper half of root tips which had been placed horizontally.

The presence of auxin in *Avena* roots was proven in another way by Thimann (1934), who acidified the roots, extracted directly with chloroform, and subsequently tested the extract, freed from chloroform and dissolved in agar, upon coleoptiles. The concentration of auxin decreased from the tip towards the base, as may be seen from Figure 30, p. 68, which summarizes his results. Boysen Jensen (1936a) confirmed that auxin could be extracted from roots by chloroform and found that more was extracted from the lower half of horizontally placed roots than from the upper.

The above experiments show that auxin is present in the root, and especially in the tip, but do not make it clear that it is actually produced there. Thimann (1934), using 10 mm. *Avena* root tips, compared the auxin obtainable by chloroform extraction with that obtainable by diffusion into dextrose agar, and stated that "the only fair conclusion seems to be that growth substance is not produced in the root tip but merely accumulates there." However, Cholodny (1934) found that, if supplied with dextrose gelatin, root tips of *Zea Mays* continue to yield auxin for 5–6 hours and Nagao (1936) obtained the same result with short (2 mm.) tips of *Avena* roots. The researches of Van Raalte (1936) go far towards clearing up this question. Using *Vicia Faba* roots, he found that addition of salts alone to the agar gives very good yields of auxin, but addition of dextrose isotonic with the salt is still more effective. Thus the dextrose acts in two ways—osmotically, by increasing the diffusion out of the root tip, and nutritively, by maintaining the root tip during the experiment. Boysen Jensen (1933a) had previously found that mannite was almost as effective as glucose and concluded from this that its action could not be nutritive. Van Raalte further showed that on dextrose agar the production of auxin by the root tip is actually greater in the second hour than in the first, and if such tips were then extracted with ether the amount of auxin extractable had increased. There is therefore little doubt that auxin is produced for a short time in the isolated root tip, when it is fed with dextrose.

Fiedler (1936), however, found that neither by diffusion into dextrose agar nor by extraction with chloroform could auxin be obtained from isolated root tips of *Zea Mays* and *Vicia Faba* in culture solutions after about 24 hours; even after 8 hours in the medium 80 to 90 per cent of the auxin originally present had disappeared. This disappearance of auxin could be largely prevented by coating the cut surface with gelatin or lanoline and is therefore probably due to enzymic oxidation (*cf.* IV *A*). Fiedler concludes that root tips in culture produce no auxin and adopts the view of Thimann (1934) that the auxin in root tips comes there from the seed or shoot.

Since there are a number of chemically different auxins, which all have the same effect on root growth, it is of special interest to know which one is present in the root tip. This question has been studied by Heyn (1935), who found, by the determination of the diffusion coefficient, that the auxin of the root tip of *Vicia Faba* has a molecular weight of about 370, which is just the same as that for the *Avena* coleoptile tip; it is therefore probably auxin *a* or *b*.

The transport of auxin in the root has been the subject of conflicting experiments and views. Went (1932) suggested that the polarity of the shoot was continuous with that of the root, so that auxin transport would be towards the root tip. Gorter (1932) investigated transport directly by using *Zea Mays* root cylinders in the same way as van der Weij with coleoptiles (Chapter VI *C*), and found that transport took place in both directions about equally (see also Heidt, 1931). The auxin appeared to be rapidly destroyed by the root. The same thing was found for *Vicia Faba* by Faber

(1936). The most basal zones of roots 60 mm. long or so, however, transported practically no auxin in either direction. The velocity of movement was about 4 mm. per hour. Nagao (1936) found in *Vicia Faba*, on the other hand, that the auxin diffusing out from cylinders taken from near the tip was greater from the basal than from the apical surface. In an experiment of Cholodny (1934), coleoptile tips were applied to the apical or the basal cut surface of decapitated roots; if these were then placed horizontally, the stumps with tips on their apical ends curved geotropically, the others not. He concluded that auxin moved only basipetally in the root, although Heidt's very similar experiment with *Sinapis alba* indicated movement in both directions. That some transport certainly takes place from base to apex is shown by the experiments of Thimann (1936*a*) on the formation of lateral roots of *Pisum* by auxin applied to the stump of the shoot (see XI *F*). He also found that auxin applied to the scutellum of *Avena* greatly inhibited the growth of the young roots, and if applied at the base of the shoot in older plants it here also—though to a lesser extent—inhibited the growth of the roots. Transport from base to apex in *Avena* roots therefore probably decreases with age. Such experiments on roots are made more difficult by the rapid destruction of auxin which takes place (Gorter, 1932; Fiedler, 1936), but there seems no doubt that transport in both directions occurs in *Pisum*, *Zea*, *Avena*, and *Vicia*, although doubtless the ratio of the transport intensities in the two directions varies.

An interesting feature of the action of auxin on roots is its production of swellings. Cholodny (1931*a*) showed that when 3 maize coleoptile tips, instead of one, were applied to the root stump there was a marked swelling in the growing zone. This swelling was mostly confined to the cortical parenchyma. Bouillenne and Went (1933) noticed that cuttings on which leaves had been grafted, and which rooted vigorously, frequently gave abnormal thickenings near the root tip, doubtless due to the excess of auxin coming from

the leaf; on removal of the leaf the roots resumed their
normal growth. Kögl, Haagen Smit, and Erxleben (1934*a*)
in showing that pure auxins inhibit growth of *Avena* roots,
mention that the short roots were abnormally thick. Subsequently numerous workers have noticed the thickenings
which are almost always produced by the action of auxin,
particularly with high concentrations. In the shortened and
thickened zone, there is radial elongation of the cells in the
cortex, which are actually shortened in the longitudinal
dimension (*u*). The thickening need not necessarily accompany inhibition of elongation, since Lane (1936) has shown
that *Avena* roots may be almost completely inhibited in
length without any appreciable thickening, by soaking the
seeds in auxin solution.

A special case of root thickening and lateral root formation is provided by the bacterial nodules on the roots of
legumes. Thimann (1936) has shown that young growing
nodules produce considerable amounts of auxin, which
diffuses both from the apical and from the basal portion.
He also showed that local application of auxin to a lateral
root at its first appearance produced its complete inhibition,
and thus deduced that nodules are due to the auxin formed
by the bacteria in the tissues; this auxin induces a lateral
root at the point of infection, but then inhibits its growth
and causes it instead to swell.

D. The Rôle of Auxin in the Growth of Roots

The formation of and response to auxin in the root is so
different from that of shoots, that the two-factor scheme,
suggested to explain the distribution of growth in shoots,
cannot be applied to roots. How then do roots grow? According to Czaja (1935) auxin in roots has fundamentally
the same function as in shoots, that is, it causes elongation.
He assumes two opposite streams of auxin, one coming
from the stem and the other from the root tip, each of which
by itself promotes growth, while the two in combination
cause a growth retardation. This view, based on a few ex-

periments only, and theoretically impossible (see VI *D*), has been disproven both by Faber (1936) and by Thimann (1936). Czaja's *experimentum crucis:* negative geotropic curvatures in decapitated roots, which should have only one auxin "stream," could not be repeated. Further, auxin, when applied to the epicotyl stump of decapitated *Pisum* seedlings does not inhibit root growth, but even slightly accelerates it (Thimann, 1936), and the presence or absence of the root tip (*i.e.* the second auxin "stream") does not affect the result. In *Avena*, in which the same treatment produces a slight inhibition, the presence or absence of the root tip is also without effect.

One obvious suggestion as to how it is that auxin inhibits root elongation is that its action is exerted on the transverse walls and thus causes thickening instead of elongation (*cf. e.g.* F. A. F. C. Went, 1935). However, since inhibition appears to be independent of thickening, there must be another explanation.

Another suggestion comes from Boysen Jensen (1936*a*). According to this, roots are much more sensitive to auxin than shoots; very low concentrations of auxin promote their growth, but the ordinary concentrations worked with are high enough to be above the optimum and thus cause inhibition. This is supported by the experiments of Amlong (1936*a*) and Fiedler (1936) on roots made very poor in auxin, whose growth is then slightly promoted by the lowest auxin concentrations (see IX *B*). A comparable inhibition of elongation is produced in stems, *e.g.* of pea and *Helianthus*, by very high concentrations of auxin. In stems, therefore, inhibition is caused only by the highest concentrations, while in roots it is caused by all but the very lowest. This raises the question as to why different roots react differently to auxin. Thus in Thimann's experiments (1936) *Avena* and *Pisum* behave in the opposite way to auxin applied basally; in Faber's experiments (1936) *Avena* and *Vicia* also react oppositely. Both have suggested that the difference is due to different concentrations of auxin already in the root, roots already low in auxin giving an acceleration, roots high in auxin a retardation. This would correspond approximately with Boysen Jensen's suggestion. Jost and Reiss (1936) also tend to adopt this view.

The other possibility is that auxin is not necessary at all for the growth of roots. The growth of isolated roots in culture is known to be dependent on sugars, salts, and traces of special substances, which are present in yeast extract (White, 1933, 1934). These may perhaps include a special root-growth promoting substance, but in any event addition of auxin does not improve the growth, and such a medium suffices for the indefinite growth of the roots of wheat and tomato. The absence of detectable amounts of auxin from such isolated roots (Fiedler, 1936) would certainly indicate that it plays no part in their growth. The fact that in these cultures roots continue to branch, however, would indicate either that they produce traces of auxin or else that the small amount of auxin in the yeast extract or other constituent is sufficient to cause both growth and branching.

Whether auxin plays any part in root elongation or not, the mechanism whereby it causes inhibition of root growth is, as stated above, not clear. Bonner (1935) has suggested that instead of diminishing the forces between the micelles of the cell wall, it increases them. However, Amlong (1936) has shown that the decapitation of *Vicia Faba* roots causes a decrease in their plasticity just as was shown by Heyn for coleoptiles (VIII *D*). Not only does this contradict Bonner's suggestion, but it raises again the question of whether the increased plasticity caused by auxin can be the direct cause of growth.

In view of the incompleteness of our knowledge as to the mechanism of elongation, it is perhaps unreasonable to expect any better understanding of the mechanism of inhibition. Doubtless further advances in the analysis of both processes may be expected in the near future.

CHAPTER X

TROPISMS

I. TROPISMS IN GENERAL

The apparent lack of feeling or of responsiveness in plants was the basis of the old distinction between plants and animals: "Saxa crescunt, plantae crescunt et vivunt; animalia crescunt, vivunt et sentiunt." However, in tropistic movements plants appear to exhibit a sort of intelligence; their movement is of subsequent advantage to them. In addition, tropisms are easily observable and lay themselves open to obvious experiments, so that it is not surprising that they have been a subject of investigation from the earliest times of plant physiology. This sensitivity, otherwise not noticeable in plants, explains why it is that in regard to tropistic responses the parallelism between plants and animals has been so much stressed. This had at first the drawback that many complex concepts of zoölogy were transferred to plants, but one of the great services which the discovery and study of the auxins has performed is that it has forced the development of new concepts independent of the zoölogical heritage—concepts not only new, but also more concrete and experimentally analyzable. It will be among the aims of this chapter to elucidate this change in thought, and with this in view, tropisms will be treated only so far as they are demonstrably due to differential growth and so far as their auxin relations have been investigated. The material in this chapter could also be regarded as an application of the knowledge of auxin which we have gained in the preceding pages. However, this would not be historically correct, because, as shown in Table I, p. 16, the early evidence for the existence and rôle of auxin came through the study of tropisms. In the recent development of the field, the center of interest has shifted away from the explanation of tropisms to more general functions of auxin in correlative processes and to the growth process itself.

A. HISTORICAL INTRODUCTION

The early work on tropisms has been reviewed by Wiesner (1878, 1880), Pringsheim (1912), F. A. F. C. Went (1929, 1931), Rawitscher (1932), du Buy and Nuernbergk (1935) and need not be further discussed here. We can thus pass over the first period, consisting first of simple mechanical explanations, and then of their gradual replacement by more and more elaborate stimulus-concepts, none of which had a really concrete physical basis. This period of complexity of thought was accompanied by simplicity of experimental approach, and work was of a purely qualitative nature. The experiments of Blaauw (1909, 1914, 1915, 1918) ushered in a new era,[1] that of quantitative work; this was associated with greater simplicity of theories. He showed that, within limits, the response is proportional to the total energy received by the plant, and he envisaged tropisms simply as a phenomenon of differential growth. Thus: "Whenever light causes a growth reaction, unequal distribution of the light will cause unequal growth, which we call phototropism" (Blaauw, 1918, p. 171).

Almost simultaneously with the first publication of Blaauw, the "stimulus" concept of tropisms received a blow from another direction. Boysen Jensen (1910, 1911, 1913) found that the transmission of the light stimulus does not involve any vital process, but can take place by simple diffusion. He concluded from his experiments, which have been discussed in II B, that the path of the phototropic stimulus is along the shaded side, that of the geotropic stimulus along the lower side, of the plant. The stimulus could cross a cut surface, but would not pass a sheet of mica; however, a slice of rattan inserted in the cut did not

---

[1] The editors of the *Zeitschrift für Botanik* received Blaauw's paper "Licht und Wachstum, *I*" (1914), with the following unusual reservation: "We publish this paper although we do not agree in every respect with the author's theoretical conceptions."

interfere with its passage. The transmission of the stimulus is therefore due to a diffusible substance. Purdy (1921) confirmed his essential results.

Soon after this first important step Paál's investigations (1914, 1919) brought another great advance. Paál found that not only after tropistic stimulation, but also in normal growth, the tip exerts an influence on the growth of the lower zones. Thus he developed the concept that the tip continuously forms growth-regulating substances. His great contribution to the field of tropisms was that he envisaged the response as due to an unequal supply of these growth regulators to the two sides (*cf.* II *C*). Considering phototropism in particular, he suggested three possible ways in which such an effect might be brought about: the regulator might "disappear," its production might be reduced, or its transport might be interfered with, on the lighted side.

The concepts of Stark (1921), Stark and Drechsel (1922), and Brauner (1922) represented a modification of Paál's theories, tinged with a return to earlier ideas. Stark showed that the traumatotropic stimulus, or the tendency of coleoptiles to curve towards a wound, could be transmitted, just as in phototropism, across a cut surface. Tips wounded on one side, *e.g.* with $AgNO_3$, were replaced on stumps and induced curvatures, in the stump, towards the wounded side. If tissues were crushed and mixed with agar, then the agar, if applied one-sidedly to stumps, caused curvatures towards that side. Hence he assumed that there are special wound-hormones, which inhibit growth. Similarly he assumed special phototropo-hormones, (active in phototropism), which increase the growth rate (*cf.* footnote to p. 114). His evidence also indicated that these tropo-hormones had definite specificity.

Brauner (1922) placed unilaterally-illuminated tips on unilluminated stumps, and unilluminated tips on unilaterally-illuminated bases; in both cases a curvature resulted, while the illumination of the stump alone caused no response. He explained these results in terms of an increased permeability on the lighted side, which he afterwards (1924, 1935) was able to measure directly. The increased permeability was assumed to allow increased transmission of growth-inhibiting substances on the lighted side. Seubert (1925) carried out experiments which can be regarded as an extension of those of Brauner. She illuminated coleoptile stumps unilaterally and found that if agar blocks containing saliva were then placed symmetrically upon them they curved towards the light; otherwise they did not.

Brauner's explanation makes it clear on how slight an experimental basis the suggested relation between growth substances and phototropism was founded. There were 4 possible explanations, namely:

1. Increased transmission of growth-promoting substance on the dark side (Boysen Jensen),
2. Decreased transmission of growth-promoting substance on the light side (Paál),
3. Increased transmission of growth-inhibiting substance on the light side (Brauner),
4. Decreased transmission of growth-inhibiting substance on the dark side.

All but the fourth were held at different times by different workers, and it was some years before it was shown that in fact both 1 and 2 simultaneously occur (Cholodny, 1927; Went, 1928).

B. THE CHOLODNY-WENT THEORY

In 1924 Cholodny published the first of a long series of valuable papers dealing with the relation between tropisms and growth hormones. Beginning with an investigation of roots he showed that decapitation removes the sensitivity of the stump to gravity, but that placing a coleoptile tip or a root tip upon the cut surface restores the geotropic sensitivity. In a somewhat similar way he later showed (1926), (cf. p. 75), that *Lupinus* hypocotyls from which the central cylinder had been bored out lose their geotropic sensitivity, but regain it if the tip of a *Zea Mays* coleoptile be inserted into the cavity (see Figure 47). He thus arrived (1926) at a number of important conclusions. In logical order these are: (1) "growth hormones play an essential rôle in the mechanism of the geotropic reaction"; (2) "in vertically placed stems and roots the growth-regulating substances are equally distributed on all sides"; (3) "as soon as these organs are placed in a horizontal position,

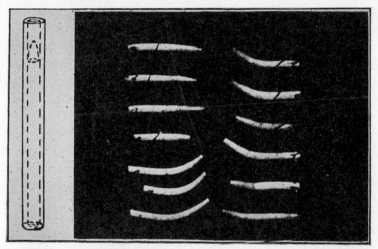

FIG. 47. Geotropism of hypocotyl cylinders of *Lupinus angustifolius*, from which the central cylinder has been removed. Upper left, four bored-out controls, no geotropic response; lower left, three intact controls, normal response. Right, six plants in the hollow of each of which a coleoptile tip of *Zea Mays* has been placed, as in diagram; geotropic sensitivity restored. (From Cholodny, *Jahrb. wiss. Bot. 65*: 447–459, 1926.)

the normal diffusion of the growth hormones is disturbed; the upper and lower cortical cells now obtain different amounts of these substances." This unequal distribution is ascribed to a physiological polarity induced by gravity, a polarity which he had tentatively postulated in 1918; (4) the opposite signs of the reactions of roots and shoots fit in with the fact that they react in opposite ways to the growth hormones coming from their tips; (5) he concludes that "the problem of geotropism can be traced back to the much simpler problem of the chemical control of growth." This passage recalls Blaauw's (1918) statement that "the problem of phototropism in itself has become void," phototropism being simply a phenomenon of growth.

Simultaneously Went (1926) came to the same conclusions as Cholodny, from his experiments on the isolation of auxin from the coleoptile tip; "geotropic perception is caused by a polar alteration in the coleoptile cells . . . instead of moving rectilinearly the growth regulators are more strongly conveyed towards that side which under geotropic stimulation was turned downwards."

Consideration of the literature on phototropism led Cholodny shortly after (1927) to the view that the apparently conflicting results of different workers could be brought into agreement by adapting his hormonal theory of geotropism as follows: "The cells of the coleoptile first become polarized under the influence of the unilateral illumination, and this causes the continuously produced growth hormones to diffuse from the light towards the dark side more rapidly than in any other direction."

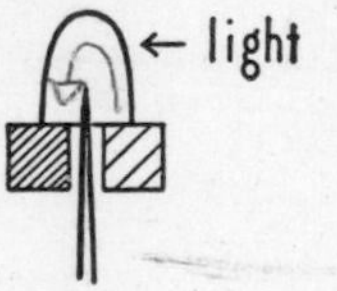

FIG. 48. Coleoptile tip, arranged so that the auxin from the light and dark sides diffuses into separate blocks. Degree of shading indicates relative amounts of auxin collected.

No sooner had this theory of phototropism been formulated than it was independently stated, and this time with experimental proof, by Went (1928). After having found that the growth hormone of coleoptile tips (auxin) can be determined quantitatively by the curvature test (see III C) and that without auxin no growth occurs, he concluded that a phenomenon of differential growth must be analyzed in terms of differential auxin relations. Having found that auxin itself is not affected directly by light, he looked for a difference in the production or distribution of auxin on the two sides of phototropically stimulated coleoptile tips. Coleoptiles were exposed unilaterally to light of a suitable intensity, the tips then cut off and placed upon two blocks of agar separated by a razor-blade in such a way that the auxin from the two sides diffused into two different blocks (see Figure 48). He found that more auxin diffuses out of the dark than out of the light side, and that the amount coming from the dark half was *more* than the amount coming from half an unilluminated tip. This shows that the principal effect of unilateral illumination is to cause the lateral transport of some auxin from the light to the dark side.

On the basis of these experiments and concepts the general theory of plant tropisms, sometimes called the Cholodny-Went theory, may be formulated as follows (see *e.g.* Cholodny, 1929):

> Growth curvatures, whether induced by internal or by external factors, are due to an unequal distribution of auxin between the two sides of the curving organ. In the tropisms induced by light and gravity the unequal auxin distribution is brought about by a transverse polarization of the cells, which results in lateral transport of the auxin.

"These researches, which are grouped around a central idea, allow us to approach step by step to the solution of one of the most interesting problems of physiology. From the standpoint of the history of science, the present [1] state of the problem is of the greatest interest. Gradually there emerges from a chaos of facts the splendid form of a theory which promises to unite and to coördinate, in the very near future, the enormous mass of varied experimental data into a single principle" (Cholodny, 1927). This prophetic statement has to a large extent come true, and it will now be necessary to consider the "enormous mass of experimental data" in more detail. In succession we shall treat geotropism, phototropism, and other tropisms so far as they are related to our subject.

II. GEOTROPISM

C. GEOTROPISM OF SHOOTS

An interesting forerunner of the Cholodny-Went theory is Loeb's view of geotropism (1917). His experiments on

[1] 1927.

the geotropism of *Bryophyllum* stems were tentatively interpreted on the basis of "specific geotropic substances or hormones . . . having the tendency to collect on the lower side of a horizontally suspended stem." His subsequent change of view is discussed in II *E*.

Some experiments of Gradmann (1925) were at first thought to be in opposition to the above theory. He split stems of *Labiatae* longitudinally and placed them horizontally: those with the cut surface uppermost curved normally and showed considerable growth, but those with the cut surface downward showed little growth or curvature. A large number of variations on this type of experiment gave similar results, and his general conclusion was that, in an intact organ, the influence of gravity produced geotropo-hormone only in the lower half and this then accelerated growth of this half. Isolated upper halves would thus have no such hormone. His interpretations have, however, been criticized both by Cholodny (1927, 1931) and Dolk (1930) on the ground that he completely neglected the effects of the wound, which are very great (see section *J*).

It remained for Dolk (1929, 1929a, 1930, 1936) to show that the Cholodny-Went theory applies completely and in its simplest form to the case of geotropism in *Avena*. He first showed that neither upon rotating coleoptiles horizontally nor upon returning them to the vertical position was there any change in growth rate, *i.e.* there is no "geo-growth reaction" (see also Cholodny, 1929a). This was afterwards confirmed by growth measurements made during the actual geotropic curvature by Navez and Robinson (1933). Correspondingly the total amount of auxin diffusing out of coleoptile tips is the same whether they have been placed horizontally or vertically. However—and this is the important point—the amount diffusing out of the lower half, when they have been placed horizontally, is 62.5 per cent, and that diffusing out of the upper half 37.5 per cent, of the total. Exactly the same distribution was found for *Zea Mays* coleoptile tips. (Navez and Robinson [1933]

subsequently found a somewhat greater difference, the lower
side giving 73 per cent of the total auxin.) Hence gravity
has no effect on the total auxin production but affects only
its distribution between the two sides. Dolk found this
difference in distribution to appear within 15 minutes after placing coleoptiles horizontally, and to disappear again
within one hour after the horizontal exposure has ceased.
In isolated coleoptile cylinders which have been symmetrically provided with auxin-agar and placed horizontally, the
same distribution takes place and the same ratio, 38 to 62,
was obtained. Polar distribution therefore may take place
in any zone of the coleoptile. Dolk also measured the curvature of different zones of the *Avena* coleoptile as a function
of time, and this brought to light a number of interesting
points. Firstly, if the exposure to gravity is short, the
curvature of the base is delayed until curvature of the upper
zones is well under way, but if the exposure is 30 minutes
or more all but the most basal zones begin to curve at about
the same time. From this, and other experiments on bases
provided with auxin and exposed to gravity, we may conclude that all zones are able to perceive gravity by redis-
tributing their auxin, but that the redistribution in the
basal zones only leads to curvature if the exposure has
been 30 minutes or longer. In this respect the response is
different from that to light (see X *H*). Secondly, as mentioned above, the unequal distribution does not last long
after the stimulus is removed, and hence the curvatures
do not go on increasing for more than 40 minutes after
exposure. On the contrary, they begin to decrease from
the top down, so that the zone of maximum curvature
appears to migrate towards the base; this straightening
Dolk explained in terms of the food factor (*cf.* V *D*). It
thus appears that all the peculiarities of the geotropic
reaction are explicable in terms of unequal auxin distribution (*cf.* also discussion in X *H*, p. 176).

Dijkman (1933, 1934) has made a similar study of geotropism in *Lupinus* hypocotyls. Having first established

that gravity has no effect on the total production of auxin, he attempted to correlate quantitatively the unequal auxin distribution with the unequal growth distribution. The unequal auxin distribution begins half an hour after the plants are placed horizontally and the curvature begins at the same time. He showed that for these objects, as for *Avena*, straight growth is proportional to auxin applied, and he could thus calculate how much growth difference between the two sides of the geotropically curved organ would be expected from the observed auxin difference. He found that from 70 to 100 per cent of the growth difference may be accounted for by the auxin difference. It is possible that the pH difference (see below), if real, plays also a minor rôle in such curvatures, but on the whole the confirmation of the Cholodny-Went theory is excellent.

Van der Laan (1934), in an investigation on the effect of ethylene, confirmed the older observation that in *Vicia Faba* seedlings exposure to ethylene causes downward bending of the shoots and found that this is correlated with an unequal auxin distribution such that the upper side has more than the lower. This, of course, is to be distinguished from the increase of auxin in the lower half of horizontally placed stems in pure air. The curious behavior of these seedlings in ethylene is thus explained.

Boysen Jensen (1936a) has applied the chloroform extraction method of Thimann (see IV A) to the direct determination of the auxin in the upper and lower halves of geotropically stimulated stems of *Phaseolus* and *Vicia Faba*. He finds that the distribution between the two sides is of the same order as that found by Dolk and Dijkman. However, the difference in auxin does not seem numerically great enough to account for the difference in growth. Boysen Jensen explains this by reference to a suggestion of Thimann (1934) that some of the auxin in the plant is present in a bound non-diffusible form, but that this is extracted by chloroform along with the free or active auxin (see discussion in VIII F). Hence the real difference between the *free* auxin on the two sides is somewhat greater than that found.

Another effect may play a rôle here. It has been found by Gundel (1933) and confirmed by Metzner (1934) that the pH of the lower side of horizontally placed stems is about 0.1 pH unit more acid than that of the upper side. According to Bonner (1934) this would increase the auxin which is in the active, free acid, form, by about 20 per cent, and thus the same total amount of auxin would give a greater growth on the lower side than on the upper.

There are two apparent disagreements with the theory so far. One is the difficulty raised by Beyer (1932) that *Taraxacum*, *Helianthus*, and other stems and hypocotyls, *just* before or after they cease growing altogether, still give geotropic curvature. It might certainly be expected that if the auxin present were not enough to cause growth it would not be enough to cause curvature. Du Buy (1936) has shown, however, that in aging material a certain minimum concentration of auxin must be present before any growth can occur—a "threshold concentration." Beyer's material, just finishing its growth, was evidently in this state, and hence the increased concentrations of auxin on the lower side, produced by gravity, would be just sufficient to exceed this threshold and so cause growth to begin again.

The other disagreement is the fact, discovered by Schmitz (1933) that mature nodes of grasses, which have ceased growing and which yield no auxin, begin to produce some auxin again if they are placed horizontally. This, of course, is connected with the well-known exceptional behavior of mature grass nodes which are still capable of geotropic response. It does not, however, agree with the Cholodny-Went theory because there is here an apparent new formation of auxin upon stimulation. It must be left for the present as an unexplained curiosity.

D. Geotropism of Roots

The fact that auxin, as has been shown in IX *B*, inhibits the growth of roots (in all but the minutest concentrations), makes it clear in what direction we must look for an explanation of the geotropism of roots. Unfortunately the facts are still partly in dispute. The experiment of Cholodny, mentioned above (1924), indicates that auxin is necessary for the response of the root to gravity (*cf.* Keeble, Nelson, and Snow, 1931; Keeble and Nelson, 1935). On the other hand, isolated roots in culture appear neither to contain nor to produce any auxin, and yet they are still able to curve geotropically (Fiedler, 1936). A possible explanation for this discrepancy may be sought in Fiedler's observation that his roots developed traces of chlorophyll when in agar media. This, as shown in IV *A* and *B*, would lead to the continuous production of traces of auxin, which might suffice for geotropic response, although not enough auxin would accumulate to be detectable by extraction methods. Since it is always difficult to prove a negative, *i.e.* the absence of auxin, we may for the present consider only the positive evidence.

It is important that, although Keeble, Nelson, and Snow (1931) state the contrary, the growth rate of the root does not depend on its position in regard to gravity, *i.e.* there is no "geo-growth reaction" (Cholodny, 1932; Navez, 1933).

Hawker (1932) investigated the distribution of auxin in geotropically stimulated root tips. *Zea Mays* roots were placed horizontally and after 3 hours the tips were cut off and separated into upper and lower halves. These halves were then applied to half the cut surface of unstimulated root stumps, and the curvature of the stumps measured. The half of the tip which had been the lower during stimulation gave three times as big a curvature as that which had been the upper. Hence auxin passes to the lower side of the root under the influence of gravity and thus the auxin distribution in roots is the same as that in coleoptiles. Direct confirmation of this by the diffusion method was obtained soon after by Boysen Jensen (1933*b*). He allowed the auxin from the upper and lower sides to diffuse into separate blocks of dextrose agar. These, when tested on

Avena, showed more auxin on the lower than on the upper side. Finally, the result was confirmed (Boysen Jensen, 1936a) by the chloroform extraction method, the auxin distribution found, 54:46, agreeing exactly with the ratio of the growth on the two sides during the action of gravity. This was not the case for stems, as mentioned above.

It is of interest that roots which have been treated with eosin or erythrosin lose their geotropic sensitivity, as was shown by Boas and Merkenschlager (1925), and such roots were correspondingly found by Boysen Jensen (1934) to be almost devoid of auxin. Of a group of roots treated, some still gave positive geotropic curvature, some curved, but not in the vertical plane ("transversal") and some were completely ageotropic. The relative amounts of auxin obtained from these groups by diffusion into dextrose agar were 1.05, 0.49, and 0.08 respectively, against 1.26 for untreated controls. Geotropic response is thus proportional to the amount of auxin in the root. This action of eosin has been explained by Skoog (1935), who showed that traces of eosin cause rapid photodynamic inactivation of solutions of indole-acetic acid. No such inactivation occurs in the dark.

The findings of Dolk can be used to explain the results of Keeble, Nelson, and Snow (1929), who carried out an experiment on roots comparable to that of Brauner (1922) on coleoptiles. They found that geotropically stimulated root tips of *Zea Mays* would induce curvature in unstimulated stumps. Correspondingly, unstimulated root tips would induce curvature in stimulated stumps, which alone do not curve. The transverse polarization of the root cells, leading to lateral transport of auxin, can thus take place in the lower zones as well as in the tip, but, in order that a markedly unequal distribution may be reached, an auxin supply from the tip must be provided.

Altogether the relations between geotropism and auxin in the root are, except for the experiments on isolated roots, in complete agreement with the Cholodny-Went theory.

E. The Mechanism of Geotropic Perception

It is interesting to recall that Czapek's theory of geotropism (1902) comes remarkably close to the auxin explanation in one particular respect. According to this theory, on geotropic (or phototropic) stimulation of plants, the reducible substances inside the cells increase, this being due mainly to the formation of homogentisic acid from tyrosine. The remarkable fact about this is that homogentisic acid, HO—⟨benzene ring⟩—CH$_2$COOH is closely related to phenyl-acetic acid, (ring with OH) —⟨benzene ring⟩—CH$_2$COOH which has definite growth-promoting activity

("primary activity") in the pea stem test.

A number of attempts have been made to explain the way in which gravity may cause the unequal distribution of auxin. Two pieces of evidence indicate that the same basic principle underlies all geotropic reactions. In the first place, Navez (1929) has compared the temperature coefficient for the respiration of *Vicia Faba* seedlings with the temperature coefficients for the geotropic presentation and reaction times of the roots. Between about 5° and 21° all have the same value ($\mu = 16,200$), from which he concludes that the geotropic response is governed by an oxidative or respiratory reaction. The rôle of a respiratory reaction in the response to auxin has been discussed in Chapter VIII.

In the second place, the percentage of the total auxin which diffuses out of the lower half of horizontally placed shoots or roots of different plants varies within rather narrow limits, as Table XIII (amplified from that of Boysen Jensen, 1936*a*) shows. It may be concluded from the uniformity of the results with different plants that the basic factor inducing lateral auxin transport is the same throughout.

A number of theories as to the mechanism of auxin distribution depend upon electrical changes. Cholodny (1926, 1927) suggested that the transverse movement of auxin is produced by an e.m.f., which is itself caused by the action of gravity. Such an e.m.f. had been observed first by Bose (1907) and was later studied by Brauner (1926, 1927, 1928). The latter found that if plant organs are placed horizontally a potential difference of the order of 5–10 mv. is established across them, the upper part always becoming negative to the lower ("geo-electric effect"). Roots and shoots behave in the same way. This behavior is not limited to living tissue, for even two electrolyte solutions separated by parchment paper show the same effect. The effect depends upon the charge of the membrane and the concentration of the electrolyte. Although Brauner and Amlong (1933) suggest a different interpretation, it seems probable that we have to do with a streaming potential between liquid and membrane.

TABLE XIII

GEOTROPICALLY STIMULATED	PER CENT OF AUXIN DIFFUSING FROM	
	Upper Side	Lower Side
Coleoptile tips of *Avena* (Dolk, 1930)	38	62
" " " " (Navez and Robinson, 1933)	28	72
" " " *Zea Mays* (Dolk, 1930)	37	63
Root tips of *Vicia Faba* (Boysen Jensen, 1933b)	37	63
Root tips of *Zea Mays* (Hawker, 1932)	25	75
Hypocotyls of *Lupinus* (Dijkman, 1934)	32	68
Epicotyls of *Vicia Faba* (van der Laan, 1934)	38	62
	AUXIN EXTRACTED WITH CHLOROFORM	
	Upper Side	Lower Side
Epicotyls of *Phaseolus* (Boysen Jensen, 1936a)	39	61
Epicotyls of *Vicia Faba* (" " ")	44	56
Roots of *Vicia Faba* (" " "):		
4 mm. tips	41	59
10 mm. tips	46	54

Although a number of experiments, including those on "electro-tropism," seem to indicate that auxin may be moved inside the plant by electric potentials, no direct evidence to prove this has ever been brought forward. In the experiments of Koch (1934) it appears that auxin is moved within *Helianthus* hypocotyls by the application of 10–100 mv. externally, but this deduction is founded only upon curvatures and not on direct auxin determinations. It is possible that these curvatures away from the + pole are due to the production of acid around this pole which would set free auxin (see VIII *F*). As has been indicated on p. 103 the evidence that electric potentials play a part in auxin transport is as yet inconclusive.

III. PHOTOTROPISM

F. AUXIN REDISTRIBUTION

We have seen that in geotropism the Cholodny-Went theory quantitatively explains the observed facts. In phototropism, however, the situation is far more complicated, and it will therefore be desirable to differentiate clearly between the auxin distribution effect and the other phenomena. We shall therefore give up the historical order of treatment and consider first the simple auxin redistribution effect and afterwards the many complicating factors.

As a beginning let us consider the *Avena* coleoptile. In the first place, the sensitivity of the extreme tip (the uppermost 0.25 mm.) to light is about 1000 times as great as that of the lower zones (Sierp and Seybold, 1926; Lange, 1927). In the second place the curvature varies periodically with the amount of light (see curve, Figure 49). Small illuminations up to 4000 MCS [1] produce the so-called "first positive curvature"; the maximum curvature is reached at about 200 MCS. Above this and up to about 40,000 MCS the plant curves away from the light—"first negative curvature." With still more light there occurs a second and then a third positive curvature separated by a zone of indifference or of slight negative curvature. The third positive

[1] MCS = meter-candle seconds, 25 meter-candles at 4360 A.U. being equal to 1 erg/cm².

curvature is that which appears in ordinary daylight (see: du Buy and Nuernbergk, 1934). All these curvatures may be brought about by illumination of the tip alone; illumination of the base gives only positive curvatures.

That the curvature depends upon a gradient of light across the coleoptile was convincingly shown by Buder (1920) and subsequently worked out for decapitated and regenerated coleoptile bases by du Buy (1934). The gradient can

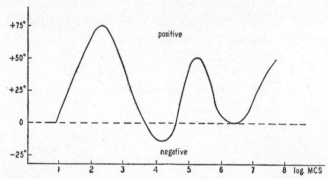

Fig. 49. Relation between phototropic curvature (ordinate) of *Avena* coleoptiles and the amount of unilateral light (abscissa). From 10 to 4000 meter-candle seconds gives the first positive curvature, 40,000 to 1,000,000 the second, and above 10,000,000 the third. Between 4000 and 40,000 negative curvature. (After du Buy and Nuernbergk, 1934.)

be reduced by pulling out the primary leaf, or still further reduced by filling the interior of the hollow coleoptile with water; if this is done the curvature is greatly reduced.

The extent to which the first positive and the first negative curvature are related to auxin distribution may be seen from Table XIV, which summarizes the results of Went (1928), van Overbeek (1933), and Asana (1936,*u*) obtained by placing unilaterally illuminated tips upon two separate agar blocks as in Figure 48. It is evident from these figures that there is the strictest parallelism between both the magnitude and the sign of curvature and the auxin distribution a few mm. below the tip. The extremely good agreement in the controls and in plants in the region of indifference gives additional confidence in the figures.

TABLE XIV

Amount of Light MCS	Type of Curvature	Extent of Curvature	Auxin Distribution in Per Cent		No. of Plants	Author
			Light Side	Dark Side		
0	Control	0°	49.9	50.1	120	Asana
20	First positive	+(10°)	41	59	24	Went
100	" "	++	26	74	48	Went
500	" "	++	36	64	48	Van Overbeek
1,000	" "	++(48°)	32	68	120	Went
?	" "	++	31	69	136	Asana
10,000	Indifferent	ca 0°	49	51	24	Went
?	First negative	—	58	42	394	Asana

Attempts to relate the phototropic curvatures quantitatively to the auxin distribution have been few. In the upper zones, auxin is not the limiting factor, so that an increase of auxin on the shaded side can cause little or no *increase* in growth rate. Thus Went (1928a) concluded that most of the curvature in the upper zones must be due to a *decrease* in the growth of the lighted side, and calculated that, in order to explain the strongest phototropic curvatures from the observed auxin distribution, the growth of the lighted side must almost cease. This was confirmed kinematographically by du Buy and Nuernbergk (1929, 1930). They found only slight acceleration of the dark side, and a very marked slowing down, or complete cessation, of growth on the lighted side. These results are the opposite of those of Boysen Jensen (1911, 1913) who concluded that the curvature was caused by a change in growth rate of the *dark* side. On the other hand, in the lower zones, where auxin is limiting growth there is both acceleration on the dark side and retardation on the lighted side.

Unlike geotropism, in which Dolk found that within an hour after returning to the vertical position the auxin distribution was again normal, in phototropism the unequal distribution persists for several hours after illumination (Went, 1928). Correspondingly, if the plants are rotated on a clinostat so that gravity does not interfere with the effect, phototropic curvatures continue to increase for 6 hours or so after illumination (see X *H*).

The above considerations hold only for auxin redistribution in the tip. Since the extreme tip is solid (*cf.* Figure 6, p. 23), it is clear that auxin redistribution can take place much more readily in it than in the lower, hollow zones. Thus, it was shown by Sierp and Seybold (1926) and by Lange (1927) that the minimum amount of light necessary to produce curvature is, if the upper 0.2 mm. are illuminated, 20 MCS; in the 0.2 mm. zone 0.8–1.0 mm. from the tip, 500 MCS; while if a 0.2 mm. zone 2 mm. below the tip is illuminated 20,000 MCS are required. We can now explain the experiment of Brauner (1922), mentioned above, in which unilluminated tips, replaced on previously illuminated stumps, caused a curvature. This result is due to the persistence of the auxin-redistributing system after unilateral illumination has ceased. The fact that the illuminated stumps not provided with tips curved scarcely at all is due to the necessity of auxin for growth (and curvature). Instead of the tip a block of agar containing auxin is equally effective in allowing curvatures to take place in the stump (Seubert, 1925; Boysen Jensen, 1933; Reinders, 1934). The effect of the decapitation itself in temporarily inhibiting lateral transport (Nuernbergk, 1933) results, however, in a delay in the onset of such curvatures.

The fact that phototropic curvature can only occur if sufficient free-moving auxin is present (*i.e.* curvature is dependent upon growth) is brought out very effectively by the work of Tsi Tsung Li (1934). A large number of coleoptiles were decapitated and then illuminated unilaterally at different time intervals after decapitation. With very short time intervals between decapitation and illumination they still gave a slight curvature, due doubtless to redistribution of the free-moving auxin still present, but afterwards the ability to curve became extremely small, *i.e.* the "free" or redistributable auxin (see VIII *F*) almost disappears. Finally, as soon as auxin was regenerated the curvatures increased markedly. The free or redistributable auxin disappears first from the upper zones and persists longest in the base (u).

The response of tip and of stump thus both rest on the same phenomenon, namely the redistribution of free auxin. The two responses differ, however, (1) in the amount of light needed to bring them about, (2) in their spectral sensitivity, and (3) in their reaction times (Haig, 1935).

Different phototropic sensitivity in different parts of the spectrum must be due to unequal absorption of light by the light-sensitive system in the coleoptile. Because of the rôle of auxin in the production of phototropic curvatures, it has been assumed that the greater sensitivity to blue and violet light is due to the absorption of these shorter wave-lengths by auxin. This, however, is not the case; the auxins have no pronounced absorption spectrum in the visible, while the phototropic sensitivity curve shows maxima at about 440 and 475 mμ. Wald and du Buy (1936) have pointed out that the spectral sensitivity of *Avena* corresponds very well with the absorption spectrum of carotene, of which they showed small amounts to be present in etiolated coleoptiles. Castle (1935) has made a similar comparison for the phototropic sporangiophores of *Phycomyces*.

The bulk of the curvature in the *Avena* coleoptile can thus be explained as due to the asymmetrical distribution of auxin, although more extensive data are very desirable. Just how the light can produce this distribution, and what rôle is played by the different pigments remains to be found out.

Our knowledge of auxin redistribution under the influence of unilateral light is even scarcer in other objects than in *Avena*. Only in *Raphanus* has a complete set of data been collected (van Overbeek, 1933). These may be summarized here. The distribution of auxin diffusing from the apical 10 mm. of the hypocotyl in darkness was symmetrical; after 3 hours' continued illumination, however, the light side gave off only 15 per cent, the dark side 85 per cent of the total. In hypocotyl cylinders supplied apically with auxin agar the same redistribution was observed; the length of these cylinders was only 6 mm. and thus one may calculate that the observed auxin difference (37 per cent on light and 63 per cent on dark side) corresponds quantitatively with the greater difference in the hypocotyl tips 10 mm. long. Van Overbeek also ascertained that the lateral auxin transport is induced only by wave-lengths less than 5460 A.U., *i.e.* by those causing phototropic curvature.

The phototropic curvature of *Phaseolus* epicotyls is also accompanied by asymmetric distribution of auxin. Boysen Jensen (1936a) determined the auxin in the light and dark halves of the epicotyl by the chloroform method and found about one third of the total on the lighted side and two thirds on the dark side.

As already mentioned, the way in which unilateral light brings about this lateral transport is not understood. Light has no direct effect on the longitudinal transport of applied auxin through cylinders of *Avena* or *Raphanus* (see VI *C*), so that the explanation of du Buy (1933), based on decreased transport rate on the lighted side, cannot be valid. As with gravity, attempts have been made to ascribe the curvatures to electric potentials. Brauner (1927) found that unilateral illumination of *Hordeum* nodes caused the light side to become negative to the dark side. Waller (1900) and Bose (1907) had found similar effects. This potential would be in the right direction to produce an electrolytic transport of the anion of auxin, but there is no evidence that it does so. It is, however, a remarkable coincidence that both in geotropism and in phototropism the auxin moves to the side which becomes positive, as would be expected from its acid properties.

G. Light-Growth Reactions

As stated above, the asymmetric distribution of auxin is only one of the factors operating to produce phototropic curvatures. There are a number of other effects of light on growth. We can imagine light having an effect on (1) auxin production, (2) auxin transport (already considered), (3) auxin destruction, or (4) on the reactivity of the plant to the auxin in it. Effects of light on permeability or on the protoplasm directly would appear, in most cases, under the last heading. As we have seen, the effect of light on lateral transport can only take place in an intact system or structure in which there is correlation between the different parts. In other words, the Cholodny-Went effect depends essentially on the behavior of the organ as a whole. This is shown very clearly by the experiments of Boysen Jensen and Nielsen (1926) and Boysen Jensen (1928), which show that direct contact between the light and dark sides of the coleoptile tip must be maintained in order to obtain good phototropic curvature. Insertion of platinum foil through the middle of the tip, perpendicular to the plane of the beam of light, practically prevents curvature.

The other effects listed above, however, can take place at a single point, and each cell may react independently, its reaction being determined by the amount of light it receives. These reactions may be grouped together as light-growth reactions, and as such have been studied intensively by Blaauw (1914, 1915, 1918) and successors (Vogt, 1915; Sierp, 1918, 1921; Koningsberger, 1922; Van Dillewijn, 1927), and in *Phycomyces* by Castle (1930). In general, the originally constant growth rate of dark-adapted or dark-grown plants changes after illumination. This light-growth reaction in higher plants consists principally of a decrease in growth rate, with a maximal retardation ½ to 1½ hours after illumination, followed by an acceleration. When plants are unilaterally illuminated it is evident that the sides towards and away from the light will receive different amounts of light, and hence will give different light-growth reactions; this will in itself cause phototropic curvatures. However, the relative parts played in phototropic curvature by these light-growth reactions and by the auxin redistribution remains a point of controversy.

It would be out of place to review the publications dealing with the qualitative comparison of light-growth reaction and phototropic curvature; our concern is with the auxin side of the phenomenon. The simplest case is found in hypocotyls of *Raphanus* (van Overbeek, 1933), which probably are comparable in their behavior to those of *Helianthus* studied by Blaauw (1915). If *Raphanus* seedlings are exposed to strong continuous light (1000–2000 meter-candles)

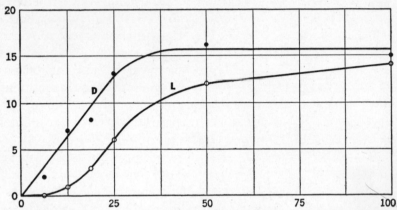

Fig. 50. Auxin curvatures of *Raphanus* hypocotyls. Ordinate, curvature in degrees; abscissa, concentration of auxin applied unilaterally. Curve D, in darkness; L, in light of about 2000 meter-candles. (From van Overbeek, *Rec. trav. bot. néerl. 30:* 537–626, 1933.)

their growth is reduced by from 50 to 60 per cent. This reduction in growth rate is not due to decreased auxin production or transport, nor to increased destruction (see, however, pp. 88, 175); it must therefore be due to a decrease in the reactivity of the cells to auxin. The same effect may be seen from the effect of light on curvatures produced by one-sided application of auxin (see Figure 50). An exactly similar effect of light in reducing straight growth from applied auxin was found in *Vicia Faba* stems by Thimann and Skoog (1934). This reduced reactivity of plant tissues in light undoubtedly plays a part in phototropic curvatures. Van Overbeek calculated that about half the phototropic curvature of *Raphanus* hypocotyls is due to auxin redistribution (Cholodny-Went effect), and about half to this light-growth reaction (Blaauw effect).

With *Helianthus* hypocotyls Blaauw measured light-growth reactions for different intensities and calculated the difference between the growth rates on the two sides, having previously found that the light side received $3\frac{1}{2}$ times as much light as the dark side. This difference accounted quantitatively for the curvature observed. Phototropism in *Helianthus* would thus appear to be largely accounted for by the Blaauw effect.

In *Avena*, however, the Blaauw effect, as we have seen above, plays little or no part in phototropic curvatures at low light intensities. This is confirmed by experiments in which a light-growth reaction was observed without any accompanying phototropic curvature (Beyer, 1928) or a phototropic curvature without any light-growth reaction (Cholodny, 1932a, 1933a). The observed light-growth reaction of *Avena* at these intensities is apparently due to a reduction of about 20 per cent in the amount of auxin diffusing out of the tip within the first hour after illumination (Went, 1928). This corresponds well with the observation that this type of growth reaction (the "long reaction") occurs only after illumination has fallen on the tip of the coleoptile. A second type of light-growth reaction (the "short reaction") reaching its maximum half an hour after illumination, occurs when the basal zones are illuminated. The response is not proportional to the total amount of light energy, as was shown by Burkhardt (1926), but appears to be more of the nature of a shock reaction or typical "stimulus"; it is ascribed by van Overbeek (1936a) to a transient decrease in sensitivity to auxin. It was shown by Cholodny (1930) that plants subjected to a gradual increase of unilateral illumination did not give this reaction, although their phototropic response was still normal. If, on the other hand, the light were applied to them suddenly, this light-growth reaction was very marked.

In this connection an analysis of the effect of all-sided

illumination on auxin curvatures has been carried out by
van Overbeek (1936*b*, 1936*c*). The effect depends upon the
auxin used. If indole-acetic acid is applied, light causes a
temporary decrease in rate of curvature, followed by an
increase, so that the net effect is small, while if auxin *a* is
used, light produces a considerable reduction in the curvature. On the other hand, if the plants are illuminated for
2 hours before the auxin is applied, the curvatures produced
by indole-acetic acid and auxin *a* are both affected in the
same way, *i.e.* they are increased. Thus we must conclude
(1) that previous lighting increases the sensitivity of coleoptiles to both auxins, but that (2) lighting while the
auxin is present decreases the response to auxin *a* only.
The two effects could be interpreted as due to destruction
of auxin *a* inside the coleoptile in the light. Thus, in (1), the
increased sensitivity to applied auxin would be due to a
reduced auxin content of the coleoptile, while in (2) the
applied auxin *a* would be partially inactivated as soon as it
enters. We saw in VI *C* that light has no effect on auxin
transport, but on the other hand the auxin which is determined in transport experiments may be distinct from the
auxin in the cell (*cf.* Table XI, p. 132). Hence light may
inactivate only the auxin inside the cell, and not the trans-
portable auxin.

Another effect of light is to cause the formation of auxin
in green parts, as discussed in Chapter IV *A*. Since the
greening of etiolated plants is itself brought about by light,
this factor may also play a part in long-period illuminations.

The so-called euphotometric movements, or bending of
leaves out of the shade into the light (see *e.g.* Raydt, 1925),
are growth reactions of the petioles. These are apparently
due to a differential distribution of auxin in the petiole,
caused by differential illumination of various parts of the
leaf-blade (*u*). Laibach and Fischnich (1936*a*) have imitated the movements by applying dots of auxin paste on
the leaf-blade of *Coleus;* if applied at one side the petiole

would bend away from the place of application. Our own experiments (*u*) have given similar results.

H. COMPARISON OF PHOTOTROPIC AND GEOTROPIC CURVATURES

The similarities and differences between the different types of curvature in *Avena* coleoptiles are difficult to appreciate

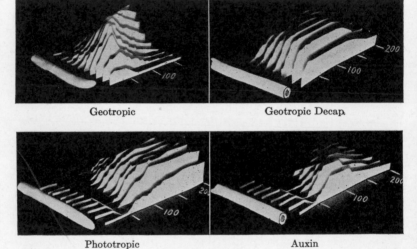

Geotropic   Geotropic Decap.

Phototropic   Auxin

FIG. 51. The course of curvatures in *Avena* coleoptiles. Ordinate: extent of curvature of each zone. Abscissae: towards right, time in minutes; towards background left, successive 2 mm. zones. At left of each diagram is a coleoptile corresponding with these zones, at the start of measurements. Top left: after 30 minutes horizontal; curvature already beginning in upper zones. Top right: the same, but decapitated immediately afterwards; autotropism delayed until after regeneration. Lower left: phototropic. Lower right: unilateral auxin application, the top two zones being removed. (After Dolk, 1930.)

from the somewhat detailed discussion above. Dolk (1930, 1936) has, however, made a comparative study of the increase of curvatures with time and with distance from the tip, which we are now in a position to interpret. Figure 51 shows a three-dimensional composite picture in which the magnitude of curvature—represented by the ordinate—is plotted against time for each 2 mm. zone of the coleoptile. The plants were rotated on a clinostat throughout so that gravity could not counteract the curvatures.

The fourth diagram shows a curvature produced by unilateral application of auxin. After an interval of 35 minutes, in which no curvature takes place, curvature begins sharply in the upper zones 3 and 4 (zones 1 and 2 being removed by decapitation). It then spreads downwards from zone to zone at an average rate of 10–12 mm. per hour, the rate being somewhat faster in the upper zones. This rate agrees exactly with the transport velocity of auxin found by van der Weij (*cf.* VI *C*). At 110 minutes after application of the agar block (= 150 minutes after decapitation) regeneration begins, and immediately the curvatures in the uppermost zones decrease. The lower zones continue to increase in curvature so that the total curvature does not decrease but moves down the coleoptile. The final state of the plant, after $3\frac{1}{2}$ hours, thus shows the curvature located mainly in the base.

The third diagram (Figure 51) shows the curvature of an intact plant after one-sided illumination with 500 MCS. At first sight it resembles the auxin curvature. There is an interval of 40 minutes, after which curvature begins in several upper zones. The rate of movement of the initial curvature is somewhat faster than the above, about 16 mm. per hour; this agrees with Went's finding (1935) that in the intact plant auxin transport is slightly faster than when decapitated. The other characteristic of this diagram is that the curvatures *do not decrease*, but continue to increase in all zones for at least 3 hours. This agrees with the fact that the auxin redistribution caused by light persists for many hours (see p. 168). The final state of the plant therefore shows a curvature throughout. The first diagram shows geotropic curvature of plants placed horizontally for 15 minutes. The difference may be seen at a glance. The interval before curvature begins is only 20 minutes and the first five zones then all begin to curve simultaneously. This is due to the detection of gravity, with its resulting redistribution of auxin, not only by the tip but also by the zones below. In the sixth and lower zones the presentation time is greater than 15 minutes and therefore curvature in these zones is dependent on transport of the redistributed auxin from above. From the fifth to the tenth zone the initial curvature therefore moves downwards at 12 mm. per hour, the rate of auxin transport. After only 30 minutes of curving the curvature begins to decrease very rapidly in the uppermost zones, so that they are straight within 2 hours ("autotropism"). This is due to the fact that the gravitational auxin redistribution does not persist and the autotropism is ascribed, as we have seen in V D, to the temporary exhaustion of the food factor at the point where growth has been rapid. The zone of maximum curvature is thus quite narrow and moves rapidly down the plant. The final state of the plant thus shows a very localized curvature in the base, the upper part being almost entirely straight. In decapitated plants this autotropic straightening is very much less marked, and is delayed until regeneration begins, 150 minutes after decapitation. This affords clear proof that autotropism is dependent upon a supply of auxin.

Thus it may be seen that all the peculiarities of the curvatures in *Avena* may be satisfactorily explained in terms of what we know about auxin and its distribution.

IV. OTHER TROPISTIC RESPONSES

J. TRAUMATOTROPISM

The curvature of plants towards or away from a wound— traumatotropism—was first ascribed by Stark (1921) to the influence of special traumatotropic hormones which were produced in the damaged tissue. Beyer, however (1925), made it clear that all organs which curve towards a wound are those whose growth is retarded by removal of the tip. Correspondingly, if the tip be removed, such organs lose their ability to curve towards the wound. Hence he deduced, in agreement with Paál, that the curvatures are due to interference with the normally present growth-promoting substance, rather than to the production of a growth-inhibiting substance. He also found that even in decapitated

Avena coleoptiles, curvatures could be induced if the wound was close to the base. This is doubtless due to interference with the upward-moving stream of substance from the seed (*cf.* V *D*). In general, all positive traumatotropic curvatures appearing above the incision (Stark, 1917; Beyer, 1925; Bünning, 1927) may probably be ascribed to interference with the upward-moving stream of food factor.

Tendeloo (1927) has shown that while *Avena* normally gives positive traumatotropic curvatures, regeneration of auxin production at the lower cut surface of the incision may subsequently give rise to a negative curvature. The negative curvatures obtained by Weimann (1929) may also be due to this cause.

Keeble and Nelson (1935) have explained the traumatotropic curvatures of roots by interference with the distribution of auxin, and there seems no reason to doubt that this is one of the principal factors operating in traumatotropism.

The effects of wounding, however, consist not only of interference with the transport, but also involve destruction of auxin by enzymes freed from the cut cells (Thimann, 1934). This phenomenon doubtless explains the results of Gradmann and Cholodny with split stems, discussed in X *C*. In Cholodny's experiments split halves of stems, placed horizontally with the cut surface downward, curve much less than those with the cut surface upward. We may tentatively explain this by saying that the auxin which accumulates under the influence of gravity on the lower side is, in the one case, partly inactivated by the wound enzymes, in the other case not. The auxin inactivation may also play an important part in positive curvatures.

In conclusion, it is evident that the whole phenomenon of traumatotropism needs to be reconsidered in the light of our present knowledge of auxins.

K. ELECTROTROPISM

Movements of shoots and roots towards electrodes have been known for a very long time; they are of interest to us

here on account of their possible connection with auxin
movements. Since all known auxins are acids, their anions
will move to the anode if solutions are electrolyzed. Such a
movement in electrolysis through agar was shown to occur
by Koch (1934). Electrolytic transport through agar also
explains the results of Kögl, Haagen Smit, and Van Hulssen
(1936) who found that the auxin curvature of decapitated
Avena coleoptiles was increased if a small current was passed
through the agar block containing auxin, the block being
made negative to the plant.

The question now arises, does this electrolytic auxin transport occur inside the plant, and if so, would it explain the
observed electrotropisms? The phenomena of electrotropism
are not altogether clear. Roots, when immersed in water
through which a current is sent, curve towards the −pole
at low current densities, and towards the + pole at high
current densities or after long exposure to smaller currents.
In air they curve towards the − pole. Coleoptiles and shoots
in air curve towards the + pole (Brauner and Bünning, 1930;
Hartmann, 1932; Amlong, 1933) and in water in the same
direction (Koch, 1934). In regard to roots there is evidence
that the curvature is due to accumulation of ions by electrolysis (Ewart and Bayliss, 1906; Navez, 1927) rather than
to a direct effect of current on the root. Nevertheless, decapitation either of roots or of shoots prevents electrotropic
curvature almost entirely (Amlong, 1933), and since decapitating roots does not retard their growth (*cf.* IX A) the
effect cannot be due to influence on the growth rate alone.
This last fact would indicate that electrolytic movement
of auxin does play a part, and this is supported by an experiment of Koch (1934). He inserted electrodes on opposite sides of *Helianthus* hypocotyls, and applied 4 volts
for 1 hour, when the plants curved towards the − pole. The
hypocotyls were halved longitudinally and the halves applied one-sidedly to *Pisum* roots. The convex side produced
more curvature than the concave.

On the whole, it must be said that the analysis of electrotropic curvatures, so far as it has been carried, is suggestive rather than convincing.

L. CHEMOTROPISM

The only study of chemotropic curvature which is at all germane is that of Amlong (1933), who applied salt solutions of different concentrations to the two sides of *Vicia Faba* roots; the curvatures so caused were interpreted as due to the potential differences set up (concentration cell e.m.f.'s.) and thus to a kind of electrotropism. Under this heading we might also list the curvatures caused by the one-sided application of acid (see III *C* 4 and VIII *F*).

M. NASTIC MOVEMENTS

By these are understood movements caused by external forces, but whose direction is determined morphologically by internal structure. The only study of the rôle of auxin in these movements is that of Uyldert (1931). She showed that in *Tradescantia* the stems give their typical epinastic response only if supplied with sufficient auxin. When the plagiotropic lateral branches are in the vertical position auxin is transported along the dorsal side only, but when in the horizontal position auxin is also transported along the ventral side. We may therefore conclude that the epinastic curvature is due to the action of gravity in causing asymmetrical auxin transport. It is thus exactly comparable to geotropism except that the auxin accumulates, not on the lower side, but on the morphologically determined side. A geotropic accumulation of auxin on the lower side may take place at the same time; an equilibrium position is then reached when the geotropic auxin distribution is equal and opposite to the plagiotropic auxin distribution.

Crocker, Zimmerman, and Hitchcock (1932) studied the epinasty of tomato petioles produced by ethylene, and found it to be due to an acceleration of growth on the upper side, with or without some shortening of the lower side. The zone which reacts is the growing zone at the base of the petiole.

Their figures give no evidence that the ethylene produces any increase in the *total* growth rate. It is most probable, therefore, that the effect of the ethylene is to influence the distribution of auxin in the petiole.

We have seen above that gravity may do the same thing, *i.e.* may cause unequal distribution of auxin. In a later paper (1935), Crocker, Hitchcock, and Zimmerman have argued that since application of auxin to the petiole can also produce unequal growth, the action of ethylene is the same as that of auxin. However, by the same argument, the action of gravity should be the same as that of auxin, *i.e.* gravity should be a growth hormone! This shows a confusion between the primary factor (auxin) and the forces which modify it, much as though the action of gasoline on an automobile were to be compared with the changing of the gears. Another unjustifiable comparison between ethylene and auxin is referred to in XI *C*.

CHAPTER XI

ROOT FORMATION

A. ROOT FORMATION AS A CORRELATION PHENOMENON

In Chapter II *A* it has been pointed out that our earliest knowledge of correlation was mainly based upon root formation. Beginning with Duhamel and Sachs, various investigators have explained root formation on cuttings by the accumulation of special root-forming substances near the basal cut surface. Beijerinck (1886) emphasized the importance of the leaves for root formation, although he was apparently thinking rather of a nutritional effect. Vöchting (*cf.* VI *B*) studied both root formation and root development, but with particular reference to polarity, the formation of the roots being considered rather as an indicator of polarity than as a problem in itself. Among the factors investigated, Vöchting stressed the importance of water, the inhibiting effect of light, and the tendency of gravity to induce root formation on the lower side of a horizontal cutting.

Of the other investigations of the various factors controlling rooting, only the more relevant need be mentioned. In the first place numerous attempts, largely unsuccessful, have been made to correlate root formation or root growth with nutritive factors, especially with the carbohydrate: nitrogen ratio (see for instance Goebel, 1902–1903; Reid, 1924; Carlson, 1929). However, it was emphasized by Mac-Callum (1905) that nutrient conditions are not the principal factors governing root formation. Morgan (1906) has shown the same thing for regeneration in animals; the rate of formation of new legs, after the removal of the original legs, was found, in *Salamanders* and other animals, to be the same when they were well-fed as when they were starved. In this connection Kupfer (1907) made the interesting observation that in *Commelina* the yellow varieties do not root while green ones do, but the difference is not due to nutrition because addition of sugar or peptone does not affect it.

In the second place the effects of various empirical treatments have been studied; Curtis (1918) found that permanganate promotes rooting of cuttings, while inorganic nutrient solutions have no effect, and a number of authors have shown that oxygen is necessary (*e.g.* Zimmerman, 1930, Graham, 1934). Treatment with carbon monoxide, ethylene, and other unsaturated gases stimulates root formation (*cf.* XI *C*). Graham and Stewart (1931) and Graham (1934, 1936) have studied the optimum experimental conditions for making cuttings of a large number of different plants. The most important factors are (1) time of year at which the cuttings are taken, which differs for different plants, (2) temperature relations of the cutting, and (3) ample watering without interference with aëration. They found that if these factors are considered, practically any plant can be induced to give 90 per cent rooting from stem or leaf cuttings.

Loeb, in 1917, suggested that root formation in *Bryophyllum* is controlled by a special root forming substance or hormone. About this hormone he made some statements which in the light of our present knowledge seem quite remarkable. Thus, "In *Bryophyllum* the hypothetical geotropic hormone is associated (or identical) with the root-forming hormone" (1917). Further, "these (bud-) inhibitory substances may be identical with or may accompany the root-forming hormones" (1917*a*). The inhibition of buds is, as will be shown in Chapter XII, also brought about by auxin. Loeb's subsequent change of view from special substances to mass action relations is discussed in II *E*. In a later study of *Bryophyllum*, F. A. F. C. Went (1930*a*) returned to the concept of root-forming substances, these substances being considered to be formed mainly in the older leaves.

B. Hormones and Root Formation

The first extensive study of root formation in which internal factors were taken into consideration was that of van der Lek (1925). He distinguished clearly between roots which develop from preëxisting "root germs" or initials, and those which are really formed anew. Since the bulk of the root germs are found in the apical part of any internode, isolated internodes do not show the usual polar distribution of roots. In longer cuttings, nevertheless, the number of root germs which develop is greater in the lower internodes, and hence a general polarity still persists. Of the cuttings he studied, *Ribes nigrum* and most species of *Salix* and *Populus* possessed numbers of root germs, while only four, *Salix caprea*, *Salix aurita*, *Populus alba* and *Vitis vinifera*, were free from them. In these latter species the polar distribution of roots is complete, even in single internodes. In all cases, the presence of a bud powerfully promotes root formation, especially if the bud is rapidly developing. Buds which are developing in the dark or which are enclosed in plaster of Paris also promote root formation, the latter only weakly, however. Removal of the buds stops root formation almost completely, especially in the species without root germs. If a portion of cortex below the bud is cut away down to the wood, root formation is reduced, showing that some influence travels through the cortex from the bud to the base of the cutting. To explain these results, van der Lek assumes that the developing bud forms one or more hormones, which are transported downwards through the phloem. These hormones he compares to the cell-division-promoting hormones postulated by Haberlandt. In a later study (1934) van der Lek found that in *Populus* cuttings taken in December or in January, the buds, which are now completely dormant, no longer promote root development, or even slightly inhibit it, but in the course of the next two months their favorable influence returns.

A corresponding effect was found in *Acalypha* cuttings

by Went (1929); the buds strongly, and the leaves less strongly, promoted formation of roots. In these experiments distinction was made for the first time between number and elongation of the roots. Debudded and defoliated cuttings formed very few roots, or under some conditions none.[1] If, however, the diffusate from *Papaya* leaves were mixed with agar and applied to the cutting, an increase in the number of roots was observed. Still greater increases were subsequently obtained by the application of diastase (which was also active after being boiled) or of extract of rice polishings (Bouillenne and Went, 1933). However, Gouwentak and Hellinga (1935) were afterwards unable to obtain rooting by the application of diastase. Sugar solution was found to have no root-forming effect, so that the action is not one of nutrition. Bouillenne and Went (1933) found that the action of the extracts is exerted only at the base of the cutting, and inversion with respect to gravity did not alter this polarity; it was therefore deduced that "the polar localization of new roots is caused by the polar transport" of the hormone. The formation of roots in seedlings is closely comparable; if the roots are removed from the base of *Impatiens* hypocotyls then the formation of new roots is greatly promoted by the presence of the cotyledons or, in the light, by leaves. The application of sugar to the hypocotyl base in these experiments increased the number of roots formed, but the cotyledons were necessary as well; there is therefore a differentiation between hormonal and nutritive factors, the influence of the cotyledons being explained as due to storage of root-forming hormone in them. It follows from these experiments that root-formation is due to a special substance or hormone (which Bouillenne and Went named "rhizocaline"); it is not itself a nutrient, is thermo-stable and is produced by leaves in the light. It is also stored up in cotyledons and buds, and its transport is basipetally polar.

[1] Graham and Stewart (1931a) subsequently obtained good rooting on isolated *Acalypha* leaves.

The production of a similar substance by bacteria would explain the results of Němec (1930), who obtained formation of new roots on root cuttings of *Cichorium intybus* by smearing the cut surface with a culture of *Bacterium tumefaciens* (*cf.* XIII *C*).

In a later paper Němec (1934) confirmed the fact that cotyledons and buds store not only food materials but also

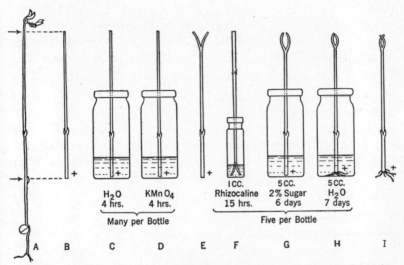

FIG. 52. Determination of root-forming activity. Basal end of cutting marked +. A, 7-day old etiolated pea seedling; B, cutting; C, D, preparation; E, slit apically; F, inverted in test solution; I, root formation after 14 days. (From Went, *Proc. Kon. Akad. Wetensch.*, Amsterdam *37*: 445–455, 1934.)

special root-forming substances or "rhizogenes." He placed isolated hypocotyls of *Helianthus* or *Lupinus* in aqueous extracts of cotyledons, terminal buds, or stems. All these extracts increased the number of roots formed at the base of the hypocotyls, distinction being again made between *number* and *length* of the roots.

For quantitative experiments neither woody cuttings like *Acalypha* nor hypocotyls with hormone-storing organs above them are suitable. Went (1934*a*) therefore introduced etiolated *Pisum* seedlings as test objects; the shoots, when 10–12 cm. long, are cut off just above the first scale-bearing node and, after washing, their bases are immersed in 0.05 per cent permanganate for four hours. This treatment disinfects the cuttings and improves their keeping quality; it also, according to Curtis (1918), improves rooting. The terminal bud is then removed, and the apex of the stem, split longitudinally for 1–2 cm., is immersed for fifteen hours in 1 cc. of the test solution or extract (see Figure 52).

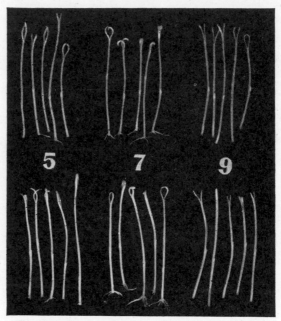

FIG. 53. Root formation on etiolated pea stems 8 days after the treatment of Figure 52. Group 5, 10 mg.; group 7, 100 mg. indole-3-acetic acid per liter; group 9, water. Note auxin curvatures of slit tops in 5 and 7. Ten plants per group.

The test solution is applied at the apex because the substance is transported polarly from apex to base, as shown above. Only with very high concentrations of active substances can roots be formed by application at the base (see XI *E*). After the treatment, the split apex is rinsed. If the test solution contained auxin, the split halves will show the inward curvature described in III *D*. Finally the cuttings

are placed for seven days with their bases in 2 per cent
sucrose solution, followed by seven days in water. The
number of roots, which by this time has reached its final
value, is then a measure of the root-forming activity of the
test solution (see Figure 53). The concentration necessary
to produce one root under constant conditions is termed one
root unit per cc. The usual procedure is to make serial
dilutions of each solution to be tested, at least 10 plants
being used for each dilution. To obtain reproducible results the sucrose should be purified by slightly acidifying
and extracting with ether, since sucrose always contains
a number of physiologically active substances. The ether
extract so obtained is definitely toxic to pea cuttings (*u*).

The buds of *Pisum* contain some of the root-forming substance, just as do the buds of *Acalypha* mentioned above.
This is shown by the fact that if all buds are removed, practically no roots are formed; the number of roots formed—in
plants not treated with any active solution—then depends
quantitatively on the number of buds left on. The rôle of
the buds is, however, dual, for in their absence roots are not
formed even if the stem is treated with active solution;
in order to carry out tests one bud must therefore be left
on. If the one bud is left on for a short time part of its
effect is exerted. Thus in one experiment pea cuttings were
treated with a hormone preparation as described above,
and in one group the bud was removed immediately after
the treatment, in another group after 12 hours, while in the
third group it was allowed to remain for the whole 15 days.
The average number of roots per 10 plants was then 4, 12,
and 22 respectively (*u*). This action of the bud cannot be
replaced by any modification of the treatment, though it
can be partially replaced by treatment with a water extract
of pea cotyledons.

Molisch (1935) also found that budless internodes of
various plants root only weakly or not at all. He concludes
not only that the buds contain a root-forming substance
but also that they prolong the life of the internode.

C. Nature of the Root-Forming Substance

The use of this method made it possible to investigate the chemical nature of the root-forming hormone (Thimann and Went, 1934). In the first place, tests on a number of pollens and other natural products showed that the root-forming hormone occurs almost always together with auxin (the latter being determined on *Avena*). In some cases there was even a good quantitative parallelism between root-forming and growth-promoting activity; the extract of *Rhizopus* medium, rich in auxin, was also very rich in root-forming hormone, and was therefore worked up. They found that the root-forming substance was extractable by organic solvents only from acid solutions and is therefore an acid; its dissociation constant, determined by shaking out from buffered solutions, was about 2.10^{-5}. The distribution between different solvents was the same as that of auxin. The activity was readily destroyed by oxidizing agents and followed that of the auxin throughout the various stages of purification, even through vacuum distillations. It was therefore clear that the substance was either identical with, or very closely related to, auxin itself.

It was then found that auxin *b* and, later, synthetic indole-3-acetic acid (Thimann and Koepfli, 1935; Kögl, 1935) were as active in root formation as the purest *Rhizopus* preparation. This provides final proof that one, at any rate, of the hormones causing root formation is identical with auxin. The names "rhizocaline" and "rhizogene," in so far as they really refer to the action of auxin, can therefore be dropped. The evidence against the identity of the root-forming substance with auxin was that the root-forming and growth-promoting activities of various natural preparations were not quantitatively parallel. The explanation for this must lie in the influence of secondary factors (*cf.* XI *E*).

As to the path of transport of the hormone in cuttings, it seems that it moves through the living cells of the phloem, since Cooper (1936) showed that ringing, after application of auxin at the top, prevents rooting at the base. The movement is longitudinal and not transverse, and in physiological concentrations is always polar. It is almost completely stopped by chilling to below 5° C. a 5 cm. section of the cutting.

The promotion of root formation by auxins has been studied on a great number of different plants; Laibach, Müller, and Schäfer (1934) and Müller (1935) found that *Tradescantia* internodes and *Helianthus* hypocotyls were induced to form roots by urine or orchid pollen applied in the form of lanoline paste; the effect was doubtless due to the auxin. Laibach (1935), Fischnich (1935), and Laibach and Fischnich (1935) subsequently obtained roots on intact plants of *Coleus*, *Vicia Faba*, and *Solanum lycopersicum* by application of indole-acetic acid in lanoline. Hitchcock (1935, 1935a) and Zimmerman and Wilcoxon (1935), also working with intact plants, induced root formation on stems by local application of lanoline pastes containing indole-acetic acid and various other related substances. Crocker, Hitchcock, and Zimmerman (1935) then compared the long-known activity of ethylene, carbon monoxide, and other gases in promoting root formation with the action of the auxins. They concluded that ethylene may itself act as a hormone (*cf.* X *M*). However, the effect of ethylene on growth by elongation is to inhibit and not to promote it. Further, Michener (1935) has shown that in *Pisum* cuttings, which root vigorously in response to auxin, no roots are produced by ethylene, nor does ethylene increase the number of roots produced by a given auxin treatment. In *Salix* cuttings, ethylene alone has a small effect in increasing the number of roots, but if they are treated with auxin, its effect is greatly increased by ethylene treatment. Thus ethylene only seems to be effective in the presence of auxin. Since the experiments of Crocker, Hitchcock, and Zimmerman were carried out on green plants in the light, rich in auxin, it is highly probable that the action of ethylene which they observed was through its effect upon the auxin already in the plant.

The same authors have made some calculations which compare the minimum effective concentrations of ethylene and auxin (*cf.* X *M*). Such calculations are without any basis in the present state of our knowledge. In the first place it is impossible to compare an effect on *Avena* cell elongation with one on apple-twig intumescences. In the second place, we do not know whether the ethylene is really distributed between the air and apple-twig tissue as its equilibrium solubility in water would indicate, or whether it is completely absorbed. It is probably absorbed especially by those cells which react, which constitute only a very small fraction of the total tissue treated. Thirdly, the minimum effective concentration of auxin is not that which will produce 10° curvature as they assume, but that which will produce a *just visible* curvature, which, using de-seeded plants and automatic recording, is nearer to 0.1° than to 10°. (The value of one part of ethylene in 100,000,000 is recorded by Wallace for the *smallest observable* intumescence.) In addition there is an error of 10 times in the arithmetic as published, and a subsequent "erratum" distributed by Crocker in 1936 introduces a further factor of 1,000 times. Reliable data on the activity and penetration of ethylene will be needed before any comparative calculation of minimum effective concentrations is possible.

It is of importance that all substances which act as auxins are, so far as they have been tested, also active in promoting root formation. Thimann (1935*b*) showed that indene-3-acetic and coumaryl-1-acetic acids, which, as discussed in VIII *G*, are active in promoting growth but appear to be poorly transported, are also active in root formation. Their activity is, however, largely local, and is best exerted when applied at the base of the test cuttings. Phenyl-acetic acid, found to be active in root formation by Zimmerman and Wilcoxon (1935) was shown to act as an auxin by Haagen Smit and Went (1935). α-Naphthalene-acetic acid is also active for both functions (*u*). Indole-3-carboxylic acid, on the other hand, is inactive for both functions, while indole-3-propionic acid has very low activity both for growth promotion and root formation (Thimann and Koepfli, 1935).

D. Effect of Light on Root Formation

The results concerning the effect of light on root formation have been very conflicting. Vöchting showed that white light inhibited root formation of *Salix* cuttings. Some plants, *e.g. Cinnamonum,* root better if the twigs are etiolated ("blanched") for 2 weeks before taking cuttings (Blackie, Graham, and Stewart, 1926). On the other hand it is well-known that leafy cuttings need light in order to root.

A number of experiments have been carried out (Went, 1935a) on the effect of different colored lights on root forma-

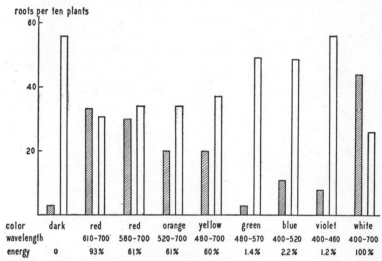

FIG. 54. Root formation on pea stems exposed for 14 days to light of the color and intensity specified. Shaded columns, one leaf present; open columns, no leaf present, but treated with indole-acetic acid (20 mg. per liter for 20 hours). 100% energy = about 100 erg/cm.²/sec.

tion. Etiolated pea cuttings, without leaves and treated with auxin in the standard way, were placed in a series of chambers illuminated through calibrated color filters for 15 days. The results (Figure 54) show that light of any wavelength reduces the number of roots formed below the number formed in darkness, white light having the greatest effect and blue the least. (The intensities of blue and green light used were, however, much lower than the others.) If, however, the leaves are left on and no auxin applied, the opposite result is obtained (Figure 54, shaded columns). Here the dark controls produce almost no roots, and the white light controls a maximum. Blue appears to be more active than its intensity would indicate but the effects of the other lights are more or less proportional to their intensity. The white columns thus represent the effect of light on the *effectiveness* of the auxin in producing roots, while the shaded columns represent a combination of this with the action of light on auxin synthesis. The importance of light for the synthesis of auxin in green parts has been discussed in IV *A*. These experiments throw some light on the conflicting results mentioned above; in cuttings with an auxin storage (deciduous plants in fall and winter, *cf.* XI *G*), root formation will be best in darkness. In leafy cuttings without auxin storage, however, light will be required for auxin formation and therefore for rooting.

E. Effects of Factors Other than Auxin

Carbohydrate. The production of roots (or any other growth) by an etiolated cutting, deprived of the food reserves in its seed, requires carbohydrate. This was clearly shown by Bouillenne and Went (1933) with *Impatiens;* in one experiment they record, after 10 days in 1.5 per cent dextrose, an average of 7.25 roots per cutting, as against an average of only 1.0 in water. Sucrose behaved similarly. Leaving the cotyledons on, however, raised the average number to 15, which we can now explain as due to the combined effects of sugar and auxin, *both* coming from the cotyledons (*cf.* the analysis of the growth of hypocotyls in V *D*). In other etiolated material the same is true; cuttings of etiolated peas, for instance, gave 25 roots per 10 plants in 2 per cent sucrose, and only 9 when in water. The sugar must be applied very soon after the auxin treatment; if the plants are first placed in water for 2 days and then in sugar practically no roots are formed (*u*).

The kind of sugar used is of considerable importance; sucrose and fructose give larger numbers of roots than dextrose under comparable conditions. The sugar also exerts an effect on the length of the roots produced, fructose giving the longest, and dextrose the shortest. Sucrose which has been purified by ether extraction (*cf.* above) gives longer roots than if unpurified (*u*). Green plant parts, producing or containing ample carbohydrate, are of course not dependent on added sugar.

Interrelations between auxins. It was mentioned above that the activity of various extracts was not always parallel to their auxin content. It has since been found (*u*) that the activity of auxin is increased by a number of other factors. One of the most interesting of these relationships is the effect of auxin *a* on the action of indole-acetic acid, of which Table XV (*u*) gives an example. In this experiment the cuttings were treated either with one auxin alone, or with indole-acetic acid in the highest concentration together with auxin *a* in varying concentrations. It will be seen that auxin *a*, even down to its lowest concentration (0.002 per cent = 2.10^{-6} mg. per cc.), increases the number of roots formed in presence of excess indole-acetic acid by about one fourth. Urine, in concentrations which are not toxic, has a similar effect, which is undoubtedly due to its auxin *a* content, as is shown by the fact that its ether extract is also active in the same way (*u*). On the other hand, the reverse procedure, namely the addition of small amounts of indole-acetic acid when auxin *a* is in excess, has no such effect.

TABLE XV

EFFECT OF AUXIN *a* ON THE ROOT FORMATION OF PEA SEEDLINGS BY INDOLE-3-ACETIC ACID. EACH FIGURE REPRESENTS THE NUMBER OF ROOTS PER 10 PLANTS AND IS A MEAN OF 30–100 PLANTS

RELATIVE CONCENTRATION OF AUXIN IN PER CENT	AUXIN *a* ALONE (20 PER CENT = 0.02 MG./CC.)	INDOLE-3-ACETIC ACID ALONE (20 PER CENT = 0.029 MG./CC.)	AUXIN *a* (CONCENTRATION IN COLUMN 1) IN PRESENCE OF INDOLE-ACETIC ACID, CONCENTRATION 20 PER CENT
20	94	79	102
4	89	73	107
1	60	44	94
0.2	49	40	102
0.04	45	35	94
0.01	50	—	96
0.002	34	—	96
0	28	28	79

The mechanism of this facilitating effect is unknown, but it is of considerable interest as indicating a physiological difference between the actions of the two auxins (*cf.* X *G* and V *F* for another difference).

These experiments with auxins were carried out by application at the apical end of the cutting. The transport of the root-forming hormone was earlier shown to be basipetal and this has been confirmed with pure auxin.

Bios. There are other substances which are like the sugars in that they must be applied to cuttings from the base, but are unlike the sugars in that the amounts of them necessary to influence root formation are extremely small. In contrast to the sugars, addition to the cuttings of various amino-acids does not promote root formation. Tryptophane, however, is an exception; if applied at the base it gives rise to a large number of roots (*u*). This is doubtless due to its conversion by the plant to indole-acetic acid.

The clearest example of a special substance, other than auxin, which is highly active when applied at the base, is that of the yeast-growth-promoting substance bios. Bios, which has been shown by Eastcott (1928) and subsequent workers to consist of a complex of at least 3 factors, is present in various sources including yeast extract itself. In a study of the effect of various additional substances on the formation of roots by pea cuttings it was found that yeast extract definitely increases the number of roots formed in presence of auxin (*u*). On this account and because ordinary amino-acids have no effect, an attempt was made to test the activity of the various constituents of bios. *i*-Inositol (Bios I) was inactive. Recently, however, one of the most important of the factors, biotin, has been isolated in a pure state by Kögl (1935, 1936) and a sample of this, from one of the last stages of purification, was tested in the same way (*u*). This work, which the authors carried out in coöperation with Professor Kögl, who supplied the biotin, showed a remarkable effect, one example of which is given in Figure 55 (*cf.* also Figure 62). Here the cuttings were treated apically with different concentrations of indole-3-acetic acid up to the maximum, which produced 102 roots per 10 plants; at this maximum concentration the biotin was subsequently applied to the base, when the number of roots formed increased in proportion to the biotin concentration and reached a second maximum of 179 roots per 10 plants. Similar

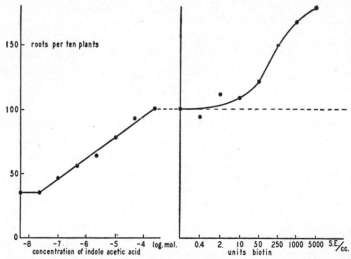

Fig. 55. Root formation on etiolated pea stems with their bases in 2% sucrose solution. Left, indole-acetic acid alone applied to the apex (abscissa, log. molar concentration); right, optimal auxin concentration applied at apex, with biotin added to the sucrose solution at base (abscissa, Saccharomyces units per cc.). (Kögl, Thimann, and Went, 1935, u.)

application of biotin at the tip gave no effect. Without auxin, biotin, applied either at tip or base, produces no roots, so that its effect is exerted *only* in presence of excess of auxin. This result is of special interest in view of the fact that up till recently biotin has only been known to exert its effect on growth of yeasts. However, Kögl and Haagen Smit (1936) have found that biotin also increases the growth in length of *Pisum* seedlings, from which the cotyledons have been cut off. It should be noted that the lowest concentration of biotin which definitely increases the number of roots is between 2 and 10 Saccharomyces units[1] per cc., *i.e.* a con-

[1] 1 mg. of biotin = 25×10^6 Saccharomyces units.

centration which just exerts a detectable effect on yeast growth.

Other factors. There is good evidence that pure theelin (female sex hormone or oestrin) also increases the number of roots produced by pure auxin, when it is applied at the base (u). The effect is very much smaller than that of biotin, but like that of biotin it does not appear in the absence of auxin. Whether theelin plays any part in root formation in nature is doubtful, although it is frequently present in plant material.

Bouillenne (1936) has stated that root formation in *Impatiens* seedlings is greatly hastened by carotene. The total number of roots produced was, however, not affected.

The rôle of sugars, substances like biotin, and the auxins, provides an excellent example of an interlocking system of limiting factors (see Figure 62). By varying the conditions any one can become limiting; the activity of each can only be shown in the presence of sufficient of the other factors. Such a relationship is further borne out by the behavior of different races of peas; some, like Alaska and Gradus, give few roots unless supplied with auxin, while others, such as Delicatesse, Dark Laxtonian and Perfection, give large numbers of roots on the controls, and auxin does not increase the number further (u). In the latter types auxin is evidently not a limiting factor. Others again give few roots even if supplied with auxin; in these evidently one of the other factors is limiting.

Thus far the factors considered have been those which influence the formation of visible roots. In which stage of development each factor exerts its influence is unknown. To produce a visible root at least three processes must take place in succession: redifferentiation of pericycle cells into root initials, formation of a root primordium by these initial cells, and the outgrowth of the root primordium. From a standpoint of morphogenetics the first two processes are the most important; physiologically speaking they can be regarded as one process. There are several reasons for thinking that it is this process which is influenced by the factors discussed above; firstly, the length of the roots which have been formed is not materially influenced by the treatment, except by sugar; secondly, examination of the pea stems has not revealed any appreciable number of root primordia; thirdly, we know that the direct effect of auxin on roots is to inhibit their growth in length. Furthermore, the total length of roots formed per cutting is more or less constant, so that the more roots are formed the shorter they are. This indicates that the *outgrowth* of the roots is influenced not by the auxin treatment, but by an internal factor, which may become distributed over a large number of root primordia. This factor is probably the one contained in the yeast extract which White (1933, 1934) finds necessary for growth of excised root tips in synthetic media (see IX *D*).

There is, however, another factor of quite different type which apparently also takes part in the first stages of root formation. If a pea cutting is divided into a number of sections and each is placed in sugar solution and treated with high concentrations of auxin (in paste form), then the sum of the numbers of root primordia formed is about the same as if the intact cutting were so treated. The majority of these primordia are formed at the point of application of the auxin. Only a small proportion of them grow out as roots, probably because of the high concentration of auxin, which inhibits growth in length (*cf.* IX *B*). In one experiment, there were 34 such primordia on the intact cutting; on 2 cuttings which were divided into 4 the sum of the primordia produced at the 4 bases and apices was 27 and 33; on 2 cuttings similarly divided into 8 the sum of the primordia was 38 and 43 (*u*). The total number of primordia is thus nearly constant and must therefore be determined by an internal factor other than the auxin, which factor only becomes limiting when auxin is in excess. Further, the distribution of this factor inside the plant can be determined from the distribution of the primordia on the dissected cuttings; the bulk of the primordia are on those sections some distance from the apex, which therefore contain the most of this factor. However, when auxin was applied to the intact cutting 30 primordia were formed at the top, but when applied to the uppermost one eighth of a cutting, only about 7 were formed at the top: the auxin may, therefore, mobilize some of the other factor from the lower parts of

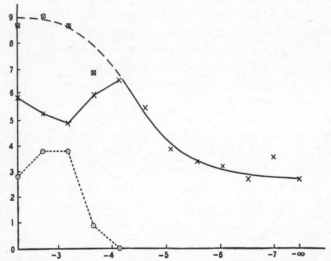

Fig. 56. Root formation on etiolated pea cuttings. Ordinate, average number of roots per plant formed near basal (crosses) and apical (circles) cut surface; abscissa, log. of the indole-acetic acid concentration in moles per liter. (From Went, "Allgemeine Betrachtungen über das Auxin-Problem," *Biol. Zentralbl. 56:* Fig. 1, P. 479, 1936; Verlag Georg Thieme, Leipzig.)

the cutting. This suggests that an important function of the auxin is to control the movement of this other factor. This is supported by another fact, namely that with increasingly high auxin concentrations, applied at the tip, the number of roots at the base reaches a maximum and then decreases; at that concentration at which the decrease begins, roots begin to appear at the top of the cutting, *i.e.* at the point of application of the auxin (see Figure 56). According to Went (1936) this means that the other factor is becoming mobilized at the tip by the very high auxin concentration and thus not enough is available for the base.

If the number of roots at the base and the tip are added the total number per cutting increases smoothly with auxin concentration as shown in Figure 56.

When auxin is applied at the apex, the lowest concentration needed to produce localized roots in this way is about 100 times that which will produce roots at the base. The concentrations needed to produce localized roots in the experiments of Hitchcock (1935a) are evidently those corresponding to these high values, since they too are of the order of 100 times the concentration which will, in our experiments, produce roots at the base. Experiments on intact plants in soil, of course, preclude observation of basal root formation. This ratio of 100 fits in very well with an observation of another sort. It was stated above that auxins must be applied at the apex to induce root formation at the base. An exception, of course, is given by those substances, such as indene-acetic and cumaryl-acetic acids, whose transport from apex to base is limited. These substances give excellent rooting when applied at the base, while if applied at the tip their activity is slight or zero (Thimann, 1935b). Thus, on pea cuttings, indene-acetic acid applied at the tip gave, per 10 plants, 19 roots, while at the base the same concentration gave 98 roots. Root formation when true auxins are applied to the base can, however, also be obtained if very high concentrations are used. In one experiment basal root formation on *Pisum* cuttings was induced by 0.02 γ per cc. of indole-acetic acid when applied at the tip, but, when applied at the base, a concentration of 20 γ per cc. was necessary. From this and other experiments the ratio of minimum effective concentrations applied at base and at tip is between 100 and 1000. Gouwentak and Hellinga (1935) report comparable data for *Coleus* cuttings. A dab of paste containing 0.01 γ indole-acetic acid caused root formation at the basal cut surface only; with 20 γ of the same compound in the paste, roots were formed at both apical and basal surfaces. When the 20 γ was applied at the base it did not, of course, produce roots at the apex. These results could be interpreted in terms of a local mobilization effect as described above.

A conclusion of a similar kind may be drawn from the experiments of Cooper (1936) in which lemon cuttings were treated with auxin at the base. If subsequently the basal 10 mm. were cut off and the cuttings again treated with auxin no roots were formed, although controls from which the bases were not cut off rooted vigorously. This indicates that the second factor has already been accumulated at the base and was thus removed with the cut-off portion.

It will be seen from this discussion that in the complex process of root formation many factors are involved. These include auxin, carbohydrates, a group of other substances such as biotin, and the internal factor discussed above. Much further study will be needed to elucidate their interactions.

F. ROOT FORMATION ON OTHER ORGANS

Although we have dealt in this chapter only with root formation on stems and hypocotyls, roots will also be formed on the petioles of isolated leaves which have been treated like cuttings (for literature and for a list of leaves tested for root formation see Hagemann, 1932, and Graham, 1934). Since leaves form auxin and food materials in light, this is not surprising; it is also evident that addition of auxin will at best speed up root formation on petioles, but not materially change their rooting response in general.

Root formation on roots might be considered as a special case, but Bouillenne and Went (1933) concluded that this was governed by the same factors as root formation on stems. They found, in *Acalypha*, that abundant hormone supply led to the formation either of a large number of sparsely branched roots, or of a few roots with numerous laterals, the controls forming only one or two roots without branches. This would indicate that if the excess hormone in the cutting is not used up in the formation of roots on the stem, it will move into the roots and cause the formation of numerous laterals on them. Zimmerman and Hitchcock

(1935) described the formation of laterals on the aërial roots of *Cissus*, after application of various auxins and auxin-like substances either as paste or in water solution to the growing zone. Application on the basal side of the elongating region was ineffective. The applied auxin, however, inhibits the growth of the main root, and to this they ascribed the branching; as soon as the main root recovered its original growth rate, the effect of the auxin paste on branching disappeared. The same phenomenon on a number of seedling roots was described by Faber (1936; see also Laibach, 1935), and by Thimann (1936). Faber obtained profuse branching of the roots at the place of application of the auxin paste. However, Thimann (1936) showed that in *Pisum* roots branching is independent of the growth of the main root. He applied auxin paste to the stump of the epicotyl, which produced no inhibition, but even a slight acceleration of the main root; nevertheless it increased branching from 0 in the controls to an average of 2.7 in the treated plants. On de-tipped roots the effect was still greater. This fact gives good evidence for acropetal auxin transport in the root (see IX *C*).

Thimann also found that branching in both *Avena* and *Pisum* roots is inhibited by the presence of the root tip; since the root tip is a source of auxin this is probably due to factors other than auxin. Correspondingly, Katunskij (1935) reported that in *Zea* roots branching is inhibited by the application of coleoptile tips. In *Avena* branching occurs very readily and is not increased by auxin application, so that auxin appears not to be the limiting factor for branching in these roots.

If an incision be made on one side of *Vicia Faba* roots the formation of laterals is prevented on the apical side of the incision for a considerable distance (de Haan and Petrick, 1935). This indicates that formation of laterals is controlled by something coming from the stem or cotyledons. All the above facts indicate that root branching is controlled both by auxin and by other factors.

G. PRACTICAL APPLICATIONS

Study of the use of auxin for rooting cuttings of commercially important plants has been begun by Cooper (1935). He obtained excellent root formation on cuttings of lemon, *Acalypha*, *Lantana*, and fig by apical application of auxin in lanoline. Subsequently the fact, mentioned above, that high concentrations of auxin cause root formation when applied at the base has been utilized successfully by Hitchcock and Zimmerman (1936) and by Cooper (1936) for cuttings of *Ilex*, *Taxus*, *Hibiscus*, *Pachysandra*, lemon, *Chrysanthemum*, and some other plants (see Figure 57). Private reports from a number of horticulturists have already extended this list considerably. In general the highest non-toxic concentration of indole-acetic acid, dissolved in water, will give the best results. This concentration varies for different plants, and is lowest for green cuttings. A treatment with 0.2 mg. per cc. for 12 to 24 hours can be recommended, but before large-scale applications are made the toxic limit for each species to be treated should be ascertained. Indole-butyric and naphthalene-acetic acids are also effective. For treatment by the lanoline method a concentration of about 1 mg. indole-acetic acid per gram of lanoline is satisfactory.

It is clear that some of the procedures used by gardeners to induce root formation have their foundation in the production and movement of auxin (see Bouillenne and Went, 1933). A curious example of this is found in the insertion, into the apical split end of cuttings, of a germinating wheat seed, as practised in parts of Holland and Scotland. As to more general principles, in non-deciduous plants leafy cuttings are always used, probably because no auxin is stored in their stems. In deciduous plants leafless cuttings are preferred because of the difficulty with water supply to the leaf, but here the bud acts as auxin supply. As one of numerous examples might be mentioned the holly cuttings of Zimmerman and Hitchcock (1929); *leafless* cuttings of the deciduous *Ilex verticillata* will root, but those of the evergreen varieties will not.

FIG. 57. Rooting of lemon cuttings. Upper row, 8 hours in tap water; lower row, 8 hours in indole-3-acetic acid (highest non-toxic concentration, 500 mg. per liter). Photographed 17 days after treatment. (From Cooper, *Plant Physiol. 10*: 789–794, 1935.)

Layering probably depends for its success on the retarding influence on auxin transport exerted by high humidities (*cf.* XIII *C*), together with geotropic accumulation of auxin on the lower side of the stem. Rooting takes place usually at nodes, probably because there the transport of auxin is interfered with. (*Clematis* is an exception, rooting better at internodes.) The practice of ringing branches, either by cutting the cortex or by tying a tight wire round during growth, obviously operates in the same way. The optimum time of year to take cuttings varies from plant to plant (Graham, 1934) and depends upon a number of factors such as auxin production, storage, and destruction, as well as water supply and ease of wilting.

Among the causes of failure of cuttings to root when treated with auxin, one of the most important is doubtless furnished by those plants in which not auxin, but one of the other factors, is limiting. Another cause is the loss of the applied auxin or other factors by exudation from the cut surface; cuttings which root with difficulty are frequently those from which much exudation takes place. Lastly, the inactivation of auxin at the cut surface, by enzymes set free in wounding, doubtless also plays a part.

In conclusion, it may be pointed out that the rôle of auxins in root formation is a good example of a piece of research in pure physiology which has an immediate practical application.

CHAPTER XII

BUD INHIBITION

A. Bud Inhibition as a Correlation Phenomenon

It has been known from earliest times that lateral buds, low down on a stem, do not develop in presence of the terminal bud. If the terminal branch of a bud or shoot be removed, some of the laterals usually grow out at once; this is the basis of all pruning. Sachs' idea of bud-forming substances was abandoned by most workers, largely because the more obvious phenomenon is the inhibition, rather than the promotion, of bud development. However, Errera (1904) ascribed apical dominance and bud inhibition phenomena to "internal secretion," or, as we would say now, hormones. Goebel, in his earlier works (*e.g.* 1903) favored Sachs' hypothesis, but later (1908) changed his views, he and his school interpreting bud inhibition as a nutrition phenomenon. Loeb carried out a number of experiments on shoot growth and inhibition in *Bryophyllum* (1915, 1917*b*, 1918*a*, 1919, 1923, 1924), at the same time as his experiments on tropisms (see X *C*). He concluded that the growth of shoots was proportional to, and determined by, the amount of nutritive substances available. Thus, if one shoot of a plant is growing rapidly it deflects food substances away from other buds, which are therefore inhibited. However, as with root formation and geotropism, Loeb expressed different views at different times, and in 1917*b* attributed the phenomenon to the influence of special inhibiting substances formed in the leaf and transported basipetally in the stem. His experiments did not, however, provide evidence in favor of either view, although his concept of bud-inhibiting substances was shown by Reed and Halma (1919) to explain satisfactorily their experiments on correlations in bud development.

A detailed study of bud inhibition was made by Dostál (1926). He placed isolated internodes of *Scrophularia nodosa* in water and found that if one of the pair of opposite leaves were removed, the bud in its axil began to develop, while the one in the opposite axil, with its leaf present, did not. The leaf, therefore, inhibits the bud in its own axil. A growing bud, however, he found to exert a greater inhibiting influence than a leaf, the effect of the leaf being merely to upset the balance between the pair of buds, so that one could get ahead of the other. Once ahead, this growing bud inhibited the other strongly. Dostál therefore made it clear that the balance between inhibition and growth is rather delicately poised. Like his predecessors, however, he interpreted his results in terms of nutrition and water relations, and his experiments were therefore not designed to throw any light on the rôle of special substances.

Evidence for a special inhibiting substance was first brought by Snow (1925a), whose results were apparently not known to Dostál. Snow's essential experiment was to split the epicotyl of a *Phaseolus* seedling longitudinally from the roots up to 2 cm. above the cotyledons; another cut at an angle to the first then divided the plant into two parts, one of which, with one cotyledon, was completely isolated from the upper part, while the other, with the other cotyledon, was connected through the split stem with the upper part of the plant. The two halves were bound tightly together, and the growth of the buds in the axils of the cotyledons measured. The bud on the decapitated half was then found to grow out somewhat more slowly than that on a control decapitated and isolated split half. An inhibiting factor must therefore have come from the buds and leaves on the other half and crossed the cut surface. In later work (1929) he showed that the principal inhibiting effect was exerted by the very young leaves. A similar result was obtained by Weiskopf (1927).

As to the path of movement of the inhibiting influence, Harvey (1920) found that if a stretch of the stem of *Phaseolus* was killed by steaming, axillary buds grew out below the dead zone although the part above remained alive; transport downwards must therefore take place only through living tissue. A similar result was obtained by Child and Bellamy (1920), by chilling a zone of the stem with a brine coil (compare also Cooper's experiment, p. 191.) Snow later (1931a) confirmed Harvey's finding, but also obtained some evidence that the inhibiting influence could—at least to some extent—travel up a lateral branch. Experiments of this kind also show that food relations play a subordinate part, since the axillary buds may develop while the top part is also developing.

It appears, then, that the inhibition travels mainly from apex to base in living tissue, and is exerted principally by the young buds and leaves; there is also some evidence that it may cross a cut surface and thus may be due to a diffusible substance.

B. BUD INHIBITION CAUSED BY AUXIN

Thimann and Skoog (1933, 1934) pointed out that if inhibition were really due to a substance, then this substance would appear to behave like auxin in the plant. They determined the auxin production in *Vicia Faba*, using the diffusion method and the *Avena* test, and found that the terminal bud was the most active auxin-producing center (see Figure 28, p. 62). The leaves produce smaller amounts of auxin, but their production decreases with age (*cf.* Avery, 1935); the dormant axillary buds produce almost none, but as soon as they begin to develop they also begin to produce auxin. These results therefore closely parallel the inhibiting power of the different parts discussed above. Finally they removed the terminal bud and applied auxin, in agar, in its place, the auxin being renewed as soon as it had all diffused in from the agar, so as to duplicate the action of the terminal bud in providing a continuous stream. The laterals were then inhibited as completely as those on intact controls (see Figure 58). Their experiments were carried out with partially purified auxin from *Rhizopus*, but were later (Skoog and Thimann, 1934) confirmed with pure auxin *b* and indole-3-acetic acid.

A clear picture of the effect of auxin in bud inhibition is given by Figure 59. The terminal bud was removed from etiolated *Pisum* seedlings, and instead pure lanoline or lanoline containing various amounts of indole-acetic acid was applied to the apical cut surface. The swellings produced by the auxin are negligible in comparison with the growth of the buds in the controls without auxin.

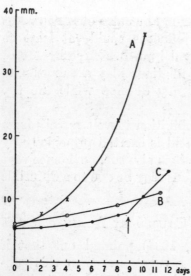

FIG. 58. Growth of axillary buds of *Vicia Faba*. Ordinate, length of bud in mm.; abscissa, time in days. A, plants decapitated, plain agar applied; B, plants intact; C, decapitated, 1600 plant units (=650 AE) of auxin applied in agar every 6 hours to apex— application stopped at arrow. (After Thimann and Skoog, *Proc. Roy. Soc. B. 114*: 317–339, 1934.)

As to the quantitative relations, Thimann and Skoog found it necessary, in order to obtain complete inhibition, to use an auxin concentration several times that which could be obtained directly from the terminal bud, but this difference is doubtless due to the inactivation of the applied auxin at the cut and the loss of auxin in non-transporting tissues. In any case the amount of auxin necessary for bud inhibition in *Vicia Faba* is considerably larger than that which causes maximal stem elongation, for, after decapitation, sufficient auxin for stem elongation, but not sufficient for bud inhibition, is produced in light by the remaining leaves. Thus only a growing bud, which is a very powerful source of auxin, can exert appreciable inhibition of lateral buds.

In this connection it is significant that many dwarfs, such as those of *Pisum*, *Vicia*, and *Zea*, have a bushy habit, *i.e.* the buds in their lower nodes develop extensively. If the dwarfing is due to a reduction in the amount of auxin present, as is true for the *nana* form of *Zea Mays* (van

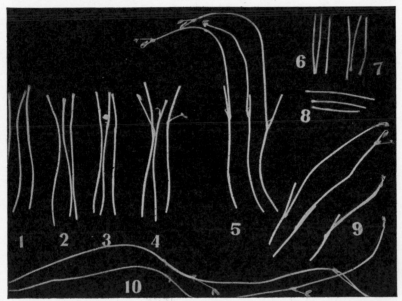

FIG. 59. Bud inhibition in etiolated *Pisum* seedlings. Nos. 1–5, decapitated below terminal bud; 6–9, decapitated below upper lateral bud; 10, intact controls. Auxin paste applied to apex immediately after decapitation. Concentrations: for 1 and 6, 10 mg.; for 2 and 7, 2.5 mg.; for 3 and 8, 0.6 mg.; for 4, 0.15 mg. indole-acetic acid per gram lanoline; for 5 and 9, plain lanoline.

Overbeek, 1935), then the branching is doubtless due to the same cause.

The above experiments leave no doubt that in *Vicia* and *Pisum* auxin is the factor inhibiting lateral bud growth. The same is true in other plants. Müller (1935) applied lanoline pastes containing urine, or orchid pollinia, to a number of decapitated plants other than those already mentioned. In *Sinapis*, *Linum*, *Antirrhinum*, *Godetia*, *Zinnia*, *Helianthus*, and *Tradescantia*, the pastes caused inhibition of lateral bud development, but in *Polygonum* and *Tropaeo-*

lum they were without effect. Both Müller and Laibach (1933) also used, instead of lateral buds, the cotyledonary buds in legume seedlings, and these also were inhibited by application of orchid pollinia to the decapitated stem. The orchid pollinia are, of course, rich in auxin. The treated stems frequently showed swelling or elongation or both, and this led Laibach and Müller to postulate the mechanism of inhibition discussed below.

If a leaf of *Bryophyllum* be cut off and replaced on its petiole, the bud in the axil continues to be inhibited, and the same result may be obtained by placing the leaf on agar, and then applying the agar block to the cut petiole (Uhrová, 1934). There is no reason to doubt that here, too, auxin is the active factor. In *Solidago*, the successive leaves of the rosette each inhibit the growth of the one following them for a time. Goodwin (1937) showed that the inhibiting power of the leaf ceases about the time that its auxin production falls off. Further, removal of one leaf accelerates the growth of the next, while application of pure auxin on the cut petiole inhibits the growth of the next. Application of pure auxin inhibits bud development in the *Aster*. In this plant the much-branched habit of *A. multiflorus* is correlated with very small auxin production by the buds, while the almost unbranched *A. novae-Angliae* produces considerably more (Delisle, 1937). We may safely assume, therefore, that the inhibiting action of auxin on bud development is very general.

Not only is the phenomenon common to a great many different plants, but it is also caused by a great many chemically different auxins. The natural auxin of the plant, pure auxin *b*, and indole-acetic acid all have the same effect. Further, indene-3-acetic and coumaryl-1-acetic acids, both of which have other properties of auxins, also strongly inhibit bud development of *Pisum* seedlings (Thimann, 1935*b*). Hitchcock (1935*a*) mentions that indole-propionic and naphthalene-acetic acids had bud-inhibiting influence when applied in high concentrations to *Nicotiana* stems.

C. Possible Mechanisms of Bud Inhibition

The auxins thus possess not only growth-promoting and organ-forming ability, but under certain circumstances they may also inhibit growth. Leaving aside those inhibitions which are produced by unphysiologically high concentrations, the growth of lateral buds and of roots are both inhibited by auxin. This raises the question of how all these different actions may be brought about. It seems clear that the auxins control some master reaction in the cell (Thimann, 1935b), which may then lead to different effects according to the age and position of the cell and the influence of other factors. However, the mechanism whereby any such action could lead to bud inhibition remains completely unexplained. Some hypotheses may be considered.

In the first place, the production of auxin within the developing bud is probably from some precursor which is stored in it. Thus Went (1934a) found that the presence of buds on etiolated pea seedlings led to the formation of roots, presumably due to auxin storage in the buds. In *Solidago* the smallest leaf in the bud, weight for weight, produces the most auxin (Goodwin, 1937), and since these small leaves are completely enclosed in the bud their auxin production cannot be directly from photosynthesis (*cf.* IV *B*). Now Thimann and Skoog (1934) suggested that the relatively high concentration of auxin reaching the lateral bud from the tip shifts the equilibrium, *Precursor* $\rightleftharpoons$ *Auxin*, towards the precursor, thus preventing the lateral buds from forming auxin themselves. Their diffusion experiments, however, showed that very little auxin diffuses out of the undeveloped lateral buds so that the amount actually in them cannot be very large.

Laibach (1933) and Müller (1935), on the other hand, assumed that the swelling and growth, accompanying application of high concentrations of auxin to the cut surface, are the cause of the inhibition. According to this view, the inhibition is only a secondary result of the increased stem growth produced by the auxin. However, this hypothesis was satisfactorily dismissed by Skoog and Thimann (1934) because in their experiments inhibition was complete without any noticeable growth increase at the top of the stem. This can be shown very clearly in peas by the inhibition of the bud in the axil of the cotyledon. Also, in Figure 59 the enormous bud development of the controls obviously represents more growth than the slight stem swelling in the auxin-treated plants, whose buds are completely inhibited.

Le Fanu (1936) has brought to light some interesting new facts in connection with the inhibition. She found, firstly, that the application of dilute solutions of indole-acetic acid to the base of stem sections of *Pisum* inhibited their elongation; if lanoline paste was used, the auxin paste decreased the growth when applied at the base, although (under somewhat different conditions) the same concentration increased the growth when applied to the apex. These results resemble those of Faber (1936) and Thimann (1936a) on roots, in which the effect of auxin also depended on its point of application (*cf.* IX *D*), and they indicate that the effect of auxin on an organ may be determined by whether it has to move with or against the normal polarity. In the second place she showed that in plants with two nearly equal shoots, the shorter, which was being inhibited by the longer, yielded only traces of auxin to agar, while normal shoots under the same conditions yielded 26 units in 3 hours. Sections of the inhibited shoot also transport practically no auxin through them, whether it is applied apically or basally. Le Fanu concludes that this evidence is against the view that the shoot can be inhibited by the direct entry of auxin into it, and supports rather the concept of some indirect means of inhibition. However, it is clear that the inhibition of stem sections by auxin at the base seems to be comparable to the inhibition of one shoot or bud by another which supplied auxin to its base.

In the hope of elucidating the mechanism of inhibition Went (1936) has attempted to assess the rôle of the other factors involved in bud growth. In etiolated *Pisum* seedlings the factor (or factors) necessary for growth in length of the stem or branch could be separated from factors governing leaf development and embryonic bud growth by cutting off different parts. The former comes mainly from the roots and to a less extent from the cotyledons, the latter mainly from the cotyledons. He suggested that the auxin coming from the terminal bud may influence the upward movement of the factor necessary for bud growth. Wherever an auxin production center is located, it would cause the bud-growth factor to move towards that place, preventing other, non-auxin producing, buds from obtaining this factor. This would be one way to explain the curious fact that the growth of laterals is inhibited by auxin coming from the terminal bud, but promoted by auxin produced in their own tissues. However, Le Fanu's (1936) observation of the inhibition due to basal application of auxin would also explain this. In XI *E* evidence has been given that auxin causes a redistribution of the specific root-forming factor, which would be comparable to the action suggested above. This view is essentially a revival of the old hypothesis (see *e.g.* Goebel, 1903; Loeb, 1915) that the growing point is a "center of attraction" for the material necessary for stem growth.

The factors controlling bud growth are apparently subject to polar distribution in rhizomes, as Schwanitz (1935) has shown. If the rhizome is cut up immediately on removal from the plant, then each piece produces about the same number of buds, but if it is first placed in the ground for 16 days or so, and then cut up, the majority of the buds are formed in the apical portion.

One of the factors for growth in length is apparently biotin, since Kögl and Haagen Smit (1936) have described how markedly it increases the growth in length of *Pisum* seedlings from which the cotyledons have been removed. Eastcott's finding (1928) that large quantities of bios are present in germinated malt seems significant in this connection. The influence of factors other than auxin may explain why some buds have a greater tendency to develop than others. Thus in woody twigs after decapitation, it is frequently the first bud below the terminal which develops (*cf*. Reed and Halma, 1919), while in herbaceous plants the lowest bud often develops under these conditions. It is easy to see how this might be related to the distribution or storage of bud-growth promoting factors. Snow (1931) considered that, in *Pisum*, the inhibiting action of the terminal bud is greatest on the buds farthest from it, *i.e.* the inhibition increases with distance. The fact is, more probably, that the *tendency* to grow out is greatest in the basal buds, so that these buds show the greatest difference in growth between decapitated and intact plants. In this connection reference may again be made to the poorly-transported auxins, such as indene-3-acetic acid; Thimann (1935b) has shown that the inhibition caused by this compound decreases very rapidly with increasing distance from the point of application. In callus formation, the activity even of readily transported auxins like auxin *a* and indole-acetic acid decreases very rapidly with distance (*cf*. XIIIc).

The mechanism of bud inhibition can probably not be understood until we know more about the fundamental mechanism of auxin action on the cell, and the rôle of other factors in bud growth. It is clear that many of the factors necessary for bud development, such as water, food, auxin, and the other substances, could, under the right conditions, become limiting factors in bud growth (*cf*. *e.g.* Denny, 1926; Moreland, 1934). However, the experiments in this chapter are concerned principally with the effects of auxin and it will be clear to the reader that the typical "apical dominance" is an auxin phenomenon.

CHAPTER XIII
OTHER ACTIVITIES OF AUXINS
A. Auxin and Cell Division

It was mentioned in Chapter II that the work of Haberlandt and his students has shown that cell division in the parenchyma of a number of plants is controlled by diffusible substances, which are present in the phloem, and which are set free from other tissues by wounding. Such attempts as have been made to characterize these cell-division substances chemically (Wehnelt, 1927; Jost, 1935*a*; Bonner, 1936 and *u*; Umrath and Soltys, 1936) give no reason to believe that they are in general identical with auxins. On the other hand, there are some conditions under which auxins certainly produce cell division.

Thus, Jost (1935*a*) in studying the parenchyma of the pods of *Phaseolus*—the material used by Wehnelt—found that the cells could be induced to divide not only by bean juice and other preparations, but also by indole-acetic acid. However, this substance acted only at the very high concentration of 0.1 per cent in water, concentrations up to 100 times those present in the plant being completely inactive. Further, the bean extract, containing only 0.5 per cent dry matter, produced more divisions than the 0.1 per cent auxin solution. Since the physiological activities of indole-acetic acid and the auxin of the plant itself differ only in a very minor degree, it is clear that the powerful action of bean juice cannot possibly be ascribed to its content of auxin, but must be due to another special substance, probably active in high dilution. A somewhat lower concentration of auxin, namely 0.01 per cent in water, caused vigorous cell division in the pith cells of the stem of *Vicia Faba*, and in the subepidermal parenchyma of the cotyledons of the white lupin. This concentration, however, is also

217

considerably higher than is likely to occur physiologically. The problem is further complicated by the fact, observed by Wilhelm (1930) and by Orth (1934), that the pith cells of *Vicia Faba* show growth and division on treatment with a variety of extracts and solutions, including sugar solution. Wehnelt (1927) and Jost (1935a) obtained cell divisions in *Phaseolus* pod parenchyma with 2 per cent levulose, 0.1 per cent NaCl, 0.01 per cent acetic acid, and 0.01 per cent citric acid. The apparent non-specificity of the reaction leads one to suspect that some of these materials may act indirectly by merely setting free the active substance in some way from the tissue, while others, such as the bean juice, really contain the active growth-promoting substance. To which type the action of auxins belongs cannot yet be definitely said. Thus both in the above work, and in that of Laibach and others on swellings (see XIII *C*), auxins bring about cell divisions in many kinds of tissue only when applied in high concentrations.

The first stages in the initiation of new roots on stems have frequently been shown to be divisions in the pericycle, and it was shown in XI *C* that such root formation is brought about, and controlled, by auxin. This fact cannot, however, be taken as proof that auxin controls cell division in general, and since the phenomena of root formation are complex, it will be better to examine first the clearest case of the action of auxin on cell division.

B. Cambial Growth

The one type of cell division which appears to be really controlled by auxins under physiological conditions is the formation of, and division in, the cambium. This applies to the cambium of the stem, and to a large extent to both cambium and pericycle of the root. It was first shown by Jost (1891, 1893) that the activity of the stem cambium of dicotyledons is greatly stimulated immediately below the growing leaves. The effect is the same even if they are etiolated, and it is transmitted only in the morphologically downward direction, no effect being observable above the leaf. In 1910, when phytohormones were not yet recognized, Keeble ascribed this transmission of cambial activity to "chemical stimulators," while the first suggestion that the activation is due to a true hormone—produced in growing parts and transmitted in the morphologically downward direction—was made by Kastens (1924).

Subsequently, in an extensive survey of cambial activity in tropical trees, Coster (1927, 1928) came to the conclusion that the young developing buds, and to a lesser extent the leaves, produce hormones which activate the cambium. These hormones may even be produced shortly before the first visible signs of bud development can be detected. In general it is observable that in trees the cambial activity in the branches begins in spring at about the time the buds begin to develop. Snow (1932) mentions that growing inflorescences and fruits of *Agrimonia*, *Spiraea*, and *Scrophularia* stimulate the activity of cambium below them, and Priestley (1930) ascribes the same effect to the flowers, buds, and growing leaves of *Fraxinus*. Gill (1933) finds that the inflorescences of *Populus serotina* and *Salix caprea*, which are within the bud at the beginning of the spring, activate the cambium immediately below them as they expand in spring; trees whose catkins are exposed throughout the winter show no such effect in spring.

Experimental evidence that cambial activation is due to a hormone was first brought by Snow in 1933. His experiments were apparently suggested by the work of Simon (1930) who found that, in grafting unrelated plants, vessel differentiation appeared to be stimulated in the neighborhood of the graft before the tissues had actually grown together. Snow therefore split longitudinally the stems of a *Pisum* and a *Helianthus* seedling for several cm., and severed half the *Pisum* stem at the lower end of the split, and half the *Helianthus* stem at the upper end. The downward-pointing half of the former was then brought into contact with the upward-pointing half of the latter, the two halves bound firmly together, and after 22 days the region of contact was sectioned and examined. Many cambial layers had formed in and between the bundles in the *Helianthus* hypocotyl, although the tissues had not (with a few exceptions) grown together. Controls not in contact showed no such effect, so that the stimulus from the *Pisum* seedling had passed across a protoplasmic discontinuity to act upon a plant of quite another family. In other experiments the upward- and downward-pointing portions were both from the same plant, *Vicia Faba*, but the stimulus passed across a piece of linen inserted in a cut in the stem.

Snow and Le Fanu (1935) then found that the cambium in the *Helianthus* hypocotyl may be activated by applying urine, or the ether extract of urine, and finally Snow (1935, 1935a) obtained excellent activation by pure auxin *a* and indole-3-acetic acid. As stated above, in high concentrations auxin may cause cell division in a variety of tissues, but in this case it is of considerable importance that the activation is brought about by low concentrations of auxin comparable with those obtaining in the normal plant. Thus, comparing his results with the auxin determinations of Thimann and Skoog (1934), Snow found that moderate cambial activity is induced by an amount of auxin *a* about 2.5 times that produced hourly by the terminal bud of *Vicia Faba*. There can thus be no doubt that the auxin formed by buds and leaves is responsible for the cambial activation below them; the polar movement of this cambial stimulus is then due to the polar transmission of the auxin. In Snow's experiments cambium was activated for 2–3 cm. below the point of application. The exact tissue in which the auxin travels in such structures as stems has not yet been determined; Cooper's experiments (1936) indicate that it must be living tissue, possibly the cambium itself. The stimulus does not seem to travel very far, although the calculations and observations of Büsgen-Münch (1929) indicate that it takes several weeks to travel from the growing buds of trees down to the trunk, which would give it about the same velocity as that found for auxin in the coleoptile (Chapter VI).

In trees the activation of cambial divisions by auxin has been studied by Söding (1936a), who showed that insertion of a crystal of indole-acetic acid into the cambium of woody twigs gives rise to a rapid growth of new secondary wood, which in the willow was up to 1 mm. wide; there was also some new production of cortex. The effect, which is due entirely to cambium activation, was only visible down to about 3 cm. below the point of application (cf. Rogenhofer, below). An interesting fact which has been described by various investigators, e.g. Coster (1927–1928) and Gouwentak and Hellinga (1935), is that wounding alone, without auxin addition, definitely produces some cambial stimulation; since, so far as we know, wounding will not produce any auxin, but will be more likely to destroy it (cf. IV A), this indicates that some other substance, probably of the type of the lepto-hormone of Haberlandt (see II E) is here involved. This fact, taken together with the relatively short distance of movement in Söding's and Snow's experiments, seems to raise the possibility that the cambial stimulus, which in nature travels very far, may not be entirely explained by the rôle of auxin. However, Avery, Burkholder, and Creighton (1937) have determined the distribution of auxin in twigs, following bud development, and find a parallelism between the downward spread of auxin and that of cambial activity.

As was stated above, the action of auxin on roots also gives rise to cell division. The thickening of roots produced by moderate concentrations of auxin (cf. Chapter IX) is largely due to enlargement of the cortical cells, but it is usually accompanied by cell divisions either in the cambium (Jost, 1935a) or in the pericycle (Thimann, 1936) or both. Divisions in these layers give rise to lateral roots, which may be produced directly as a result of auxin application (cf. XI F), and at physiologically low concentrations. The induction of divisions in the stem or root pericycle is evidently comparable with the formation of cambium in the stem; both must be ascribed to the "sensitivity," or "readiness to divide," of a certain layer of cells. Cells which have not this sensitivity can apparently not be stimulated to divide by auxin, except perhaps in unphysiologically high concentrations, and these cells therefore require the other factor or factors discussed above. Thus Snow (1935a) observed that an auxin concentration sufficient to produce marked activation of the cambium produced no divisions in the cortex or pith. We may perhaps conclude, though as yet without experimental support, that cell division results from the interaction of several factors, of which one is auxin; the distribution of these factors differs for different tissues, and those tissues, such as stem and root cambium and root pericycle, which divide readily on the application of auxin, do so because they already contain the other factors, and auxin is therefore limiting. Cells like those of the *Phaseolus* pericarp which do not respond to auxin must therefore be considered as having the other factors limiting. Finally, cells containing only traces of these other factors could respond to them if extremely high concentrations of auxin were added. The cambium or callus cultures of Gautheret (1934, 1935), which continued to proliferate on culture medium, presumably contained auxin and other factors in storage.

C. CALLUS AND STEM SWELLINGS

One of the most obvious results of the application of auxin to young tissues, especially if high concentrations are used, is the swelling of the tissue. This aspect of auxin activity has unfortunately not been studied very quantitatively, so that we cannot say just how the concentrations needed to produce swelling compare with those present in nature. The application of these findings to normal physiological processes is therefore difficult, and more exact work is needed, but it seems probable that they will have a bearing on pathology and teratology. In woody cuttings these swellings have their counterpart in the formation of callus at the basal cut surface. Such callus formation, which involves both cell enlargement and division, was observed in *Acalypha* cuttings by Bouillenne and Went (1933) after application of diastase or extract of rice polishings. They concluded that the callus was caused by a special substance, analogous to, but probably not identical with the root-forming hormone.

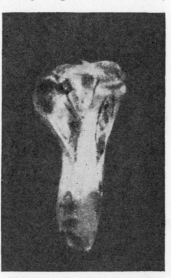

It was reported by Laibach (1933) that orchid pollinia, applied to decapitated epicotyls of *Vicia Faba*, cause a marked increase in thickness. The same result was obtained on other plants by Laibach, Mai, and Müller (1934), Mai (1934), and Müller (1935), both with orchid pollinia and with ether extracts of these and of urine.[1] Later the same effect was obtained with pure indole-3-acetic acid in lanoline by Laibach (1935) (see Figure 60), by Hitchcock (1935), the authors (*u*), and others, while similar results from the application of indole-butyric,

FIG. 60. Swelling and callus formation at apical cut surface of decapitated epicotyl of *Vicia Faba*, after treatment with indole-acetic acid paste. (From Laibach, *Ber. d. bot. Ges. 53:* 359–364, 1935.)

naphthalene-acetic, and other acids have been mentioned by Zimmerman and Wilcoxon (1935).

The only quantitative work so far carried out is that of Laibach and Fischnich (1935a) on swellings, and of Rogenhofer (1936) on callus proper. The former found that the extent of thickening of *Vicia Faba* epicotyls is proportional to the logarithm of the concentration of auxin applied, using lanoline paste. Rogenhofer determined the callus produced

---

[1] These workers proposed to call the active substance causing swellings "Meristine," but since it is identical with auxin the name can be dropped.

on sections of *Populus* twigs by separating and weighing it. The amount of callus formed by auxin decreases rapidly with distance from the point of application, approaching zero at about 3 cm. below it. If applied simultaneously at two points on the twig, the callus produced was equal to the sum of the amounts which would be produced by single applications at the same points; the method is thus satisfactory for quantitative work. Auxin *a* was somewhat less active in callus formation than indole-acetic acid.

As to the histology of the thickening, it involves both cell enlargement and division, the enlargement, which is partly radial and partly isodiametric, being mostly confined to the cortical parenchyma and the pith cells (*u*). Laibach and Fischnich (1935) found that the proportion of divisions to enlargement was always about the same in *Vicia Faba*, and therefore use the total swelling as measure of the cell division; [1] they correspondingly speak of the swellings as "callus." However, the term callus has usually been applied to the formation of undifferentiated and random-oriented cells at wound surfaces, whereas these swellings show at least in part the character of the stem; further, since enlargement of parenchyma accounts for a large part of the increase in volume, and in some cases (as claimed by Czaja, 1935*b* [1]) for all of it, it seems better simply to use the term "swellings." Within the swellings secondary lignification of the cell walls may often be observed, so that it seems possible that auxin controls or stimulates such secondary wall formation.

Czaja (1935) has put forward the view that the effect of auxin depends largely on the direction of its application. If applied directly to the transversal cut surface of the *Helianthus* hypocotyl he finds increase in elongation to be the principal effect, but if applied externally, to the epidermis, the principal effect is swelling. His published measurements,

---

[1] The controversy between Czaja and Laibach as to whether the auxin swellings are due to cell division or enlargement is easily explained: when auxin is applied, enlargement of the parenchyma cells takes place first, and cell divisions follow after a few days (Went, 1936).

however, do not bear this out, nor could Jost and Reiss (1936), nor the authors (*u*), confirm it. It is true that the place of application of auxin is in some cases important for its effect; this is shown in roots (Chapter IX) and also for the elongation or inhibition of stem growth (Le Fanu, p. 214). Czaja's theory, discussed in VI *D*, that the polarity of cells and tissues is caused by the direction of the prevailing auxin stream was based upon these experiments. Went (1936) has suggested a mechanism for the formation of swellings in terms of the interaction between auxin and other factors.

The formation of callus at the base of a cutting is often, though not always, associated by gardeners with good rooting of the cutting. In the light of the above, it is probable that a cutting which forms much callus does so because it is rich in auxin, and the root formation is then due to the auxin; the roots are not as a rule formed from the callus, but both result from the same internal cause, namely the auxin. The many exceptions to this rule provide further evidence of the rôle of other, non-auxin, factors in both processes.

The auxin swellings bear a close resemblance to the phenomena observed in some of the galls and other pathological outgrowths, and there is good evidence that auxin plays an important part in such growths. The root nodules of leguminous plants are active auxin-forming centers when still growing, and their initiation and growth are almost certainly due to the auxin produced by the invading bacteria (Thimann, 1936*b*; *cf.* IX *C*). These can therefore be considered as root-galls, arising by pathological swelling of a lateral root initial. The crown-gall organism, *Pseudomonas tumefaciens*, also produces auxin, since Brown and Gardner (1936) have obtained typical swellings and outgrowth by extracts from cultures of this bacterium (see also Duyfjes, 1935). They have also produced large galls on *Phaseolus* by long-period application of pure indoleacetic acid at a cut surface (see Figure 61). The experiment of Němec (p. 187) also indicates auxin production by this bacterium. The apparently widespread ability of bacteria and fungi to produce indole-acetic acid from tryptophane, or possibly other auxins from other amino-acids (*cf.* IV *E*), is doubtless of great significance in this connection.

Fig. 61. Gall, produced in 5 months on *Phaseolus* stem by decapitating and smearing wound with indole-acetic acid paste (20 mg. per gram of lanoline). (From Brown and Gardner, *Phytopath.* *26:* 708–713, 1936.)

The intumescences on leaves of *Populus grandidentata*, which are not caused by microörganisms but arise under conditions of high humidity (La Rue, 1933) may be perfectly imitated by injection of indole-acetic acid in very low concentration; if in some way the action of auxin in the leaf is intensified by high humidity this would explain them

(La Rue, 1936). Probably many other pathological out-growths are explicable in terms of auxin—a development which will open important fields in plant pathology.

D. MISCELLANEOUS EFFECTS

A number of other effects of auxin have been recorded. Laibach (1933) has described how tendrils of *Cucurbita* coil up when auxin paste is applied on one side, the reaction not being restricted to the place of application. This, how-ever, is not generally true, for tendrils of *Passiflora*, similarly treated, show only local curvatures (u).

The reactions of leaves are of some interest. Laibach (1934) found that when *Phaseolus* leaves are smeared over with auxin in lanoline, they bulge and curl, while Avery (1935) found that the midrib of the *Nicotiana* leaf curves readily away from auxin paste applied on one side. The authors' experiments (u) indicate that auxin causes elonga-tion of the cells of the midrib and lateral veins, but not increase of surface of the mesophyll. This results in dif-ferential growth with bulging of the leaf-blade (particularly marked in *Aristolochia*). In varieties like *deformis* of tobacco (Honing, 1923) or *wiry* of tomato (Leslie, 1928), mesophyll growth is practically absent in the mature plant, so that the leaves are restricted to a midrib, with the lateral veins, which are still present, contracted against it. Thus the *deformis* and *wiry* genes affect only mesophyll growth. On the other hand, *Aphids* (see Maresquelle, 1935) and "curly-top" virus cause curling of the leaf, due to deficient vein growth, while the blade develops normally. Grieve (1936) has indicated that in "spotted wilt" virus this curling may be due to lack of auxin. It is significant that it is usually associated with reduction in total growth. All these cases fit in with the view that auxin causes elongation of leaf veins, while the growth of mesophyll depends on other factors, such as that postulated by Gregory (1928).

Certain other effects are not readily explicable on the basis of growth promotion. Thus if the leaf-blade of *Coleus* be removed, the petiole subsequently falls off; but if urine or auxin paste be applied to the petiole it remains in position for a much longer time (Laibach, 1933a; Uhrová, 1934; La Rue, 1935). Application of large amounts of indole-acetic, indole-butyric, or other related acids to the soil, 3 to 5 weeks before flowering was due, has been reported to hasten the formation of flower buds in Turkish tobacco (Hitchcock and Zimmerman, 1935). A hastening of flowering has been found to be produced in various plants by application to the soil of female sex hormones (see XIV B). Hastening of flowering has also been recorded in peas and beans as resulting from application of yeast extract (Virtanen and Hausen, 1933, 1934). Little can be said about the mechanism of such phenomena pending more careful study.

Interesting, particularly from a historical standpoint, is the rôle which is apparently played by auxin in the phenomena of post-floration of some orchids. It was shown by Fitting in 1910 that the falling off of the flower and swelling of the gynostemium of some tropical orchids after flowering were brought about by the presence of the pollen grains, and could also be caused by water extracts of the pollinia (see II E). The action was ascribed to a hormone in the pollen, and this was the first use of the term hormone in connection with plants. It was shown by Laibach (1932a) that this substance is extractable with ether, behaving like an acid in the extraction, and further that the extracts were active on *Avena*. *Hibiscus* pollen gave similar results. Laibach and Maschmann (1933) subsequently showed that ether extracts of urine and animal tissue behaved in the same way, and that action on the orchid gynostemium was parallel with auxin action on *Avena*, all extracts which had the one action having the other. The activity on the orchid was destroyed by H_2O_2. The swelling was entirely due to cell enlargement. It was thus deduced that the effect is due to the auxin in the pollinia, so that Fitting's "Pollenhormon," which may fairly be called the first plant hormone, is identical with auxin. Experiments have not been carried out with pure auxins, but there seems no reason to doubt the identity. In this case we have a combination of the growth-promoting effect with another effect resulting in flower fall, the mechanism of which is as yet unknown.

We have seen that the auxins play a protean rôle in the development of plants, and influence a large number of processes, both normal and pathological. It is important to note that, as discussed in Chapters VIII and XII, in all cases investigated a substance which shows one of the effects of auxin shows them all. Its activity may sometimes be concealed, as in those substances which cause no *Avena* curvature, or which produce root formation only locally, but it may be demonstrated by special experiments. Many of the apparently different effects are to be traced to different types of cell enlargement, but others, such as root formation, are more complex. It is difficult to avoid the conclusion that "all these functions arise from one primary reaction in the cell; which physiological effect is produced depends upon the nature and position of the tissues affected. The actual primary reaction becomes, then, of greater interest than ever. It is a kind of master reaction governing the activities of the cell." So far as attempts have been made to analyze further the nature of this primary reaction, they have been summarized in Chapter VIII. It remains now to consider the rôle of auxin in comparison with some other aspects of growth and development.

CHAPTER XIV

GENERAL CONCLUSIONS

In the preceding pages we have seen how from analyzing the complexities of correlation and of tropisms there has emerged a clear concept of hormones and of the rôle they play in the plant. It could hardly be expected, however, that, after only about 10 years of research this concept would have led us to a finished explanation of all the processes in which auxin is involved. Still less could we be expected to have progressed in our knowledge beyond this one group of hormones, the auxins. Our knowledge of the auxins has, as a matter of fact, laid open to experimental attack many problems concerned with other factors in the plant. However, it is fair to say that we already see the auxins and their properties as a continuous thread connecting most of the developmental and growth processes in the plant. Thus the auxins bring tropisms into that close relation with growth upon which Blaauw insisted in 1918; they bring growth, in the general sense of development and organ formation, into the same terms as growth in the special sense of cell elongation; and lastly, they bring the concept of correlation, which by its very name has previously defied causal analysis, into the realm of direct experimental attack. Perhaps the best example of this last phase is the meaning which is now given to the formerly elusive conception of polarity; polarity can now be expressed quantitatively as a function of the transport of a known substance in the tissues. Finally, few fields can have benefited so much from close interaction between the biological and chemical approaches, and the remarkable discoveries on the chemical side have made possible equally remarkable progress in the physiology. It has even been possible to inquire somewhat into the inner mechanism of the relation between auxins and their substrate.

A. Quantitative Relations between Auxin and Growth

The development of our knowledge of auxins has brought out the fact that their activity is quantitative as well as qualitative. The extent of growth, of root formation, etc., is directly dependent on the amount or concentration of auxin present. Since these quantitative relations have been proven for the simplified cases of direct experiment it is interesting to consider their bearing in general on growth and correlation.

Thus absolute size, among individual plants of a species (within normal environmental conditions), remains fairly constant and is even used as a taxonomic character. The experiments described in Chapter VI allow us to ascribe this to genetically determined rates of auxin production.

Among relative size relationships, one of the most stressed is that between the above-ground and below-ground parts of the plant, the "shoot-root ratio." Such constancy as this ratio shows is probably due to a reciprocal control system in the plant. On the one hand the number and size of buds and leaves determines the rate of auxin production, and this auxin, reaching the roots, influences the development of the root system (*cf.* XI *F*). On the other hand, the root system probably forms a factor or factors necessary for shoot growth (*cf.* XII *C*) and hence the increased root system increases the shoot.

Another interesting relation is that between the place of auxin production and the length of the growing zone in a stem. In many stems (*e.g.* most seedlings and annuals— *Pisum, Vicia, Nicotiana*), the growing region is restricted to a few cm. below the terminal bud, and in these stems auxin production is mainly in the terminal bud and youngest leaves. Other plants exhibit growth over a longer region, and in these auxin production is probably vigorous in axillary buds or lower leaves as well as in the terminal bud. Examples are *Asparagus* (Oosterhuis, 1931), *Polygonum* (Figure 33), *Tradescantia* (Uyldert, 1931), and *Bambusa* (*u*); probably the shoots of all trees and shrubs with periodic growth behave in this way.

The correlation between the amount of auxin which diffuses from buds of different plants and the rates of growth of the shoots below them (Zimmermann, 1936) may also be mentioned.

All such observations support the view that *quantitative relations between different parts of the plant are expressions of the quantitative relation between auxin and its growth effects.* This generalization can now supersede the older view that such growth relations are determined by the amounts of food material present.

B. COMPARISON WITH ANIMAL HORMONES

The progress of the work on phytohormones compares very favorably with that which has been made in other fields. This may be attributed to the relative simplicity of the relation between the plant and its hormones, as contrasted with the apparent complexity in animals. The hormonal correlation between different parts of an organism will be the more complex the larger the number of parts; the plant, with few organs, is thus a relatively favorable organism for study. One important complexity in animals is that the action of hormones is so often indirect, so that the hormonal activity of one gland may be expressed through its effect on the activity of another gland. The pituitary exerts an effect on the gonads, vitamin D may act through the parathyroid, and so on. Where there are introduced in this way additional links in the chain of action the mechanism of the process is correspondingly harder to elucidate. This does not necessarily mean that in plants the fundamental process is itself any simpler, but it does mean that it is more open to attack, as is shown by the fact that it has been possible to separate the primary processes in which auxin takes part from the secondary ones which prepare for its action.

There are important contrasts between the hormones of the plant and animal kingdoms. In animals, of course, the foods and hormones all travel along the same path, namely that of the blood stream. This has the effect that all cells receive the same hormonal stimulus and the result will depend upon their ability to respond to it. Plants, on the other hand, have no true circulation and the movement of hormones in them is mainly unidirectional, independent of the mass movements of water and foods. Thus hormones and foods move by different paths and hence every cell is not in a position to respond; this results in local growth zones and phenomena such as apical growth.

However, the fact that the term "hormone," first coined for animal physiology, has been used for the auxins shows that there are important parallelisms. The fundamental function of hormones, namely that of chemical messengers, is the same in plants as in animals;—the phytohormones are true hormones. Further, the activity is in both cases exerted in concentrations too low to allow of their making up an appreciable part of the cell (cf. VIII E). Table XVI summarizes very approximately the minimal active doses per gram of fresh weight of the test organism, for some different hormones. These figures, however, are not really comparable, not only because the molecular weights are different, but also because we do not know the actual concentrations at the place of action.

It is interesting to compare the specificity of the animal

TABLE XVI

HORMONE	ORGANISM	MINIMUM ACTIVE DOSE IN γ PER GRAM OF ORGANISM
Oestriol	Mouse	0.1
Androsterone	Capon	0.1
Biotin	Yeast	0.1
Insulin	Rabbit	0.25
Testosterone	Capon	0.01
Thyroxin	Man	0.01
Histamine	Cat	0.01
Oestrone (folliculin)	Mouse	0.001
Auxin	Oat	0.0001

hormones with that of auxin. There is little or no species specificity in either case, that is, one hormone performs the same function in large classes of organisms. On the other hand there is specificity of function, and this is far more marked in animals than in plants. Thus the auxins bring about a number of different effects, while the animal hormones in general have one special function. The latter are not as a rule merely growth-promoting, and their assay— except in the case of the pituitary hormone—is not based on growth measurements. An exception might be made for the sex hormones, which certainly act to produce a rapid growth of special tissues and which have actually been referred to as "Wuchsstoffe" (Butenandt, 1935, 1936). The specificity of function in animal hormones is strictly dependent on their molecular structure, so that in the sterols, for instance, small changes in the molecule completely alter certain functions of the substance: hydrogenation of one aromatic ring converts a female to a male sex hormone. In the auxins small changes merely alter the quantitative activity of the substance, but do not change the functions it performs. However, quantitative changes in activity with small changes in the molecule also occur in the sex hormones. Whether these changes are due to differences in secondary properties, such as penetration, inactivation, etc., as with the auxins (see VIII *G*), has not yet been ascertained. It is, however, very suggestive that the relative activity of two substances in two different tests may be quite different. Thus if the activity of androstandiol, a male sex hormone, is taken as 1 in both the capon and the rat test, then iso-androstandiol has an activity of 0.04 in the capon and 0.23 in the rat test (Butenandt, 1936). It seems justifiable, therefore, to suggest that the difference in relative activity between two such substances in the two tests is due to differences in their secondary properties.

The effect of animal hormones on plant growth scarcely falls within the scope of this review, but may be mentioned briefly. There is evidence that oestrone in particular has the effect of increasing the growth and development of a number of different plants. This is shown by increased production, dry weight, etc., in wheat, rye, barley, beans, and sugar-beets (Scharrer and Schrop, 1935) and tomatoes (Schoeller and Goebel, 1935). The effect can be ascribed to a stimulation of the earlier growth stages. Stimulation of flowering, either by an increase in the number of flowers or by the earlier opening of the first flowers, has also been reported (Schoeller and Goebel, 1935). This also seems to be correlated with better growth. The experimental conditions necessary to obtain positive results are of great importance, since various investigators were unable to confirm Schoeller and Goebel's earlier work (1931–1934) (*e.g.* Harder and Störmer, 1934; Virtanen, Hausen, and Saastamoinen, 1934). Indications that oestrone has an effect on root formation are mentioned in XI *E*.

Comparison has recently been made between the phenomena of crown-gall disease and animal cancer (Levine, 1936). This comparison, which was first made 20 years ago by E. F. Smith, rests upon very superficial similarities and appears quite unjustified. Conversely, little comparison can be drawn between the auxins and the animal carcinogenic substances. These substances, which are hydrocarbons (see Fieser, 1936), are very slow in acting, and it seems probable that their effect is to induce normal cells to change into cancerous cells rather than to promote cell growth directly.

C. COMPARISON WITH GROWTH SUBSTANCES OF LOWER PLANTS

In contrast to the above true hormones stand the growth promoting substances for fungi and microörganisms. While free movement of these substances may take place within the organism it is not an essential part of their activity; this is particularly obvious for unicellular microörganisms, in which correlations as ordinarily understood cannot occur. While microörganisms, therefore, cannot, by definition, have hormones, the question as to what name should be given to their growth-promoting substances remains in doubt. The term vitamin has the definite connotation of a food factor absorbed from the medium, while these growth substances are in some cases produced by the organisms themselves. On this account Kögl (1935) was led to term bios a phytohormone, because although yeasts require bios for growth, they also have the ability, though not usually in sufficient degree, to produce bios for themselves. According to Huxley's nomenclature (1935) we should name such substances local or intracellular activators.

The reason why these growth substances have been mentioned here is because there are some interesting parallels between them and the phytohormones. The group includes bios, vitamin B_1, "Wuchsstoff B," and the substances active on bacteria and protozoa. Vitamin B_1 is necessary for the growth of a few yeasts and numerous fungi. Wuchsstoff B is the term given by Nielsen and Hartelius (1932) to a substance, insoluble in ether, produced by *Rhizopus* cultures and active in promoting growth of *Aspergillus*. (The name should not be confused with auxin *b*.) Apparently both an organic growth substance and a group of accessory inorganic substances are involved (Nielsen and Hartelius, 1933).

The term bios is specifically restricted to substances active in promoting the growth of yeasts. Bios is of particular interest here because it was the first example of a system of interlocking substances, the action of each of which is increased by the presence of the others. That any one bios produces an effect alone is probably to be ascribed to the presence within the cell of small amounts of the other factors. The work of the Toronto school has shown that bios consists of at least 3 fractions, of which bios I was shown by Eastcott (1928) to be *i*-inositol, and another, bios II, has recently been isolated, under the name of "biotin," by Kögl and Tönnis (1936). Like auxin, biotin is active at extremely high dilution, 1 part in 4×10^{11} of solution having a detectable effect; however, in terms of the weight of organism affected its activity is not particularly high (see Table XVI). The following table from Kögl (1935) exemplifies clearly the interlocking action of the 3 fractions:

TABLE XVII

ADDITIONS TO A MEDIUM CONTAINING 42 GRAMS OF DEXTROSE AND 23 GRAMS OF SALTS	YIELD PER GRAM OF INOCULUM IN 10 HOURS
Control	1–1.5
Bios I, 4 g.	1–1.5
Bios III, 2 g.	1–1.5
Bios I, 4 g. + Bios III, 2 g.	1–1.5
0.167 γ Biotin	4
1.67 γ Biotin	7
1.67 γ Biotin + 4 g. Bios I	10
1.67 γ Biotin + 4 g. Bios I + 2 g. Bios III	14

The strain of yeast here used evidently contains none of the biotin, which thus acts as a limiting factor, but in the presence of a sufficient amount of biotin the other constituents become limiting and must be added to obtain · maximal growth. Some yeasts, like that of Williams *et al.* (1933), need only one of the bios factors, presumably being able to synthesize sufficient of the others. This parallels closely the root formation of the different strains of *Pisum* discussed in XI *E*, where some varieties respond to auxin application and others not at all. In some of these, auxin is already in excess, as is shown by the large number of roots formed by untreated controls; in others some additional factor is lacking, for roots are not produced by any treatment.

Root formation in *Pisum* provides a particularly good example of a system of limiting factors in higher plants, there being at least 3 substances known whose action interlocks. These 3 factors, sugar, auxin, and biotin are all available in the pure state and hence their interlocking action is easily studied (*cf.* XI *E*). A graphic representation of the interaction of these factors, drawn in a manner comparable to that of Blackman (1905), is shown in Figure 62. It will be seen that each factor reaches a concentration at which it is no longer limiting, and at this concentration root formation may be increased by adding the next factor, the increase being proportional to the amount added. The activity of any one factor alone is zero, the action of sugar alone being ascribable to the presence of small amounts of auxin in the plant. We thus have a complete parallel to the interaction of bios I, II, and III on yeast growth, or that of the Wuchsstoff B and Co-Wuchsstoff on *Aspergillus* growth; or, to go still further, to the interaction of enzymes and co-enzymes. Such interlocking systems of limiting factors are widely distributed in nature and probably will be encountered in any process which is sufficiently analyzed.

While bios, a growth substance for fungi, plays a part in the growth of higher plants, there is no evidence that auxins have any action on fungi or other lower organisms. Boysen Jensen (1932), Nielsen and Hartelius (1932), Bonner (1932), and Bünning (1934) all found that the auxin produced by fungi has no effect upon their own growth. Ronsdorf (1935) failed to find any effect of the addition of auxin *a* to the culture medium of various fungi; the auxin, however, was apparently destroyed in the medium. Similar destruction of indole-acetic acid in *Rhizopus* cultures was also noted by Thimann and Dolk (1933) after the time of maximum auxin production had been passed. The above experiments make it highly improbable that the action of plant exudates on growth of *Phytophthora* can be due to auxins, as supposed by Leonian (1935).

The report of Popoff (1933) that the excysting action of plant extracts on *Euglena* is due to auxin is probably equally unfounded. For the excystment of *Colpoda* Thimann and Barker (1934) found that at least two substances are involved; one is present in impure auxin preparations but is not identical with auxin, the other is completely unrelated to auxin. Pure indole-acetic acid and other auxins have no excysting action on *Colpoda* or some other protozoa (*u*).

D. REGENERATION

We have made comparisons between the *active substances* of higher plants and those of lower plants and of animals.

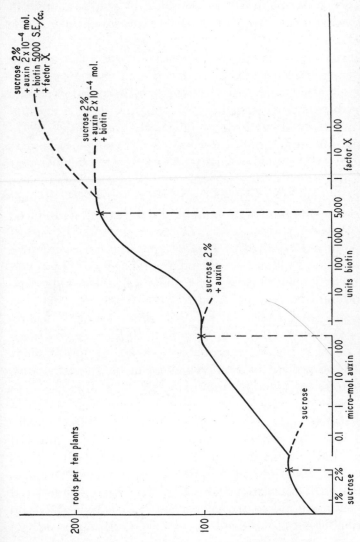

FIG. 62. Diagram illustrating Blackman's principle of limiting factors as operating in root-formation on etiolated pea cuttings. Ordinate, roots per 10 plants; abscissa, concentration (log. scale) of the factor which is limiting root formation. Each curve is continued a little beyond its maximum, in broken lines, for clarity.

239

We can now attempt some comparisons between the *processes* in which these substances are involved, in plants and animals. The analysis which we have made in the case of root formation enables us to consider organ formation in more general terms, and especially organ formation on isolated parts—the so-called "regeneration."

It is clear that the substances and processes acting to form roots are doing so continuously in the normal intact plant. In a cutting these factors will continue to operate *in the same way* as they would have done in the intact plant, the place of accumulation being now, of course, different. Thus the auxin which normally would have moved from the buds to the base of the shoot, or even into the roots, will now move merely to the base of the cutting. It follows that the roots so formed are not new formations ("*regenerates*"), nor is their formation in any way a *response* to the loss of the others. On the contrary it is merely the normal generation going on in an atypical—that is, an artificially conditioned—place, and thus has nothing to do with any "tendency towards completion (Ganzheit)."

In animals, if a part is removed, there is a tendency to replace it, and this is very pronounced in the Coelenterates, which furnish the best comparison with root formation. These animals show apical growth, and, what is important from our point of view, they have no true circulation of food. Correspondingly, their growth is not diffuse, as in higher animals, but is typically polar. This must be due to the polar transport of one or more growth substances, which in higher animals would be carried in the blood stream instead. In view of the neglect of this subject in recent years, it would be of great interest now to transfer our knowledge of "regeneration" in plants back to such animals, with special reference to the rôle of growth substances and of their probable *polar transport*.

A well-analyzed case of regeneration in a very interesting object is the work of Hämmerling (1934, 1935, 1936) on the alga *Acetabularia*. This bears out all the points previously discussed. In this large uninuclear siphonaceous cell, the apical end of any isolated middle section will regenerate apical organs; the basal end, on the other hand, will regenerate rhizoids.' Sections containing the nucleus regenerate rapidly and completely, but without the nucleus regeneration is only complete if the section is fairly old and has therefore been under the influence of the nucleus for some time. Hämmerling interprets his results as due to polar movement in opposite directions of two substances whose production is controlled by the nucleus, one apex-forming and the other base-forming. The percentage of regenerates, and the rate at which they form, are both proportional to the size of the isolated piece, and therefore, as he concludes, to the amounts of organ-forming substances present. The conclusions are supported by numerous additional experiments, but it must nevertheless be emphasized that as yet no direct evidence for the postulated organ-forming substances has been brought forward.

A comparable case is that of *Griffithsia bornetiana*. By passing an electric current through this alga, Schechter (1934) could induce rhizoids to form at the side facing the positive pole. The number of rhizoids was increased by increasing the current density. Schechter suggests that the formation of rhizoids is induced by some material inside the cell, which moves in an electric field. Centrifugal forces have a comparable effect (Schechter, 1935); shoots appear on the side where the heavier matter collects. Similar electrical control of polarity was reported for the zygotes of *Fucus* by Lund (1923); the rhizoids grow out towards the positive pole. Thus, the inherent polarity in lower plants, or single cells, may be affected by electrophoresis of organ-forming materials resulting from applied potentials. This is not true for higher plants.

To explain differences between types of regenerates, and between growth rates at different points, the concept of "gradients" or "fields" has been introduced. So long as the gradient is one of something intangible it is not open to experimental attack, and is only a restatement of the observations in different terms. If, however, the term be interpreted as a gradient in the concentration of active substances it not only becomes experimentally analyzable but is in close agreement with the situation in plants. Plants have, in fact, a gradient of auxin concentration which is set up either by the apical auxin formation or by the polarity, the latter probably being the cause of the former. Heretofore polarity was only detected by its effect on regeneration or organ formation, and as so many other factors affect this process it was a doubtful criterion even for the existence of polarity. But now, by measuring the rate and capacity of polar auxin transport we can measure polarity quantitatively and this undoubtedly will lead to a better understanding of this remarkable property of living matter. Apex-to-base polarity provides an example of the simplest type of "field."

E. ORGANIZATION

As we have seen, the factors operating in regeneration are those operating in normal development, and this suggests that the same principles also underlie development in the embryo. The effects of auxin in the plant compare very interestingly with embryonic development in the animal. Organization in the animal embryo, which may be defined as differentiation according to a definite pattern, is slightly different from Sachs' concept of organization referred to in VIII A. In the amphibian gastrula, any part of the ectoderm is apparently able to differentiate into a neural tube. That only one is formed is ascribed to the "organizer," viz., the dorsal lip of the blastopore, which as Spemann and his school have shown will, after invagination, induce the formation of a neural tube in that part of the ectoderm against which it comes to lie. Recently attempts have been made to isolate chemically the active principle of the organizer (see the review of Weiss, 1935). As a result, certain substances have been found to have the power of causing the differentiation of a neural tube. The chemical nature of these differentiating substances or "evocators" (Waddington, 1934) does not appear to be highly specific. Fischer *et al.* (1935) have found that similar effects can be produced by highly purified oleic acid, linolenic acid, and 12-octadecenic acid-1, as well as by muscle adenylic acid. Saturated acids, including stearic acid, were not active. From these results they conclude that the induction can be regarded as a stimulation by acid ("Säure-Reiz"). Such a stimulation might be interpreted in the same way as the effect of acid on growth of plants, namely that the acids set free a certain amount of active substance, but have no activity themselves (*cf.* VIII *F*). The failure of the saturated acids to act may be due to their lower ability to enter the cell. The results of Waddington, Needham, *et al.* (1935) cannot be interpreted in this way, and the active sterols and hydrocarbons studied by them apparently possess evocator activity of their own.

It must be emphasized that such evocations are not to be confused with the action of the living organizer, which not only differentiates the neural tube but also controls all other differentiations, *i.e.* it imposes a pattern on the embryo. This pattern-formation seems to call for the assumption of some kind of "field," of the same type as the polarity of auxin transport in the plant.

In organization in the plant, such as root formation, the "field" is the polar transport of the active substances; the evocator itself can be compared with auxin. Although auxin is formed or present in many different tissues, organization takes place only in that special location which is determined by the polar accumulation of the auxin. Correspondingly, in animal embryos, the evocator may be present in other parts of the embryo, as Holtfreter (1935) showed; the lack of a "field," however, is probably the reason why it does not act there. There is thus a close parallelism between auxin and the evocator; both are present in many parts of the organism, but their effects are limited by an existing "field," *i.e.* by their polarized accumulation. As to the organizer, it appears to furnish *both* field *and* evocator, and it must therefore be compared to the sum of auxin and polarity.

F. THE STIMULUS CONCEPT AND THE NATURE OF AUXIN ACTION

As has been shown in the latter half of this book, auxins bring about a number of different responses in plants. These are, specifically: growth by cell-elongation; the formation of roots—both on stems and on roots themselves; the inhibition of buds; the activation of the cambium; inhibition of root growth, and certain growth phenomena which involve cell enlargement and division together. We have seen already that a number of different substances can bring about the same growth response. It is also true that *any one* of the active substances can bring about *all* these different responses. This raises the question of the mechanism of these effects. There are two possibilities which may be considered; (1) the auxins bring about some master-reaction within the cell, the results of which will be determined by the presence and amount of other factors ("condition of the cell"), and by the conditions of the experiment; or (2) the auxins are stimulating substances setting free the energies stored up in the living protoplasm ("latente Reizbarkeiten"). This latter view has recently been emphasized by Fitting (1936); "I am convinced that we are right in including the hormones with the 'stimulus-substances' (*Reizstoffe*). By these are understood, following physiological usage, all those compounds which exert their physiological action through the intervention of the living substance, *i.e.* whose first point of attack is the living plasma. The typical physiological actions of stimulus substances show all the characteristics of stimulations. . . ." By the latter are meant latent time, presentation time, threshold concentration, excitation of the protoplasm, anti-reaction and recovery, etc.

To make this somewhat old-fashioned idea clear to the modern reader it is necessary to picture the organism as continuously in touch with its surroundings: every quality of the surroundings, such as light, gravity, or chemical change, acts as a stimulus on the organism, and the perception of this stimulus is followed by a response. These stimuli do not supply the organism with the energy which it uses in its response, any more than a lighthouse supplies a ship with the energy to move out of its way. The stimulus is perceived by the helmsman and the response of the ship is achieved by the release of much larger amounts of energy. According to Fitting's definition the perception of the light stimulus must necessarily be through the living protoplasm of the helmsman, although this is not entirely true because the helmsman can very well be replaced by a photoelectric cell. (A similar example has been given by Loeb [1918] in his "heliotropic machine.")

However, it must be made clear that the responses of plants to auxin are by no means typical stimulus responses. Let us take as example the effect of light in causing phototropism. It was at first believed that the light acted by releasing the stored-up "bending tendency" in the plant. Blaauw and Fröschel's "Reizmengengesetz" dealt a serious blow to this concept by establishing a quantitative relation between the amount of energy applied (intensity × time) and the amount of response. Not only this, but the curvature of an *Avena* coleoptile is, as we now know, principally due to the redistribution of auxin between the light and dark sides. This redistribution requires far less energy than is supplied by the light which causes it (Went, 1936). The ship is, in fact, being steered by the photoelectric cell itself. Thus one of the most typical properties of a stimulus, *i.e.* its action through the release of stored-up energy of the protoplasm, is here absent, and for phototropism, therefore, the stimulus concept is an unnecessary complication.

The relation between auxin and growth also has nothing in common with stimulation. We have seen in the foregoing chapters, especially in III *C* and III *D*, that a given amount of auxin produces, if the conditions are constant, a given amount of growth, the curve of proportionality being a straight line within well-defined limits. Under other conditions, of course (as for instance at other temperatures), the proportionality factor will be different. Old coleoptiles do not give the same amount of growth for a given auxin application as do young ones (du Buy, 1936) but in these, of course, it is the conditions which are not comparable. Further, there is no evidence for any threshold in the response of young *Avena* coleoptiles to auxin; the curve of auxin applied against growth produced passes directly through the origin (Figure 19, p. 41). As a matter of fact, even in phototropism the significance of the threshold has been made doubtful by the measurements of Arisz (1915), who showed that its value depended on the method of detection of the minimum curvature. Thus the use of the microscope reduced the apparent threshold illumination from about 5 MCS to 1.4 MCS. A final blow to the stimulus concept of auxin action is dealt by the stoichiometric relations in the pea test, in which the activity of a number of substances, at the lower limit of response, approaches the same value per mole (VIII *G*). This, together with the linear proportionality just mentioned, means that the auxins enter into a definite stoichiometric reaction with some constituent of the cell. The concept of stimulus, and all that it implies, has therefore no useful bearing on auxin problems.

There remains the other possibility mentioned on pp. 229, 244, that of a master-reaction. According to this view auxin acts by taking part in some reaction in the cell, from which a chain of reactions leads to the observed response. The type of response then depends on the other factors, both internal and external, influencing the reaction-chain (Thimann, 1935*b*). Thus it was shown in V *B* that growth is controlled not only by auxin but also by another factor or group of factors; the most rapidly growing zone is that in which both are present in optimal concentrations. The auxin at the extreme tip of the coleoptile cannot cause growth because the other factors are limiting; the auxin at the extreme base of the coleoptile cannot cause growth because the cells can no longer respond to it. Root formation furnishes a still more striking example. Here, as shown in XI E, the formation of roots is dependent upon the cooperation of a number of factors. The concentration of auxin determines not only the number of roots formed, but also the cells which will form them. In general, the response in organ formation is localized. To explain this localization of the action Went (1936) has suggested that in addition to its master-reaction effect, auxin acts by affecting the transport of the other factors, so that they become accumulated at the point of highest auxin concentration. However this may be, it is clear that when the influence of the other factors is taken into account, the apparently mysterious action of the auxins in bringing about so many responses no longer seems so obscure. It is true that we do not yet know the nature of the fundamental master-reaction, but there is good reason to hope that it is within our reach.

G. Abnormal Growth

If internal or external factors affect growth, they must do it through the growth-controlling system we have discussed. In some cases this will be through their effects on auxin.

Numerous examples of this have been given. The effects of external factors, particularly radiation, are numerous, and a number of them have been analyzed in terms of auxin. In the case of visible light, these include phototropism (X E), auxin production (IV A), and sensitivity to auxin (X B); in the case of x-rays, their general inhibiting effect on growth has been explained (V F). Of the effects of internal factors, only one group has yet been considered to any extent, namely the genes. The genes set up a chain of internal reactions which terminate in the observed effect; but the last link in this chain, where genes affecting growth are concerned, is the effect on auxin. This has been partly analyzed in V E.

Many of the infections to which plants are susceptible

become incorporated in the plant to such an extent that they may be regarded as internal factors. There are a number of diseases in which growth correlations are destroyed or new ones established, and in these auxin must play a part. Thus, in "curly-top," one of the virus diseases, the growth of the shoot is greatly reduced, and Grieve (1936) has obtained evidence for a corresponding reduction in auxin content in the infected plant. Galls may be due to the opposite effect, namely production of growth hormones by the infective agent. Indeed, both Sachs (1882) and Beijerinck (1897) based their views on growth correlations partly on such pathological growths (cf. Figure 2). In a study of *Erineum* outgrowths on leaves (intumescences) La Rue (1935, 1936a) has shown that auxin will produce similar effects, while Brown and Gardner (1936) have shown the same thing for crown gall. In the case of root nodules there is good evidence that they are due to auxin produced by the infective agent, *Rhizobium leguminosarum* (see IX *C*). Comparable evidence for the production of auxin by the crown-gall organism has been given in XIII *C*. The galls due to gall-wasps (*Cynipidae*) and gall-midges (*Cecidomyidae*), which show elaborate differentiation, can probably not be considered in such simple terms.

Another suggestive observation for the interpretation of abnormal growth is that of Laibach and Mai (1936), who have described malformations of leaves and buds caused by repeated application of concentrated auxin pastes to the growing point.

H. Outlook

This survey of the rapidly developing field of phytohormones shows that many problems have been solved and few really important points are still subjects of disagreement. This result has not been achieved without effort. In the first place emphasis has been laid from the very beginning on quantitative work. In the second place the development of the chemistry has made it possible to check all findings with pure substances. However, the recent increasing use of these substances in unphysiologically high concentrations constitutes a danger, because the results do not necessarily have any bearing on the functions of auxin in the normal plant. Lastly, until quite recently it has been customary to investigate as far as possible every point bearing on a theory before the theory was enunciated, so that most of the views reached were well-founded and could be used as basis for further work. In the last year or two this procedure has not been so rigidly adhered to; examples of generalizations without sufficient experimental foundation are furnished by the comparison between the action of ethylene and auxin discussed in XI C, by the theory of the rôle of acids in producing growth directly (VIII F), by the interpretation of experiments on the movement of auxin in the transpiration stream (VI D), and by the two-stream theory of inhibition by auxin (VI D, IX D). There is danger, in any rapidly developing field, of an accumulation of unclassified facts and unproven theories which makes further development much less certain. In the field of phytohormones this is particularly unjustifiable, because the experimental procedure is relatively simple and the equipment necessary is not too elaborate. If the criteria of high-class experimental work continue to be observed, then we may look forward in the next few years to the rapid solution of a great many of the interesting problems of growth and development.

BIBLIOGRAPHY

AGRICOLA, G. A., 1716. Neu und nie erhörter doch in der Natur und Vernunft wohlgegründeter Versuch der Universal-Vermehrung aller Bäume, Stauden und Blumen-Gewächse. Regensburg, 1716.

AMLONG, H. U., 1933. Untersuchungen über die Beziehungen zwischen geoelektrischen Effekt und Geotropismus. *Planta 21:* 211–250.

AMLONG, H. U., 1936. Der Einfluss des Wuchsstoffes auf die Wanddehnbarkeit der *Vicia-Faba-Wurzel. Ber. d. bot. Ges. 54:* 271–275.

AMLONG, H. U., 1936a. Zur Frage der Wuchsstoffwirkung auf das Wurzelwachstum. *Jahrb. wiss. Bot. 83:* 773–780.

ANDERSON, D. B., 1935. The structure of the walls of higher plants. *Bot. Rev. 1:* 52–76.

APPLEMAN, C. O., 1918. Special growth-promoting substances and correlation. *Science 48:* 319–320.

ARISZ, W. H., 1915. Untersuchungen über den Phototropismus. *Rec. trav. bot. néerl. 12:* 44–216.

AVERY JR., G. S., 1930. Comparative anatomy and morphology of embryos and seedlings of maize, oats, and wheat. *Bot. Gaz. 89:* 1–39.

AVERY JR., G. S., 1935. Differential distribution of a phytohormone in the developing leaf of *Nicotiana*, and its relation to polarized growth. *Bull.* Torrey Bot. Club *62:* 313–330.

AVERY JR., G. S. and P. R. BURKHOLDER, 1936. Polarized growth and cell studies on the *Avena* coleoptile, phytohormone test object. *Bull.* Torrey Bot. Club *63:* 1–15.

AVERY, G. S., P. R. BURKHOLDER, and H. B. CREIGHTON, 1937. Production and distribution of growth hormone in shoots of *Aesculus* and *Malus*, and its probable rôle in stimulating cambial activity. *Am. J. Bot. 24:* 51–58.

BABIČKA, J., 1934. Die Wuchsstoffe. *Beih. Bot. Centralbl. 52:* 449–484.

BAUGUESS, L. C., 1935. Plant responses to some indole derivatives. (Abstract). *Am. J. Bot. 22:* 910.

BAYLISS, W. M., 1927. Principles of general physiology. 4th Ed. London, 1927.

BAYLISS, W. M. and E. STARLING, 1904. The chemical regulation of the secretory process. *Proc. Roy. Soc. B 73:* 310–322.

BEIJERINCK, M. W., 1885. Die Galle von *Cecidomyia Poae* an *Poa nemoralis*. Entstehung normaler Wurzeln in Folge der Wirkung eines Gallenthieres. *Bot. Zeit. 43:* 306–315, 320–331.

BEIJERINCK, M. W., 1886. Beobachtungen und Betrachtungen über Nebenwurzeln. *Verz. Geschr.* II: 7–122.

BEIJERINCK, M. W., 1888. Über das *Cecidium* von *Nematus Capreae* auf *Salix amygdalina. Bot. Zeit. 46:* 1–11, 17–27.

BEIJERINCK, M. W., 1897. Sur la cécidiogénèse et la génération alternante chez le *Cynips calicia. Verz. Geschr.* III: 199–232.

BEYER, A., 1925. Untersuchungen über den Traumatotropismus der Pflanzen. *Biol. Zentralbl. 45:* 683–702, 746–768.

BEYER, A., 1927. Zur Keimungsphysiologie von *Avena sativa. Ber. d. bot. Ges. 45:* 179–187.

BEYER, A., 1928. Experimentelle Studien zur Blaauwschen Theorie. II. *Planta 5:* 478–519.

BEYER, A., 1928a. Beiträge zum Problem der Reizleitung. *Z. f. bot. 20:* 321–417.

BEYER, A., 1932. Untersuchungen zur Theorie der pflanzlichen Tropismen. *Planta 18:* 509–524.

BLAAUW, A. H., 1909. Die Perzeption des Lichtes. *Rec. trav. bot. néerl. 5:* 209–372.

BLAAUW, A. H., 1914. Licht und Wachstum. I. *Z. f. Bot. 6:* 641–703.

BLAAUW, A. H., 1915. Licht und Wachstum. II. *Z. f. Bot. 7:* 465–532.

BLAAUW, A. H., 1918. Licht und Wachstum. III. *Med. Landbouwhoogeschool 15:* 89–204.

BLACKIE, J. J., R. J. D. GRAHAM, and L. B. STEWART, 1926. Propagation of camphor. *Kew Bulletin,* 380–381.

BLACKMAN, F. F., 1905. Optima and limiting factors. *Ann. Bot. 19:* 281–295.

BOAS, F. and F. MERKENSCHLAGER, 1925. Reizverlust, hervorgerufen durch Eosin. *Ber. d. bot. Ges. 43:* 381–390.

BONNER, J., 1932. The production of growth substance by *Rhizopus suinus. Biol. Zentralbl. 52:* 565–582.

BONNER, J., 1933. The action of the plant growth hormone. *J. gen. Physiol. 17:* 63–76.

BONNER, J., 1933a. Studies on the growth hormone of plants. IV. On the mechanism of the action. *Proc. Nat. Acad. Sc. 19:* 717–719.

BONNER, J., 1934. The relation of hydrogen ions to the growth rate of the *Avena* coleoptile. *Protoplasma 21:* 406–423.

BONNER, J., 1934a. Studies on the growth hormone of plants. V. The relation of cell elongation to cell wall formation. *Proc. Nat. Acad. Sc. 20:* 393–397.

BONNER, J., 1935. Zum Mechanismus der Zellstreckung auf Grund der Micellarlehre. *Jahrb. wiss. Bot. 82:* 377–412.

BONNER, J., 1936. Plant tissue cultures from a hormone point of view. *Proc. Nat. Acad. Sc. 22:* 426–430.

BONNER, J., 1936a. The growth and respiration of the *Avena* coleoptile. *J. gen. Physiol. 20:* 1–11.

BONNER, J. and K. V. THIMANN, 1935. Studies on the growth hormone of plants. VII. The fate of growth substance in the plant and the nature of the growth process. *J. gen. Physiol. 18:* 649–658.

BOSE, J. C., 1907. Comparative electro-physiology. London, 1907.

BOTTELIER, H. P., 1934. Über den Einfluss äusserer Faktoren auf die Protoplasmaströmung in der *Avena*-koleoptile. *Rec. trav. bot. néerl. 31:* 474–582.

BOTTELIER, H. P., 1935. Oxygen as limiting factor of the protoplasmic streaming in *Avena* coleoptiles of different ages. *Rec. trav. bot. néerl. 32:* 287–292.

BOUILLENNE, R. and F. W. WENT, 1933. Recherches expérimentales sur la néoformation des racines dans les plantules et les boutures des plantes supérieures. *Ann. Jard. bot. Buitenzorg 43:* 25–202.

BOYD, L. and G. S. AVERY JR., 1936. Grass seedling anatomy: the first internode of *Avena* and *Triticum*. *Bot. Gaz. 97:* 765–779.

BOYSEN JENSEN, P., 1910. Über die Leitung des phototropischen Reizes in *Avena*-keimpflanzen. *Ber. d. bot. Ges. 28:* 118–120.

BOYSEN JENSEN, P., 1911. La transmission de l'irritation phototropique dans l'*Avena*. *Bull. Acad. Roy.* Danmark 1911, No. 1: 3–24.

BOYSEN JENSEN, P., 1913. Über die Leitung des phototropischen Reizes in der *Avena*-koleoptile. *Ber. d. bot. Ges. 31:* 559–566.

BOYSEN JENSEN, P., 1928. Die phototropische Induktion in der Spitze der *Avena*-koleoptile. *Planta 5:* 464–477.

BOYSEN JENSEN, P., 1931. Über Wachstumsregulatoren bei Bakterien. *Biochem. Zeits. 236:* 205–210.

BOYSEN JENSEN, P., 1931a. Über Bildung eines Wachstumsregulators durch *Aspergillus niger*. *Biochem. Zeits. 239:* 244–249.

BOYSEN JENSEN, P., 1932. Über die Bildung und biologische Bedeutung des Wachstumsregulators bei *Aspergillus niger*. *Biochem. Zeits. 250:* 270–280.

BOYSEN JENSEN, P., 1933. Über die durch einseitige Lichtwirkung hervorgerufene transversale Leitung des Wuchsstoffes in der *Avena*-koleoptile. *Planta 19:* 335–344.

BOYSEN JENSEN, P., 1933a. Über den Nachweis von Wuchsstoff in Wurzeln. *Planta 19:* 345–350.

BOYSEN JENSEN, P., 1933b. Die Bedeutung des Wuchsstoffes für das Wachstum und die geotropische Krümmung der Wurzeln von *Vicia Faba. Planta 20:* 688–698.

BOYSEN JENSEN, P., 1934. Über Wuchsstoff in Wurzeln, die mit Erythrosin vergiftet sind. *Planta 22:* 404–410.

BOYSEN JENSEN, P., 1935. Die Wuchsstofftheorie und ihre Bedeutung für die Analyse des Wachstums und der Wachstumsbewegungen der Pflanzen. Jena, 1935.

BOYSEN JENSEN, P., 1936. Growth hormones in plants. Translated and revised by G. S. Avery Jr., and P. R. Burkholder. New York, 1936.

BOYSEN JENSEN, P., 1936a. Über die Verteilung des Wuchsstoffes in Keimstengeln und Wurzeln während der phototropischen und geotropischen Krümmung. *Kgl. Danske Videnskab. Selskab., Biol. Med. 13:* 1–31.

BOYSEN JENSEN, P. and N. NIELSEN, 1926. Studien über die hormonalen Beziehungen zwischen Spitze und Basis der *Avena*-koleoptile. *Planta 1:* 321–331.

BRAUNER, L., 1922. Lichtkrümmung und Lichtwachstumsreaktion. *Z. f. Bot. 14:* 497–547.

BRAUNER, L., 1924. Permeabilität und Phototropismus. *Z. f. Bot. 16:* 113–132.

BRAUNER, L., 1926. Über das geo-elektrische Phänomen. *Kolloidchem. Beihefte, Ambronn-Festschr., 23:* 143–152.

BRAUNER, L., 1927. Untersuchungen über das geoelektrische Phänomen. *Jahrb. wiss. Bot. 66:* 381–428.

BRAUNER, L., 1928. Untersuchungen über das geoelektrische Phänomen. II. Membranstruktur und geoelektrischer Effekt. *Jahrb. wiss. Bot. 68:* 711–770.

BRAUNER, L., 1935. Über den Einfluss des Lichtes auf die Wasserpermeabilität lebender Pflanzenzellen. *Rev. Fac. Sc. Univ. d'Istanbul 1:* 50–55.

BRAUNER, L. and H. U. AMLONG, 1933. Zur Theorie des geoelektrischen Effekts. *Protoplasma 20:* 279–292.

BRAUNER, L. and E. BÜNNING, 1930. Geoelektrischer Effekt und Elektrotropismus. *Ber. d. bot. Ges. 48:* 470–476.

BRECHT, F., 1936. Der Einfluss von Wuchsstoff- und Säurepasten auf das Wachstum von *Avena*- und *Helianthus*-keimlingen und seine Abhängigkeit vom Sauerstoffgehalt der Luft. *Jahrb. wiss. Bot. 82:* 581–612.

BROWN, N. A. and F. E. GARDNER, 1936. Galls produced by plant hormones, including a hormone extracted from *Bacterium tumefaciens. Phytopath. 26:* 708–713.

BUDER, J., 1920. Neue phototropische Fundamentalversuche. *Ber. d. bot. Ges. 38:* 10–19.

BUCK, L., 1935. Dehnungsversuche an pflanzlichen Membranen. *Beih. Bot. Centralbl. 53:* 340–377.

BÜNNING, E., 1927. Untersuchungen über traumatische Reizung von Pflanzen, *Z. f. Bot. 19:* 433–476.

BÜNNING, E., 1928. Zur Physiologie des Wachstums und der Reizbewegungen der Wurzeln. *Planta 5:* 635–659.

BÜNNING, E., 1934. Wachstum und Stickstoffassimilation bei *Aspergillus niger* unter dem Einfluss von Wachstumsregulatoren und von Vitamin B. *Ber. d. bot. Ges. 52:* 423–444.

BURKHARDT, H., 1926. Untersuchung über die Gültigkeit des Reizmengengesetzes für die Lichtkrümmung der *Avena*-koleoptile. *Z. f. Bot. 18:* 273–317.

BURKOM, J. H. VAN, 1913. Het verband tusschen den bladstand en de verdeeling van de groeisnelheid over den stengel. Diss. Utrecht, 1–188.

BÜSGEN, M. and E. MÜNCH, 1929. Structure and life of forest trees. Trans. by T. Thomson. New York, Wiley.

BUTENANDT, A., 1935. Über die stoffliche Charakterisierung der Keimdrüsenhormone: ihre Konstitutionsermittlung und künstlicne Herstellung. *Deutsche Med. Wochenschrift* 781.

BUTENANDT, A., 1936. Ergebnisse und Probleme in der biochemischen Erforschung der Keimdrüsenhormone. *Naturwissensch. 24:* 529–536 and 545–552.

BUY, H. G. DU, 1931. Über die Bedingungen, welche die Wuchsstoffproduktion beeinflussen. *Proc. Kon. Akad. Wetensch.* Amsterdam *34:* 277–288.

BUY, H. G. DU, 1933. Über Wachstum und Phototropismus von *Avena sativa. Rec. trav. bot. néerl. 30:* 798–925.

BUY, H. G. DU, 1934. Der Phototropismus der *Avena* Koleoptile und die Lichtabfallstheorie. *Ber. d. bot. Ges. 52:* 531–559.

BUY, H. G. DU, 1936. The change in the response of *Avena* coleoptiles to growth regulators produced by aging. *Proc. Nat. Acad. Sc. 22:* 272–275.

BUY, H. G. DU and E. NUERNBERGK, 1929. Über das Wachstum der Koleoptile und des Mesokotyls von *Avena sativa* unter verschiedenen Aussenbedingungen. *Proc. Kon. Akad. Wetensch.* Amsterdam *32:* 614–624.

BUY, H. G. DU and E. NUERNBERGK, 1929a. Weitere Untersuchungen über den Einfluss des Lichtes auf das Wachstum von Koleoptile und Mesokotyl bei *Avena sativa.* II. *Proc. Kon. Akad. Wetensch.* Amsterdam *32:* 808–817.

BUY, H. G. DU and E. NUERNBERGK, 1930. Über das Wachstum der Koleoptile und des Mesokotyls von *Avena sativa* unter verschiedenen Bedingungen (III). *Proc. Kon. Akad. Wetensch.* Amsterdam *33:* 542–556.

BUY, H. G. DU and E. NUERNBERGK, 1932. Phototropismus und Wachstum der Pflanzen. *Ergeb. Biol. 9:* 358–544.

BUY, H. G. DU and E. NUERNBERGK, 1934. Phototropismus und Wachstum der Pflanzen. II. *Ergeb. Biol. 10:* 207–322.

BUY, H. G. DU and E. NUERNBERGK, 1935. Phototropismus und Wachstum der Pflanzen. III. *Ergeb. Biol. 12:* 325–543.

CARLSON, M. C., 1929. Microchemical studies of rooting and non-rooting rose cuttings. *Bot. Gaz. 87:* 64–80.

CASTLE, E. S., 1930. Phototropism and the light-sensitive system of *Phycomyces. J. gen. Physiol. 13:* 421–435.

CASTLE, E. S., 1935. Photic excitation and phototropism in single plant cells. *Cold Spring Harbor Symposia 3:* 224–229.

CHILD, C. M. and A. W. BELLAMY, 1920. Physiological isolation by low temperature in *Bryophyllum. Bot. Gaz. 70:* 249–267.

CHOLODNY, N., 1918. Über den Einfluss der Metallionen auf die Reizerscheinungen bei den Pflanzen. *Schriften d. Univers. Kiew* 1918: 1–33.

CHOLODNY, N., 1924. Über die hormonale Wirkung der Organspitze bei der geotropischen Krümmung. *Ber. d. bot. Ges. 42:* 356–362.

CHOLODNY, N., 1926. Beiträge zur Analyse der geotropischen Reaktion. *Jahrb. wiss. Bot. 65:* 447–459.

CHOLODNY, N., 1927. Wuchshormone und Tropismen bei den Pflanzen. *Biol. Zentralbl. 47:* 604–626.

CHOLODNY, N., 1928. Beiträge zur hormonalen Theorie von Tropismen. *Planta 6:* 118–134.

CHOLODNY, N., 1929. Einige Bemerkungen zum Problem der Tropismen. *Planta 7:* 461–481.

CHOLODNY, N., 1929a. Über das Wachstum des vertikal und horizontal orientierten Stengels in Zusammenhang mit der Frage nach der hormonalen Natur der Tropismen. *Planta 7:* 702–719.

CHOLODNY, N., 1930. Mikropotometrische Untersuchungen über das Wachstum und die Tropismen der Koleoptile von *Avena sativa. Jahrb. wiss. Bot. 73:* 720–758.

CHOLODNY, N., 1931. Verwundung, Wachstum und Tropismen. *Planta 13:* 665–694.

CHOLODNY, N., 1931a. Zur Physiologie des pflanzlichen Wuchshormons. *Planta 14:* 207–216.

CHOLODNY, N., 1932. Ist die Wachstumsgeschwindigkeit der Wurzel von deren Lage abhängig? *Planta 17:* 794–800.

CHOLODNY, N., 1932a. Lichtwachstumsreaktion und Phototropismus. II. *Ber. d. bot. Ges. 50:* 317–320.

CHOLODNY, N., 1933. Zum Problem der Bildung und physiologischen Wirkung des Wuchshormons bei den Wurzeln. *Ber. d. bot. Ges. 51:* 85–98.

CHOLODNY, N., 1933a. Beiträge zur Kritik der Blaauwschen Theorie des Phototropismus. *Planta 20:* 549–576.

CHOLODNY, N., 1934. Über die Bildung und Leitung des Wuchshormons bei den Wurzeln. *Planta 21:* 517–530.

CHOLODNY, N., 1935. Über das Keimungshormon von Gramineen. *Planta 23:* 289–312.

CHOLODNY, N. G., 1935a. Investigations on the growth hormone of plants in U.S.S.R. *Herbage Rev. 3:* 210–214.

CLARK, W. G., 1935. Note on the effect of light on the bioelectric potentials in the *Avena* coleoptile. *Proc. Nat. Acad. Sc. 21:* 681–684.

COOPER, W. C., 1935. Hormones in relation to root formation on stem cuttings. *Plant Physiol. 10:* 789–794.

COOPER, W. C., 1936. Transport of root-forming hormone in woody cuttings. *Plant Physiol. 11:* 779–793.

COSTER, C., 1927, 1928. Zur Anatomie und Physiologie der Zuwachszonen und Jahresringbildung in den Tropen. *Ann. Jard. Bot. Buitenzorg 37:* 49–160; *38:* 1–114.

CROCKER, W., P. W. ZIMMERMAN, and A. E. HITCHCOCK, 1932. Ethylene-induced epinasty of leaves and the relation of gravity to it. *Contrib. Boyce Thompson Inst. 4:* 177–218.

CROCKER, W., A. E. HITCHCOCK, and P. W. ZIMMERMAN, 1935. Similarities in the effects of ethylene and the plant auxins. *Contrib. Boyce Thompson Inst. 7:* 231–248.

CURTIS, O. F., 1918. Stimulation of root growth in cuttings by treatment with chemical compounds. *Cornell Univ. Agr. Expt. Sta. Mem. 14.*

CZAJA, A. TH., 1931. Der Einfluss von Korrelationen auf Restitution und Polarität von Wurzel- und Sprossstecklingen. *Ber. d. bot. Ges. 49:* (67)–(71).

CZAJA, A. TH., 1934. Der Nachweis des Wuchsstoffes bei Holzpflanzen. *Ber. d. bot. Ges. 52:* 267–271.

CZAJA, A. TH., 1935. Polarität und Wuchsstoff. *Ber. d. bot. Ges. 53:* 197–220.

CZAJA, A. TH., 1935a. Wurzelwachstum, Wuchsstoff und die Theorie der Wuchsstoffwirkung. *Ber. d. bot. Ges. 53:* 221–245.

CZAJA, A. TH., 1935b. Die Wirkung des Wuchsstoffes in parallelotropen Pflanzenorganen (Eine Entgegnung). *Ber. d. bot. Ges. 53:* 478–490.

CZAPEK, F., 1902. Stoffwechselprocesse in der geotropisch gereizten Wurzelspitze und in phototropisch sensiblen Organen. *Ber. d. bot. Ges. 20:* 464–470.

DARWIN, C., 1880. The power of movement in plants. London, 1880.

DELISLE, A. F., 1937. The influence of auxin on secondary branching in two species of Aster. *Am. J. Bot. 24:* 159–167.

DENHAM, W. S. and T. LONSDALE, 1928. Testing instruments for yarns and fibres. *J. Sci. Instr. 5:* 348–354.

DENNY, F. E., 1926. Effect of thiourea upon bud inhibition and apical dominance of potato. *Bot. Gaz. 81:* 297–311.

DIJKMAN, M. J., 1933. A quantitative analysis of the geotropical curvature in Dicotyledons. *Proc. Kon. Akad. Wetensch.* Amsterdam *36:* 749–758.

DIJKMAN, M. J., 1934. Wuchsstoff und geotropische Krümmung bei *Lupinus. Rec. trav. bot. néerl. 31:* 391–450.

DILLEWIJN, C. VAN, 1927. Die Lichtwachstumsreaktionen von *Avena. Rec. trav. bot. néerl. 24:* 307–581.

DOLK, H. E., 1926. Concerning the sensibility of decapitated coleoptiles of *Avena sativa* for light and gravitation. *Proc. Kon. Akad. Wetensch.* Amsterdam *29:* 1113–1117.

DOLK, H. E., 1929. Über die Wirkung der Schwerkraft auf Koleoptilen von *Avena sativa. Proc. Kon. Akad. Wetensch.* Amsterdam *32:* 40–47.

DOLK, H. E., 1929a. Über die Wirkung der Schwerkraft auf Koleoptilen von *Avena sativa.* II. *Proc. Kon. Akad. Wetensch.* Amsterdam *32:* 1127–1140.

DOLK, H. E., 1930. Geotropie en groeistof. Diss. Utrecht, 1930. English translation in *Rec. trav. bot. néerl. 33:* 509–585, 1936.

DOLK, H. E. and K. V. THIMANN, 1932. Studies on the growth hormone of plants. I. *Proc. Nat. Acad. Sc. 18:* 30–46.

DOLLFUS, H., 1936. Wuchsstoffstudien. *Planta 25:* 1–21.

DOSTÁL, R., 1926. Über die wachstumsregulierende Wirkung des Laubblattes. *Acta Soc. Sci. Nat. Moravicae 3:* 83–209.

DUGGAR, B. M., 1936. Biological effects of radiation. New York, 1936. 1343 pp.

DUHAMEL DU MONCEAU, 1758. La Physique des arbres. Paris, 1758.

DUYFJES, H. G. P., 1935. Het probleem der actieve immunisatie van planten tegen *Pseudomonas tumefaciens* Smith en Town. Diss. Utrecht, 1935. 100 pp.

EASTCOTT, E. V., 1928. Wildiers' Bios. The isolation and identification of "Bios I." *J. physical Chem. 32:* 1094–1111.

ERRERA, L., 1904. Conflits de préséance et excitations inhibitoires chez les végétaux. *Bull. Soc. Roy. Bot. Belgique 42:* 27.

ERXLEBEN, H., 1935. Über die Chemie und Physiologie der Auxine. *Ergeb. Physiol. exp. Pharm. 37:* 186–209.

EWART, A. J. and J. S. BAYLISS, 1906. On the nature of the galvanotropic irritability of roots. *Proc. Roy. Soc. B 77:* 63–66.

FABER, E. R., 1936. Wuchsstoffversuche an Keimwurzeln. *Jahrb. wiss. Bot. 83:* 439–469.

FIEDLER, H., 1936. Entwicklungs- und reiz-physiologische Untersuchungen an Kulturen isolierter Wurzelspitzen. *Z. f. Bot. 30:* 385–436.

FIESER, L. F., 1936. The chemistry of natural products related to phenanthrene. *A.C.S. Monograph*, New York, 1936.

FISCHER, F. G., E. WEHMEIER, H. LEHMANN, L. JÜHLING, and K. HULTZSCH, 1935. Zur Kenntnis der Induktionsmittel in der Embryonal-Entwicklung. *Ber. d. chem. Ges. 68:* 1196–1199.

FISCHNICH, O., 1935. Über den Einfluss von β-indolylessigsäure auf die Blattbewegungen und die Adventivwurzelbildung von *Coleus*. *Planta 24:* 552–583.

FITTING, H., 1907. Die Leitung tropistischer Reize in parallelotropen Pflanzenteilen. *Jahrb. wiss. Bot. 44:* 177–253.

FITTING, H., 1909. Die Beeinflussung der Orchideenblüten durch die Bestäubung und durch andere Umstände. *Z. f. Bot. 1:* 1–86.

FITTING, H., 1910. Weitere entwicklungsphysiologische Untersuchungen an Orchideenblüten. *Z. f. Bot. 2:* 225–267.

FITTING, H., 1927. Untersuchungen über Chemodinese bei *Vallisneria*. *Jahrb. wiss. Bot. 67:* 427–596.

FITTING, H., 1929. Über die Auslösung von Plasmaströmung durch optisch-aktive Aminosäuren. *Jahrb. wiss. Bot. 70:* 1–25.

FITTING, H., 1930. Untersuchungen über endogene Chemonastie bei *Mimosa pudica. Jahrb. wiss. Bot. 72:* 700–775.

FITTING, H., 1932. Untersuchungen über die Empfindlichkeit und das Unterscheidungsvermögen der *Vallisneria*-protoplasten für verschiedene α-Aminosäuren. *Jahrb. wiss. Bot. 77:* 1–103.

FITTING, H., 1933. Untersuchungen über den Plasmaströmung auslösenden Reizstoff in den Blattextrakten von *Vallisneria. Jahrb. wiss. Bot. 78:* 319–398.

FITTING, H., 1936. Die Hormone als physiologische Reizstoffe. *Biol. Zentralbl. 56:* 69–86.

FITTING, H., 1936a. Untersuchungen über die chemischen Eigenschaften des Reizstoffes von *Mimosa pudica. Jahrb. wiss. Bot. 83:* 270–314.

FITTING, H., 1936b. Über Auslösung von Protoplasmaströmung bei *Vallisneria* durch einige Histidinverbindungen. *Jahrb. wiss. Bot. 82:* 613–624.

FLIRY, M., 1932. Zur Wirkung der Endknospe auf die Hypokotylstreckung des Dikotylenkeimlings. *Jahrb. wiss. Bot. 77:* 150–184.

FREY-WYSSLING, A., 1935. Die Stoffausscheidung der höheren Pflanzen. *Monogr. ges. Physiol. Pflanzen Tiere 32:* 378 pp. Berlin, Springer.

FREY-WYSSLING, A., 1936. Der Aufbau der pflanzlichen Zellwände. *Protoplasma 25:* 261–300.

FRIEBER, W., 1921. Beiträge zur Frage der Indolbildung und der Indolreaktionen sowie zur Kenntniss des Verhaltens indolnegativer Bakterien. *Zentralbl. f. Bakt., I Abt. 87:* 254–277.

FRIEDRICH, G., 1936. Untersuchungen über die Wirkung des natürlichen Wuchsstoffes und der β-Indolyl-Essigsäure auf den Stoffwechsel der Pflanze. *Planta 25:* 607–647.

GARBARINI, G., 1909. Reinigung von Äther (abstract). *Chem. Zentralbl. 80:* 1126.

GAUTHERET, R. J., 1934. Culture du tissu cambial. *Compt. rend. Acad. Sci. 198:* 2195.

GAUTHERET, R. J., 1935. Recherches sur la culture des tissus végétaux. *Thèse.* Paris.

GILL, N., 1933. The relation of flowering and cambial activity. *New Phytol. 32:* 1–12.

GLOVER, J., 1936. Skatole as a growth-promoting substance. *Nature 137:* 320–321.

GOEBEL, K., 1903. Regeneration in plants. *Bull. Torrey Bot. Club 30:* 197–205.

GOEBEL, K., 1905. Allgemeine Regenerationsprobleme. *Flora 95:* 384–411.

GOEBEL, K., 1908. Einleitung in die experimentelle Morphologie der Pflanzen. Leipzig, 1908.

GOODWIN, R. H., 1937. The role of auxin in leaf development in *Solidago* species. *Am. J. Bot. 24:* 43–51.

GORTER, C. J., 1927. On the occurrence of growth-accelerating and growth-retarding substances. *Proc. Kon. Akad. Wetensch.* Amsterdam *30:* 728–733.

GORTER, C. J., 1932. Groeistofproblemen bij Wortels. Diss. Utrecht, 1932.

GOUWENTAK, C. A. and G. HELLINGA, 1935. Beobachtungen über Wurzelbildung. *Med. Landbouwhoogeschool Wageningen 39:* 1–6.

GRADMANN, H., 1925. Untersuchungen über geotropische Reizstoffe. *Jahrb. wiss. Bot. 64:* 201–248.

GRADMANN, H., 1928. Die Lateralwirkung bei den Windepflanzen. *Jahrb. wiss. Bot. 68:* 46–78.

GRAHAM, R. J. D., 1934. The work of Laurence Baxter Stewart. *Trans. Bot. Soc. Edin. 31:* 450–459.

GRAHAM, R. J. D., 1936. Laurence Baxter Stewart's methods of vegetative propagation at Edinburgh. *Sci. Hort. 4:* 97–113.

GRAHAM, R. J. D. and L. B. STEWART, 1931. Special methods of practical utility in vegetative propagation of plants. *Proc. XIth Int. Horticultural Congress, 1930,* 159–164.

GRAZE, H. and G. SCHLENKER, 1936. Versuche zur Klärung der reziproken Verschiedenheiten von *Epilobium*-Bastarden. III. Vergleichende Untersuchungen über den Wuchsstoffgehalt bei verschiedenen Biotypen von *Epilobium hirsutum. Jahrb. wiss. Bot. 82:* 687–695.

GREGORY, F. G., 1928. Studies in the energy relations of plants. II. The effect of temperature on increase in area of leaf surface and in dry weight of *Cucumis sativus. Ann. Bot. 42:* 469–507.

GRIEVE, B. J., 1936. Spotted Wilt virus and the hormone heteroauxin. *Nature 138:* 128.

GUNDEL, W., 1933. Chemische und physikalisch-chemische Vorgänge bei geischer Induktion. *Jahrb. wiss. Bot. 78:* 623–664.

GUTTENBERG, H. VON, 1913. Über akropetale heliotropische Reizleitung. *Jahrb. wiss. Bot. 52:* 333–350.

GUTTENBERG, H. VON, 1933. Reizperzeption und Wuchsstoffwirkung. *Planta 20:* 230–232.

GUTTENBERG, H. VON, 1932, 1933, 1934, 1935, 1936. Wachstum und Bewegung. in: *Fortschritte der Botanik* I, II, III, IV, V. Berlin, 1932, 1933, 1934, 1935, 1936.

HAAGEN SMIT, A. J., 1935. Over auxinen. *Chem. Weekblad 32:* 398–403.

HAAGEN SMIT, A. J. and F. W. WENT, 1935. A physiological analysis of the growth substance. *Proc. Kon. Akad. Wetensch.* Amsterdam *38:* 852–857.

HAAN, I. DE and L. PETRICK, 1935. Polaire wortelvorming. *Natuurw. Tijdsch. 17:* 117–127.

HAAS, R. HORREUS DE, 1929. On the connection between the geotropic curving and elasticity of the cell-wall. *Proc. Kon. Akad. Wetensch.* Amsterdam *32:* 371–373.

HABERLANDT, G., 1913. Zur Physiologie der Zellteilung. *Sitz. ber. k. preuss. Akad. Wiss.* 1913: 318–345.

HABERLANDT, G., 1914. Zur Physiologie der Zellteilung. *Sitz. ber. k. preuss. Akad. Wiss.* 1914: 1096–1111.

HABERLANDT, G., 1921. Wundhormone als Erreger von Zellteilungen. *Beitr. allg. Bot. 2:* 1–53.

HAGEMANN, A., 1932. Untersuchungen an Blattstecklingen. *Gartenbauwiss. 6:* 69–195.

HAIG, C., 1935. The phototropic responses of *Avena* in relation to intensity and wave-length. *Biol. Bull. 69:* 305–324.

HÄMMERLING, J., 1934. Über formbildende Substanzen bei *Acetabularia mediterranea*, ihre räumliche und zeitliche Verteilung und ihre Herkunft. *Arch. Entwicklungsmech. 131:* 1–81.

HÄMMERLING, J., 1935. Über Genomwirkungen und Formbildungsfähigkeit bei Acetabularia. *Arch. Entwicklungsmech. 132:* 424–462.

HÄMMERLING, J., 1936. Studien zum Polaritätsproblem. I–III. *Zool. Jahrb. 56:* 440–486.

HANSTEIN, J., 1860. Versuche über die Leitung des Saftes durch die Rinde und Folgerungen daraus. *Jahrb. wiss. Bot. 2:* 392–467.

HARDER, R. and I. STÖRMER, 1934. Über den Einfluss des Follikelhormons auf das Blühen von Pflanzen. *Jahrb. wiss. Bot. 80:* 1–19.

HARTMANN, H., 1931. Reaktionen von Koleoptilen und Wurzeln im elektrischen Feld. *Beitr. Biol. Pfl. 19:* 287–333.

HARVEY, E. N., 1920. An experiment on regulation in plants. *Amer. Nat. 54:* 362–367.

HAWKER, L. E., 1932. Experiments on the perception of gravity by roots. *New Phytol. 31:* 321–328.

HEIDT, K., 1931. Über das Verhalten von Explantaten der Wurzelspitze in nährstofffreien Kulturen. *Arch. Exp. Zellforsch. 11:* 693–724.

HESS, K., C. TROGUS, and W. WERGIN, 1936. Untersuchungen über die Bildung der pflanzlichen Zellwand. *Planta 25:* 419–437.

HEYN, A. N. J., 1930. On the relation between growth and extensibility of the cell wall. *Proc. Kon. Akad. Wetensch.* Amsterdam *33:* 1045–1058.

HEYN, A. N. J., 1931. Further experiments on the mechanism of growth. *Proc. Kon. Akad. Wetensch.* Amsterdam *34:* 474–484.

HEYN, A. N. J., 1931a. Der Mechanismus der Zellstreckung. *Rec. trav. bot. néerl. 28:* 113–244.

HEYN, A. N. J., 1932. Recherches sur les relations de la plasticité des membranes cellulaires et la croissance des végétaux. *Compt. rend. Acad. Sci. 194:* 1848–1850.

HEYN, A. N. J., 1932a. Sur la methode de détermination de plasticité des membranes cellulaires. *Compt. rend. Acad. Sci. 195:* 494–496.

HEYN, A. N. J., 1933. Further investigations on the mechanism of cell elongation and the properties of the cell wall in connection with elongation. I. The load extension relationship. *Protoplasma 19:* 78–96.

HEYN, A. N. J., 1933a. X-ray investigations of the cellulose in the wall of young epidermic cells. *Proc. Kon. Akad. Wetensch.* Amsterdam *36:* 560–565.

HEYN, A. N. J., 1934. Die Plastizität der Zellmembran unter Einfluss von Wuchsstoff. *Proc. Kon. Akad. Wetensch.* Amsterdam *37:* 180–182.

HEYN, A. N. J., 1934a. Weitere Untersuchungen über den Mechanismus der Zellstreckung und die Eigenschaften der Zellmembran. II. Das Röntgendiagramm von jungen wachsenden Zellwänden und parenchymatischen Geweben. *Protoplasma 21:* 299–305.

HEYN, A. N. J., 1934b. Weitere Untersuchungen über den Mechanismus der Zellstreckung und die Eigenschaften der Zellmembran. III. Die Änderungen der Plastizität der Zellwand bei verschiedenen Organen. *Jahrb. wiss. Bot. 79:* 753–789.

HEYN, A. N. J., 1935. The chemical nature of some growth hormones as determined by the diffusion method. *Proc. Kon. Akad. Wetensch.* Amsterdam *38:* 1074–1081.

HEYN, A. N. J., 1936. Auxine. *Handb. biol. Arbeitsmethoden 5:* 823–861.

HEYN, A. N. J. and J. VAN OVERBEEK, 1931. Weiteres Versuchsmaterial zur plastischen und elastischen Dehnbarkeit der Zellmembran. *Proc. Kon. Akad. Wetensch.* Amsterdam *34:* 1190–1195.

HINDERER, G., 1936. Versuche zur Klärung der reziproken Verschiedenheiten von Epilobium-Bastarden. II. Wuchsstoff und Wachstum bei reziprok verschiedenen Epilobium-Bastarden. *Jahrb. wiss. Bot. 82:* 669–686.

HITCHCOCK, A. E., 1935. Indole-3-n-propionic acid as a growth hormone and the quantitative measurement. *Contrib. Boyce Thompson Inst. 7:* 87–95.

HITCHCOCK, A. E., 1935a. Tobacco as a test plant for comparing the effectiveness of preparations containing growth substances. *Contrib. Boyce Thompson Inst. 7:* 349–364.

HITCHCOCK, A. E. and P. W. ZIMMERMAN, 1935. Absorption and movement of synthetic growth substances from soil as indicated by the responses of aerial parts. *Contrib. Boyce Thompson Inst. 7:* 447–476.

HITCHCOCK, A. E. and P. W. ZIMMERMAN, 1936. Effect of growth substances on the rooting response of cuttings. *Contrib. Boyce Thompson Inst. 8:* 63–79.

HOLTFRETER, J., 1935. Der Einfluss thermischer, mechanischer und chemischer Eingriffe auf die Induzierfähigkeit von Triton-Keimteilen. *Arch. Entwicklungsmech. 132:* 225–306.

HONERT, T. H. VAN DEN, 1932. On the mechanism of the transport of organic materials in plants. *Proc. Kon. Akad. Wetensch.* Amsterdam *35:* 1104–1111.

HONING, J. A., 1923. *Nicotiana deformis n. sp.* und die Enzymtheorie der Erblichkeit. *Genetica 5:* 455–476.

HUXLEY, J. S., 1935. Chemical regulation and the hormone concept. *Biol. Rev. 10:* 427–441.

JANSE, J. M., 1926. On new phenomena caused by irritation of roots. *Proc. Kon. Akad. Wetensch.* Amsterdam *29:* 834–842.

JOST, L., 1891. Über Dickenwachsthum und Jahresringbildung. *Bot. Zeit. 49:* 485–630.

JOST, L., 1893. Über Beziehungen zwischen der Blattentwicklung und der Gefässbildung in der Pflanze. *Bot. Zeit. 51:* 89–138.

JOST, L., 1935. Über Wuchsstoffe. *Z. f. Bot. 28:* 260–274.

JOST, L., 1935a. Wuchsstoff und Zellteilung, *Ber. d. bot. Ges. 53:* 733–750.

JOST, L. and E. REISS, 1936. Zur Physiologie der Wuchsstoffe. II. Einfluss des Heteroauxins auf Längen- und Dickenwachstum. *Z. f. Bot. 30:* 335–376.

JUEL, I., 1936. Über die Genauigkeit der Wuchsstoffbestimmungs-methode. *Planta 25:* 307–310.

KASTENS, E., 1924. Beiträge zur Kenntnis der Funktion der Siebröhren. *Mitt. Inst. Allg. Bot.* Hamburg *6:* 33–70.

KATUNSKIJ, V. M., 1935. Growth promoting substance as a factor in the formation of plant organism. *Compt. rend. Acad. Sci. U.R.S.S. 1:* 665–667.

KEEBLE, F., 1910. Plant-Animals. *Camb. Univ. Press,* 163 pp.

KEEBLE, F. and M. G. NELSON, 1935. The integration of plant behaviour. V. Growth substance and traumatic curvature of the root. *Proc. Roy. Soc. B 117:* 92–119.

KEEBLE, F., M. G. NELSON, and R. SNOW, 1929. The Integration of Plant Behavior. I. Separate Geotropic Stimulations of Tip and Stump in Roots. *Proc. Roy. Soc. B 105:* 493–498.

KEEBLE, F., M. G. NELSON, and R. SNOW, 1930. A wound substance retarding growth in roots. *New Phytol. 29:* 289–293.

KEEBLE, F., M. G. NELSON, and R. SNOW, 1931. The Integration of Plant Behavior. III. The Effect of Gravity on the Growth of Roots. *Proc. Roy. Soc. B 108:* 360–365.

KEEBLE, F., M. G. NELSON, and R. SNOW, 1931a. Integration of Plant Behavior. IV. Geotropism and Growth-Substance. *Proc. Roy. Soc. B 108:* 537–545.

KISSER, J., 1931. Die stofflichen Grundlagen pflanzlicher Reizkrümmun-gen. *Verh. Zool. Bot. Ges. Wien. 81:* (34)–(38).

KOCH, K., 1934. Untersuchungen über den Quer- und Längstransport des Wuchsstoffes in Pflanzenorganen. *Planta 22:* 1–33.

KÖGL, F., 1932. Über die Chemie des Auxins, eines pflanzlichen Wuchs-stoffs. *Chem. Weekblad 29:* 317–318.

KÖGL, F., 1932a. Über die Chemie des Auxins und sein Vorkommen im Pflanzen- und Tierreich. *Forsch. und Fortschr. 8:* 409–410.

KÖGL, F., 1933. Über Auxine. *Z. Angew. Chem. 46:* 469–484.

KÖGL, F., 1933a. Die Chemie des Auxins und sein Vorkommen im Pflan-zen- und Tierreich. *Naturwiss. 21:* 17–21.

KÖGL, F., 1933b. On plant growth hormones (Auxin A and auxin B) *Rep. British Assoc.* 600–609.

KÖGL, F., 1933c. Chemische und physiologische Untersuchungen über Auxin, einen Wuchsstoff der Pflanzen. *Angew. Chemie 46:* 166–167.

KÖGL, F., 1935. Über Wuchsstoffe der Auxin- und der Bios-Gruppe. *Ber. d. chem. Ges. 68:* 16–28.

KÖGL, F., 1935a. Untersuchungen über pflanzliche Wuchsstoffe. *Naturwiss. 23:* 839–843.

KÖGL, F., 1936. Untersuchungen über pflanzliche Wuchsstoffe. *Proc. 6th Int. Bot. Congress. 1:* 97–107.

KÖGL, F., 1936a. Über pflanzliche Wuchshormone. *Svensk Kem. Tidskr. 48:* 145–155.

KÖGL, F. and H. ERXLEBEN, 1934. Über die Konstitution der Auxine *a* und *b.* X. Mitteilung über pflanzliche Wachstumsstoffe. *Z. physiol. Chem. 227:* 51–73.

KÖGL, F. and H. ERXLEBEN, 1935. Synthese der "Auxin-glutarsäure" und einiger Isomerer. XV. Mitteilung. *Z. physiol. Chem. 235:* 181–200.

KÖGL, F., H. ERXLEBEN, and A. J. HAAGEN SMIT, 1933. Über ein Phytohormon der Zellstreckung. Zur Chemie des krystallisierten Auxins. V. Mitteilung. *Z. physiol. Chem. 216:* 31–44.

KÖGL, F., H. ERXLEBEN, and A. J. HAAGEN SMIT, 1934. Über die Isolierung der Auxine a und b aus pflanzlichen Materialen. IX. Mitteilung. *Z. physiol. Chem. 225:* 215–229.

KÖGL, F. and A. J. HAAGEN SMIT, 1931. Über die Chemie des Wuchsstoffs. *Proc. Kon. Akad. Wetensch.* Amsterdam *34:* 1411–1416.

KÖGL, F. and A. J. HAAGEN SMIT, 1936. Biotin und Aneurin als Phytohormone. Ein Beitrag zur Physiologie der Keimung. XXIII. Mitteilung. *Z. physiol. Chem. 243:* 209–226.

KÖGL, F., A. J. HAAGEN SMIT, and H. ERXLEBEN, 1933. Über ein Phytohormon der Zellstreckung. Reindarstellung des Auxins aus menschlichem Harn. IV. Mitteilung. *Z. physiol. Chem. 214:* 241–261.

KÖGL, F., A. J. HAAGEN SMIT, and H. ERXLEBEN, 1933a. Studien über das Vorkommen von Auxinen im menschlichen und im tierischen Organismus. VII. Mitteilung. *Z. physiol. Chem. 220:* 137–161.

KÖGL, F., A. J. HAAGEN SMIT, and H. ERXLEBEN, 1934. Über ein neues Auxin ("Heteroauxin") aus Harn. XI. Mitteilung. *Z. physiol. Chem. 228:* 90–103.

KÖGL, F., A. J. HAAGEN SMIT, and H. ERXLEBEN, 1934a. Über den Einfluss der Auxine auf das Wurzelwachstum und über die chemische Natur des Auxins der Graskoleoptilen. XII. Mitteilung. *Z. physiol. Chem. 228:* 104–112.

KÖGL, F., A. J. HAAGEN SMIT, and C. J. VAN HULSSEN, 1936. Über den Einfluss unbekannter äusserer Faktoren bei Versuchen mit *Avena sativa.* XIX. Mitteilung. *Z. physiol. Chem. 241:* 17–33.

KÖGL, F., A. J. HAAGEN SMIT, and B. TÖNNIS, 1933. Über das Vorkommen von Auxinen und von Wachstumsstoffen der "Bios"-Gruppe in Carcinomen. VIII. Mitteilung. *Z. physiol. Chem. 220:* 162–172.

Kögl, F. and D. G. F. R. Kostermans, 1934. Hetero-auxin als Stoffwechselprodukt niederer pflanzlicher Organismen. Isolierung aus Hefe. XIII. Mitteilung. *Z. physiol. Chem. 228:* 113–121.

Kögl, F. and D. G. F. R. Kostermans, 1935. Über die Konstitutions-Spezifität des Hetero-auxins. XVI. Mitteilung. *Z. physiol. Chem. 235:* 201–216.

Kögl, F. and B. Tönnis, 1936. Über das Bios-Problem. Darstellung von krystallisiertem Biotin aus Eigelb. *Z. physiol. Chem. 242:* 43–73.

Kok, A. C. A., 1931. Über den Einfluss der Plasmarotation auf den Stofftransport. *Proc. Kon. Akad. Wetensch.* Amsterdam *34:* 918–929.

Kok, A. C. A., 1932. Über den Transport von Kaffein und $LiNO_3$ durch parenchymatisches Gewebe. *Proc. Kon. Akad. Wetensch.* Amsterdam *35:* 241–250.

Koning, H. C., 1933. Het winden der slingerplanten. Diss. Utrecht, 1933.

Koningsberger, C., 1936. De auto-inactiveering der Auxinen. Diss. Utrecht, 1936.

Koningsberger, V. J., 1922. Tropismus und Wachstum. *Rec. trav. bot. néerl. 19:* 1–136.

Kornmann, P., 1935. Die Aufhebung der Wuchsstoffwirkung durch lebende Pflanzenteile. *Ber. d. bot. Ges. 53:* 523–527.

Kraus, E. J. and H. R. Kraybill, 1918. Vegetation and reproduction with special reference to the tomato. *Ore. Agr. Expt. Sta. Bull. 149.*

Kropp, B. and W. J. Crozier, 1934. The production of the crustacean chromatophore activator. *Proc. Nat. Acad. Sc. 20:* 453–456.

Kupfer, E., 1907. Studies in plant regeneration. *Mem. Torrey Bot. Club 12.*

Laan, P. A. van der, 1934. Der Einfluss von Aethylen auf die Wuchsstoffbildung bei *Avena* und *Vicia. Rec. trav. bot. néerl. 31:* 691–742.

Laibach, F., 1932. Interferometrische Untersuchungen an Pflanzen. II. Die Verwendbarkeit des Interferometers in der Pflanzenphysiologie. *Jahrb. wiss. Bot. 76:* 218–282.

Laibach, F., 1932a. Pollenhormon und Wuchsstoff. *Ber. d. bot. Ges. 50:* 383–390.

Laibach, F., 1933. Wuchsstoffversuche mit lebenden Orchideenpollinien. *Ber. d. bot. Ges. 51:* 336–340.

Laibach, F., 1933a. Versuche mit Wuchsstoffpaste. *Ber. d. bot. Ges. 51:* 386–392.

Laibach, F., 1934. Zum Wuchsstoffproblem. *Der Züchter 6:* 49–53.

Laibach, F., 1935. Über die Auslösung von Kallus- und Wurzelbildung durch β-Indolylessigsäure. *Ber. d. bot. Ges. 53:* 359–364.

LAIBACH, F. and O. FISCHNICH, 1935. Künstliche Wurzelneubildung mittels Wuchsstoffpaste. *Ber. d. bot. Ges. 53:* 528–539.

LAIBACH, F. and O. FISCHNICH, 1935a. Über eine Testmethode zur Prüfung der kallusbildenden Wirkung von Wuchsstoffpasten. *Ber. d. bot. Ges. 53:* 469–477.

LAIBACH, F. and O. FISCHNICH, 1936. Die Wuchsstoffleitung in der Pflanze. I. *Planta 25:* 648–659.

LAIBACH, F. and O. FISCHNICH, 1936a. Über Blattbewegungen unter dem Einfluss von künstlich zugeführtem Wuchsstoff. *Biol. Zentralbl. 56:* 62–68.

LAIBACH, F. and P. KORNMANN, 1933. Zur Methodik der Wuchsstoffversuche. *Planta 19:* 482–484.

LAIBACH, F. and P. KORNMANN, 1933a. Zur Frage des Wuchsstofftransportes in der Haferkoleoptile. *Planta 21:* 396–418.

LAIBACH, F. and G. MAI, 1936. Über die künstliche Erzeugung von Bildungsabweichungen bei Pflanzen. *Arch. Entwicklungsmech. 134:* 200–206.

LAIBACH, F., G. MAI, and A. MÜLLER, 1934. Über ein Zellteilungshormon. *Naturwiss. 22:* 288.

LAIBACH, F. and E. MASCHMANN, 1933. Über den Wuchsstoff der Orchideenpollinien. *Jahrb. wiss. Bot. 78:* 399–430.

LAIBACH, F. and F. MEYER, 1935. Über die Schwankungen des Auxingehaltes bei *Zea Mays* und *Helianthus annuus* im Verlauf der Ontogenese. *Senckenbergiana 17:* 73–86.

LAIBACH, F., A. MÜLLER, and W. SCHÄFER, 1934. Über wurzelbildende Stoffe. *Naturwiss. 22:* 588–589.

LAMPRECHT, W., 1918. Über die Kultur und transplantation kleiner Blattstücken. *Beitr. allg. Bot. 1:* 353–398.

LANE, R. H., 1936. The inhibition of roots by growth hormone. *Am. J. Bot. 23:* 532–535.

LANGE, S., 1927. Die Verteilung der Lichtempfindlichkeit in der Spitze der Haferkoleoptile. *Jahrb. wiss. Bot. 67:* 1–51.

LARSEN, P., 1936. Über einen wuchsstoffinaktivierenden Stoff aus Phaseolus-Keimpflanzen. *Planta 25:* 311–314.

LA RUE, C. D., 1933. Intumescences on poplar leaves. I and II. *Am. J. Bot. 20:* 1–17 and 159–175.

LA RUE, C. D., 1935. The rôle of auxin in the development of intumescences on poplar leaves; in the production of cell outgrowths in the tunnels of leaf-miners; in the leaf-fall in *Coleus. Am. J. Bot. 22:* 908.

LA RUE, C. D., 1936. Tissue cultures of spermatophytes. *Proc. Nat. Acad. Sc. 22:* 201–209.

LA RUE, C. D., 1936*a*. Intumescences on poplar leaves. III. The rôle of plant growth hormones in their production. *Am. J. Bot. 23:* 520–524.

LE FANU, B., 1936. Auxin and correlative inhibition. *New Phytol. 35:* 205–220.

LEHMANN, E., 1936. Versuche zur Klärung der reziproken Verschiedenheiten von Epilobium-Bastarden. I. Der Tatbestand und die Möglichkeit seiner Klärung durch differente Wuchsstoffbildung. *Jahrb. wiss. Bot. 82:* 657–668.

LEK, H. A. A. VAN DER, 1925. Over de wortelvorming van houtige stekken. (With summary: Root development in woody cuttings). Diss. Utrecht, 1925.

LEK, H. A. A. VAN DER, 1934. Over den invloed der knoppen op de wortelvorming der stekken. (With summary: On the influence of the buds on root-development in cuttings). *Meded. Landbouwhoogeschool Wageningen 38 (2):* 1–95.

LEONIAN, L. H., 1935. The effect of auxins upon *Phytophthora cactorum. J. Agr. Res. 51:* 277–286.

LESLIE, J. W. and M. M., 1928. The "wiry" tomato. *J. Hered. 19:* 337–344.

LEVINE, M., 1936. Plant tumors and their relation to cancer. *Bot. Rev. 2:* 439–455.

LI, T.-T., 1930. The appearance of the new physiological tip of the decapitated coleoptiles of *Avena sativa. Proc. Kon. Akad. Wetensch.* Amsterdam *33:* 1201–1205.

LI, T.-T., 1934. Phototropism of decapitated coleoptile of *Avena sativa. Rep. Nat. Tsinghua Univ. 2:* 1–10.

LOEB, J., 1915. Rules and mechanism of inhibitions and correlation in the regeneration of *Bryophyllum calycinum. Bot. Gaz. 60:* 249–276.

LOEB, J., 1917. Influence of the leaf upon root formation and geotropic curvature in the stem of *Bryophyllum calycinum* and the possibility of a hormone theory of these processes. *Bot. Gaz. 63:* 25–50.

LOEB, J., 1917*a*. The chemical basis of regeneration and geotropism. *Science 46:* 115–118.

LOEB, J., 1917*b*. The chemical basis of axial polarity in regeneration. *Science 46:* 547–551.

LOEB, J., 1918. Forced movements, tropisms, and animal conduct. Philadelphia, 1918.

LOEB, J., 1918a. Chemical basis of correlation. I. Production of equal masses of shoots by equal masses of sister leaves in *Bryophyllum calycinum*. *Bot. Gaz. 65:* 150–174.

LOEB, J., 1919. The physiological basis of morphological polarity in regeneration. I. *J. gen. Physiol. 1:* 337–362.

LOEB, J., 1923. Theory of regeneration based on mass action. *J. gen. Physiol. 5:* 831–852.

LOEB, J., 1924. Regeneration from a physicochemical viewpoint. New York, 1924.

LOEHWING, W. F. and L. C. BAUGUESS, 1936. Plant growth effects of hetero-auxin applied to soil and plants. *Science 84:* 46–47.

LOEWE, S., 1933. Analyse der Pflanzenhormone. *Handb. Pflanzenanalyse 4:* 1005–1041.

LUND, E. J., 1923. Electrical control of organic polarity in the eggs of *Fucus*. *Bot. Gaz. 76:* 288–301.

MACCALLUM, W. B., 1905. Regeneration in plants. I and II. *Bot. Gaz. 40:* 97–120 and 241–263.

MAI, G., 1934. Korrelationsuntersuchungen an entspreiteten Blattstielen mittels lebender Orchideenpollinien als Wuchsstoffquelle. *Jahrb. wiss. Bot. 79:* 681–713.

MALOWAN, S. L., 1934. Wuchsstoffe und Pflanzenwachstum. *Protoplasma 21:* 306–322.

MALPIGHI, M., 1675. Anatome Plantarum. (Die Anatomie der Pflanzen.) *Ostwald's Klassiker 120*. Leipzig, 1901.

MANGHAM, S., 1917. On the mechanism of translocation in plant tissues. An hypothesis, with special reference to sugar conduction in sieve-tubes. *Ann. Bot. 31:* 293–311.

MANSKE, R. H. F. and L. C. LEITCH, 1936. The synthesis of δ- (3-indolyl)-valeric acid and the effects of some indol acids in plants. *Can. J. Res. B 14:* 1–5.

MARESQUELLE, H. J., 1935. Défaut d'allongement et dépolarisation de la croissance dans les morphoses parasitaires. *Rev. gén. Bot. 47:* 129–143, 193–214, 273–293.

MASCHMANN, E., 1932. Der Wuchsstoff bösartiger Geschwülste. *Naturwiss. 20:* 721–722.

MASCHMANN, E. and F. LAIBACH, 1932. Über Wuchsstoffe. *Biochem. Z. 255:* 446–452.

MASCHMANN, E., and F. LAIBACH, 1933. Das Vorkommen von Wuchsstoff in tierischem und pflanzlichem Material. *Naturwiss. 21:* 517.

MEESTERS, A., 1936. The influence of heteroauxin on the growth of root hairs and roots of *Agrostemma Githago L. Proc. Kon. Akad. Wetensch.* Amsterdam *39:* 91–97.

MEISSNER, K. W., 1932. Interferometrische Untersuchungen an Pflanzen. I. Über ein handliches Präzisions- Instrument zur Messung von Dimensionsänderungen auf Grund des interferometrischen Messprinzips. *Jahrb. wiss. Bot. 76:* 208–217.

METZNER, P., 1928. Das Mikroskop. Leipzig, 1928.

METZNER, P., 1934. Zur Kenntnis der Stoffwechseländerungen bei geotropisch gereizten Keimpflanzen. *Ber. d. bot. Ges. 52:* 506–522.

MEYER, F., 1936. Über die Verteilung des Wuchsstoffes in der Pflanze während ihrer Entwicklung. Diss. Frankfurt, 1936.

MICHENER, H. D., 1935. Effects of ethylene on plant growth hormone. *Science 82:* 551.

MOISSEJEWA, M., 1928. (Zur Frage nach den Wuchshormonen des Getreides.) Visnik, Kiivsk Bot. *(Bull. Jard. Bot. Kieff),* 7/8: 1–16 (Ukrainian with German summary).

MOLISCH, H., 1935. Das knospenlose Internodium als Steckling behandelt. *Ber. d. bot. Ges. 53:* 575–586.

MORELAND, C. F., 1934. Factors affecting the development of the cotyledonary buds of the common bean, *Phaseolus vulgaris. Cornell Univ. Agr. Expt. Sta. Mem. 167:* 3–28.

MORGAN, T. H., 1906. The physiology of regeneration. *J. exp. Zool. 3:* 457–500.

MÜLLER, A. M., 1935. Über den Einfluss von Wuchsstoff auf das Austreiben der Seitenknospen und auf die Wurzelbildung. *Jahrb. wiss. Bot. 81:* 497–540.

NAGAO, M., 1936. Studies on the growth hormones of plants. I. The production of growth substance in root tips. *Rep. Tohoku Imp. Univ. 10:* 721–731.

NAVEZ, A. E., 1927. "Galvanotropism" of roots. *J. gen. Physiol. 10:* 551–558.

NAVEZ, A. E., 1929. Respiration and geotropism in *Vicia Faba. J. gen. Physiol. 12:* 641–667.

NAVEZ, A. E., 1933. Geo-growth reaction of roots of lupinus. *Bot. Gaz. 94:* 616–618.

NAVEZ, A. E., 1933. "Growth-promoting substance" and elongation of roots. *J. gen. Physiol. 16:* 733–739.

NAVEZ, A. E., 1933a. Growth-promoting substance and illumination. *Proc. Nat. Acad. Sc. 19:* 636–638.

NAVEZ, A. E. and B. KROPP, 1934. The growth-promoting action of crustacean eye-stalk extract. *Biol. Bull. 67:* 250–258.

NAVEZ, A. E. and T. W. ROBINSON, 1933. Geotropic curvature of *Avena* coleoptiles. *J. gen. Physiol. 16:* 133–145.

NĚMEC, B., 1930. Bakterielle Wuchsstoffe. *Ber. d. bot. Ges. 48:* 72–74.

NĚMEC, B., 1934. Ernährung, Organogene und Regeneration. *Věst. Král. Čes. Spol. Nauk. Ir.* II: 1–34.

NIELSEN, N., 1924. Studies on the transmission of stimuli in the coleoptile of *Avena. Dansk. Bot. Arkiv. 4* (8).

NIELSEN, N., 1928. Untersuchungen über Stoffe, die das Wachstum der Avenacoleoptile beschleunigen. *Planta 6:* 376–378.

NIELSEN, N., 1930. Untersuchungen über einen neuen wachstumsregulierenden Stoff: Rhizopin. *Jahrb. wiss. Bot. 73:* 125–191.

NIELSEN, N., 1931. Über Wuchsstoffe der Hefe. *Biochem. Z. 237:* 244–246.

NIELSEN, N., 1931a. The effect of rhizopin on the production of matter of *Aspergillus niger. Compt. Rend. Lab. Carlsberg 19* (5): 1–10.

NIELSEN, N., 1932. Über das Vorkommen von Wuchsstoff bei *Boletus edulis. Biochem. Z. 249:* 196–198.

NIELSEN, N. and V. HARTELIUS, 1932. The separation of growth-promoting substances. *Compt. Rend. Lab. Carlsberg 19* (8): 1–17.

NUERNBERGK, E., 1932. Physikalische Methoden der pflanzlichen Lichtphysiologie. *Handb. biol. Arbeitsmethoden 4* (5): 739–950.

NUERNBERGK, E., 1933. Über den Auxin-Quertransport und den Geotropismus der *Avena*-koleoptile: Einfluss der Dekapitation. *Flora 128:* 99–110.

NUERNBERGK, E. and H. G. DU BUY, 1930. Über Methoden zur Analyse von Wachstumserscheinungen. *Rec. trav. bot. néerl. 27:* 417–520.

NUERNBERGK, E. and H. G. DU BUY, 1932. Die Analyse von pflanzlichen Wachstumsvorgängen. *Handb. biol. Arbeitsmethoden 9* (4): 951–1014.

ÖHOLM, L. W., 1912. Die freie Diffusion der Nichtelektrolyte. Meddel. *Vet.-Akad. Nobelinst. 2,* No. 23.

OOSTERHUIS, J., 1931. Der Einfluss der Knospen auf das Stengelwachstum von *Asparagus plumosus* und *A. Sprengeri. Rec. trav. bot. néerl. 28:* 20–74.

ORTH, H., 1934. Die Wirkung des Follikelhormons auf die Entwicklung der Pflanze. *Z. f. Bot. 27:* 565–607.

OVERBECK, F., 1934. Beiträge zur Kenntnis der Zellstreckung. (Untersuchungen am Sporogonstiel von *Pellia epiphylla.*) *Z. f. Bot. 27:* 129–170.

OVERBEEK, J. VAN, 1932. An analysis of phototropism in dicotyledons. *Proc. Kon. Akad. Wetensch.* Amsterdam *35:* 1325–1335.

OVERBEEK, J. VAN, 1933. Wuchsstoff, Lichtwachstumsreaktion und Phototropismus bei *Raphanus. Rec. trav. bot. néerl. 30:* 537–626.

OVERBEEK, J. VAN, 1935. The growth hormone and the dwarf type of growth in corn. *Proc. Nat. Acad. Sc. 21:* 292–299.

OVERBEEK, J. VAN, 1936. Growth hormone and mesocotyl growth. *Rec. trav. bot. néerl. 33:* 333–340.

OVERBEEK, J. VAN, 1936a. Light growth response and auxin curvatures of *Avena. Proc. Nat. Acad. Sc. 22:* 421–425.

OVERBEEK, J. VAN, 1936b. Different action of auxin-*a* and of heteroauxin (Preliminary note). *Proc. Nat. Acad. Sc. 22:* 187–190.

OVERBEEK, J. VAN, 1936c. Growth substance curvatures of *Avena* in light and dark. *J. gen. Physiol. 20:* 283–309.

PAÁL, A., 1914. Über phototropische Reizleitungen. *Ber. d. bot. Ges. 32:* 499–502.

PAÁL, A., 1919. Über phototropische Reizleitung. *Jahrb. wiss. Bot. 58:* 406–458.

PERRY, J. L., 1932. A possible hormone-secreting region in the grass coleoptile. *Science 76:* 215–216.

PFAELTZER, J. W., 1934. Lengtekracht, groeistof en groei bij het coleoptiel van *Avena sativa.* Diss. Utrecht. 121 pp.

PISEK, A., 1929. Wuchsstoff und Tropismen. *Österr. Bot. Z. 78:* 168–186.

POHL, R., 1935. Über den Endospermwuchsstoff und die Wuchsstoffproduktion der Koleoptilspitze. *Planta 24:* 523–526.

POHL, R., 1936. Die Abhängigkeit des Wachstums der *Avena*-Koleoptile und ihrer sogenannten Wuchsstoff-produktion von Auxingehalt des Endosperms. *Planta 25:* 720–750.

POPOFF, M., 1933. Über die pflanzlichen Auxine und ihre Wirkung auf Einzellige. *Biol. Zentralbl. 53:* 661–668.

PRIESTLEY, J. H., 1930. Studies in the physiology of cambial activity. III. The seasonal activity of the cambium. *New Phytol. 29:* 316–354.

PRINGSHEIM, E. G., 1912. Die Reizbewegungen der Pflanzen. Berlin, 1912.

PURDY, H. A., 1921. Studies on the path of transmission of phototropic and geotropic stimuli in the coleoptile of *Avena. Kgl. Danske Videnskab. Selskab., Biol. Medd. 3:* 3–29.

RAALTE, M. H. VAN, 1936. On the influence of glucose on auxin production by the root tip of *Vicia Faba. Proc. Kon. Akad. Wetensch.* Amsterdam *39:* 261–265.

RAMSHORN, K., 1934. Experimentelle Beiträge zur elektrophysiologischen Wachstumstheorie. *Planta 22:* 737–766.

RAWITSCHER, F., 1932. Der Geotropismus der Pflanzen. Jena, 1932.

RAYDT, G., 1925. Über die Bewegungen euphotometrischer Blätter. *Jahrb. wiss. Bot. 64:* 731–769.

REED, H. S. and F. F. HALMA, 1919. On the existence of a growth inhibiting substance in the Chinese lemon. *Univ. Calif. Publ. Agr. Sci. 4:* No. 3, 99–112.

REICHE, H., 1924. Über Auslösung von Zellteilungen durch Injektion von Gewebesäften und Zelltrümmern. *Z. f. Bot. 16:* 241–278.

REID, M. E., 1924. Quantitative relations of carbohydrates to nitrogen in determining growth responses in tomato cuttings. *Bot. Gaz. 77:* 404–418.

REINDERS, D. E., 1934. The sensibility for light of the base of normal and decapitated coleoptiles of *Avena. Proc. Kon. Akad. Wetensch.* Amsterdam *37:* 308–314.

RICCA, U., 1916. Solution d'un problème de physiologie: la propagation de stimulus dans la Sensitive (résumé). *Arch. ital. Biol. 65:* 219–232.

ROBINSON, T. W. and G. L. WOODSIDE, 1937. Auxin in the chick embryo. I. *J. Cell. Comp. Physiol. 9:* 241–260.

RONSDORF, L., 1935. Vergleichende Untersuchungen über die Wirkung verschiedener Wuchsstoffe auf das Wachstum einiger Pilze. *Arch. Mikrobiol. 6:* 309–325.

ROTHERT, W., 1894. Über Heliotropismus. *Cohn's Beitr. Biol. Pfl. 7:* 1–212.

SACHS, J., 1880, 1882. Stoff und Form der Pflanzenorgane. I and II. *Arb. Bot. Inst. Würzburg 2:* 452–488 and 689–718.

SACHS, J., 1893. Ueber Wachsthumsperioden und Bildungsreize. Physiologische Notizen VI. Marburg.

SCHARRER, K. and W. SCHROPP, 1935. Die Wirkung von Follikelhormon-Kristallisaten auf das Wachstum einiger Kulturpflanzen. *Biochem. Z. 281:* 314–328.

SCHECHTER, V., 1934. Electrical control of rhizoid formation in the red alga, *Griffithsia bornetiana. J. gen. Physiol. 18:* 1–21.

SCHECHTER, V., 1935. The effect of centrifuging on the polarity of an alga, *Griffithsia bornetiana. Biol. Bull. 68:* 172–179.

SCHILLING, E., 1915. Über hypertrophische und hyperplastische Gewebewucherungen an Sprossachsen, verursacht durch Paraffine. *Jahrb. wiss. Bot. 55:* 177–258.

SCHLENKER, G. and G. MITTMANN, 1936. Versuche zur Klärung der reziproken Verschiedenheiten von *Epilobium*-Bastarden. IV. Internodienwachstum und Zellstreckung bei *Epilobium hirsutum* unter dem Einfluss synthetischer β-Indolylessigsäure. *Jahrb. wiss. Bot. 83:* 315–323.

SCHMITZ, H., 1933. Über Wuchsstoff und Geotropismus bei Gräsern. *Planta 19:* 614–635.

SCHOELLER, W. and H. GOEBEL, 1931. Die Wirkung des Follikelhormons auf Pflanzen. *Biochem. Z. 240:* 1–11.

SCHOELLER, W. and H. GOEBEL, 1932. Die Wirkung des Follikelhormons auf Pflanzen. II. Über den Einfluss des kristallinischen β-Follikelhormons. *Biochem. Z. 251:* 223–228.

SCHOELLER, W. and H. GOEBEL, 1934. Die Wirkung des Follikelhormons auf Pflanzen. III. *Biochem. Z. 272:* 215–221.

SCHOELLER, W. and H. GOEBEL, 1935. Die Einwirkung östrogener Substanzen auf Pflanzen. IV. *Biochem. Z. 278:* 298–311.

SCHUMACHER, W., 1936. Untersuchungen über die Wanderung des Fluoresceins in den Haaren von *Cucurbita Pepo*. *Jahrb. wiss. Bot. 82:* 507–533.

SCHWANITZ, F., 1935. Beiträge zur Analyse der pflanzlichen Polarität. *Beih. Bot. Centralbl. 54 A:* 520–530.

SEUBERT, E., 1925. Über Wachstumsregulatoren in der Koleoptile von *Avena*. *Z. f. Bot. 17:* 49–88.

SIERP, H., 1918. Ein Beitrag zur Kenntniss des Einflusses des Lichtes auf das Wachstum der Koleoptile von *Avena sativa*. *Z. f. Bot. 10:* 641–729.

SIERP, H., 1921. Untersuchungen über die durch Licht und Dunkelheit hervorgerufenen Wachstumsreaktion bei der Koleoptile von *Avena sativa* und ihr Zusammenhang mit den phototropischen Krümmungen. *Z. f. Bot. 13:* 113–172.

SIERP, H. and A. SEYBOLD, 1926. Untersuchungen über die Lichtempfindlichkeit der Spitze and des Stumpfes in der Koleoptile von *Avena sativa*. *Jahrb. wiss. Bot., 65:* 592–610.

SILBERSCHMIDT, K., 1928. Untersuchungen über die Abhängigkeit des pflanzlichen Wachstumsverlaufes und der erreichten Endlänge von konstanten Temperaturgraden. *Bibliotheca Botanica 97*, Stuttgart.

SIMON, S. V., 1930. Transplantationsversuche zwischen *Solanum melongena* und *Iresine Lindeni*. *Jahrb. wiss. Bot. 72:* 137–160.

SKOOG, F., 1934. The effect of x-rays on growth substance and plant growth. *Science 79:* 256.

SKOOG, F., 1935. The effect of x-irradiation on auxin and plant growth. *J. Cell. Comp. Physiol. 7:* 227–270.

SKOOG, F., 1937. A deseeded *Avena* test method for small amounts of auxin and auxin precursors. *J. gen. Physiol. 20:* 311–334.

SKOOG, F. and K. V. THIMANN, 1934. Further experiments on the inhibition of the development of lateral buds by growth hormone. *Proc. Nat. Acad. Sc. 20:* 480–485.

SNOW, R., 1924. Conduction of excitation in stem and leaf of *Mimosa pudica. Proc. Roy. Soc. B 96:* 349–374.

SNOW, R., 1925. Conduction of excitation in the leaf of *Mimosa Spegazzinii. Proc. Roy. Soc. B 98:* 188–201.

SNOW, R., 1925a. The correlative inhibition of the growth of axillary buds. *Ann. Bot. 39:* 841–859.

SNOW, R., 1929. The young leaf as the inhibiting organ. *New Phytol. 28:* 345–358.

SNOW, R., 1931. Experiments on growth and inhibition. I. The increase of inhibition with distance. *Proc. Roy. Soc. B 108:* 209–223.

SNOW, R., 1931a. Experiments on growth and inhibition. II. New phenomena of inhibition. *Proc. Roy. Soc. B 108:* 305–316.

SNOW, R., 1932. Growth-regulators in plants. *New Phytol. 31:* 336–353.

SNOW, R., 1933. The nature of cambial stimulus. *New Phytol. 32:* 288–296.

SNOW, R., 1935. Activation of cambial growth by pure hormones. *Nature 135:* 876.

SNOW, R., 1935a. Activation of cambial growth by pure hormones. *New Phytol. 34:* 347–360.

SNOW, R., 1936. Upward effects of auxin in coleoptiles and stems. *New Phytol. 35:* 292–304.

SNOW, R. and B. LE FANU, 1935. Activation of cambial growth. *Nature 135:* 149.

SÖDING, H., 1923. Werden von der Spitze der Haferkoleoptile Wuchshormone gebildet? *Ber. d. bot. Ges. 41:* 396–400.

SÖDING, H., 1925. Zur Kenntnis der Wuchshormone in der Haferkoleoptile. *Jahrb. wiss. Bot. 64:* 587–603.

SÖDING, H., 1926. Über den Einfluss der jungen Infloreszenz auf das Wachstum ihres Schaftes. *Jahrb. wiss. Bot. 65:* 611–635.

SÖDING, H., 1927. Über Wuchshormone. *Zellstimulationsforsch. 2:* 381–392.

SÖDING, H., 1929. Weitere Untersuchungen über die Wuchshormone der Haferkoleoptile. *Jahrb. wiss. Bot. 71:* 184–213.

Söding, H., 1931. Wachstum und Wanddehnbarkeit bei der Haferkoleoptile. *Jahrb. wiss. Bot. 74:* 127–151.

Söding, H., 1932. Hormone und Pflanzenwachstum. *Beih. Bot. Centralbl. 59:* 469–481.

Söding, H., 1932a. Über das Streckungswachstum der Zellwand. *Ber. d. bot. Ges. 50:* 117–123.

Söding, H., 1932b. Über das Wachstum der Infloreszenzschäfte. *Jahrb. wiss. Bot. 77:* 627–656.

Söding, H., 1934. Über die Wachstumsmechanik der Haferkoleoptile. *Jahrb. wiss. Bot. 79:* 231–255.

Söding, H., 1935. Die Ausführung des Wentschen Auxintestes am Tageslicht. *Ber. d. bot. Ges. 53:* 331–334.

Söding, H., 1935a. Über den Wuchsstoff in der Basis der Haferkoleoptile. *Ber. d. bot. Ges. 53:* 843–846.

Söding, H., 1935b. Review of: Boysen Jensen, Die Wuchsstofftheorie etc. *Z. f. Bot. 28:* 466–467.

Söding, H., 1936. Wirkt der Wuchsstoff artspezifisch? *Jahrb. wiss. Bot. 82:* 534–554.

Söding, H., 1936a. Über den Einfluss von Wuchsstoff auf das Dickenwachstum der Bäume. *Ber. d. bot. Ges. 54:* 291–304.

Söllner, K., 1933. Zur Aufklärung einiger Membranvorgänge. *Kolloid-Z. 62:* 31–37.

Soltys, A. and K. Umrath, 1936. Über die Erregungssubstanz der Mimosoideen. *Biochem. Z. 284:* 247–255.

Stanley, W. M., 1936. The isolation from diseased Turkish tobacco plants of a crystalline protein possessing the properties of tobacco mosaic virus. *Phytopath. 26:* 305–320.

Stark, P., 1917. Beiträge zur Kenntnis des Traumatotropismus. *Jahrb. wiss. Bot. 57:* 461–552.

Stark, P., 1921. Studien über traumatotrope und haptotrope Reizleitungsvorgänge mit besonderer Berücksichtigung der Reizübertragung auf fremde Arten und Gattungen. *Jahrb. wiss. Bot. 60:* 67–134.

Stark, P., 1927. Das Reizleitungsproblem bei den Pflanzen im Lichte neuerer Erfahrungen. *Ergeb. Biol. 2:* 1–94.

Stark, P. and O. Drechsel, 1922. Phototropische Reizleitungsvorgänge bei Unterbrechung des organischen Zusammenhangs. *Jahrb. wiss. Bot. 61:* 339–371.

Stiles, W., 1935. Recent advances in science;—plant physiology. *Sci. Progress, 30:* 313–317.

STRUGGER, S., 1932. Die Beeinflussung des Wachstums und des Geotropismus durch die Wasserstoffionen. *Ber. d. bot. Ges. 50:* (77)–(92).

STRUGGER, S., 1933. Über das Wachstum dekapitierter Keimpflanzen. *Ber. d. bot. Ges. 51:* 193–209.

STRUGGER, S., 1934. Beiträge zur Physiologie des Wachstums. I. Zur protoplasma-physiologischen Kausalanalyse des Streckungswachstums. *Jahrb. wiss. Bot. 79:* 406–471.

SWINGLE, W. T., 1928. Metaxenia in the Date Palm. *J. Hered. 19:* 257–268.

TAMMES, P. M. L., 1931. Über den Verlauf der geotropischen Krümmung bei künstlich tordierten Koleoptilen von *Avena*. *Rec. trav. bot. néerl.* 28: 75–81.

TENDELOO, N., 1927. Onderzoekingen over zoogenaamde traumatotropische krommingen bij kiemplanten van *Avena sativa*. *Proc. Kon. Akad. Wetensch*. Amsterdam *36:* 661–666.

TETLEY, U. and J. H. PRIESTLEY, 1927. The histology of the coleoptile in relation to its phototropic response. *New Phytol. 26:* 171–186.

THIMANN, K. V., 1934. Studies on the growth hormone of plants. VI. The distribution of the growth substance in plant tissues. *J. gen. Physiol. 18:* 23–34.

THIMANN, K. V., 1935. Growth substances in plants. *Ann. Rev. Biochem. 4:* 545–568.

THIMANN, K. V., 1935a. On the plant growth hormone produced by *Rhizopus suinus*. *J. Biol. Chem. 109:* 279–291.

THIMANN, K. V., 1935b. On an analysis of the activity of two growth-promoting substances on plant tissues. *Proc. Kon. Akad. Wetensch.* Amsterdam *38:* 896–912.

THIMANN, K. V., 1936. On the physiology of the formation of nodules on legume roots. *Proc. Nat. Acad. Sc. 22:* 511–514.

THIMANN, K. V., 1936a. Auxins and the growth of roots. *Am. J. Bot. 23:* 561–569.

THIMANN, K. V., 1936b. The physiology and chemistry of the plant hormones. *Current Science 4:* 716–721.

THIMANN, K. V. and H. A. BARKER, 1934. Studies on the excystment of *Colpoda cucullus*. II. The action of the excystment inducing substance. *J. exp. Zool. 69:* 39–57.

THIMANN, K. V. and J. BONNER, 1932. Studies on the growth hormone of plants. II. The entry of growth substance into the plant. *Proc. Nat. Acad. Sc. 18:* 692–701.

THIMANN, K. V. and J. BONNER, 1933. The mechanism of the action of the growth substance of plants. *Proc. Roy. Soc. B 113:* 126–149.

THIMANN, K. V. and H. E. DOLK, 1933. Conditions governing the production of the plant growth hormone by *Rhizopus* cultures. *Biol. Zentralbl. 53:* 49–66.

THIMANN, K. V. and J. B. KOEPFLI, 1935. Identity of the growth-promoting and root-forming substances of plants. *Nature 135:* 101.

THIMANN, K. V. and F. SKOOG, 1933. Studies on the growth hormone of plants. III. The inhibiting action of the growth substance on bud development. *Proc. Nat. Acad. Sc. 19:* 714–716.

THIMANN, K. V. and F. SKOOG, 1934. On the inhibition of bud development and other functions of growth substance in *Vicia Faba*. *Proc. Roy. Soc. B 114:* 317–339.

THIMANN, K. V. and F. W. WENT, 1934. On the chemical nature of the root-forming hormone. *Proc. Kon. Akad. Wetensch.* Amsterdam *37:* 456–459.

UHROVÁ, A., 1934. Über die hormonale Natur der Hemmungswirkung der Blätter bei *Bryophyllum crenatum*. *Planta 22:* 411–427.

UMRATH, K., 1927. Über die Erregungssubstanz der Mimosoideen. *Planta 4:* 812–817.

UMRATH, K., 1935. Review of: Boysen Jensen, Die Wuchsstofftheorie etc. *Protoplasma 23:* 143–144.

UMRATH, K. and A. SOLTYS, 1936. Über die Erregungssubstanz der Papilionaceen und ihre zellteilungsauslösende Wirkung. *Jahrb. wiss. Bot. 84:* 276–289.

URSPRUNG, A. and G. BLUM, 1924. Eine Methode zur Messung des Wand- und Turgordruckes der Zelle, nebst Anwendungen. *Jahrb. wiss. Bot. 63:* 1–110.

UYLDERT, I. E., 1927. The influence of the growth-promoting substances on decapitated flower-stalks of *Bellis perennis*. *Proc. Kon. Akad. Wetensch.* Amsterdam *31:* 59–61.

UYLDERT, I. E., 1931. De invloed van groeistof op planten met intercalaire groei. Diss. Utrecht, 1931.

VIRTANEN, A. I. and S. VON HAUSEN, 1933, 1934. Effect of yeast extract on the growth of plants. *Nature 132:* 408–409; *133:* 383.

VIRTANEN, A. I., S. VON HAUSEN, and S. SAASTAMOINEN, 1934. Die Einwirkung des Follikelhormons auf das Blühen der Pflanzen. *Biochem. Z. 272:* 32–35.

VÖCHTING, H., 1878 and 1884. Über Organbildung im Pflanzenreich. I and II. Bonn, 1878, 1–258; 1884, 1–200.

280   BIBLIOGRAPHY

VÖCHTING, H., 1892. Über Transplantation am Pflanzenkörper. Tübingen, 1892, 1–162.

VÖCHTING, H., 1908. Untersuchungen zur experimentellen Anatomie und Pathologie des Pflanzenkörpers. Tübingen, 1908, 1–318.

VOGT, E., 1915. Über den Einfluss des Lichts auf das Wachstum der Koleoptile von *Avena sativa*. *Z. f. Bot. 7:* 193–270.

VRIES, H. DE, 1885. Über die Bedeutung der Circulation und der Rotation des Protoplasma für den Stofftransport in der Pflanze. *Bot. Zeit. 43:* 1–6 and 17–26.

WADDINGTON, C. H., 1934. Experiments on embryonic induction. I, II, and III. *J. exp. Biol. 11:* 211–227.

WADDINGTON, C. H. and D. M. NEEDHAM, 1935. Studies on the nature of the amphibian organization centre. II. Induction by synthetic polycyclic hydrocarbons. *Proc. Roy. Soc. B 117:* 310–317.

WADDINGTON, C. H., J. NEEDHAM, W. W. NOWINSKI, and R. LEMBERG, 1935. Studies on the nature of the amphibian organization centre. I. Chemical properties of the evocator. *Proc. Roy. Soc. B 117:* 289–310.

WALD, G. and H. G. DU BUY, 1936. Pigments of the oat coleoptile. *Science 84:* 247.

WALLER, A. D., 1900. The electrical effects of light upon green leaves. *Proc. Roy. Soc. B 67:* 129–137.

WARNER, T., 1928. Über den Einfluss der geotropischen Reizung auf den Zucker- und Säuregehalt von Sprossen. *Jahrb. wiss. Bot. 68:* 431–498.

WEBER, U., 1931. Wachstum und Krümmung einzelner Zonen geotropisch gereizter Gerstenkeimlinge. *Jahrb. wiss. Bot. 75:* 312–376.

WEHNELT, B., 1927. Untersuchungen über das Wundhormon der Pflanzen. *Jahrb. wiss. Bot. 66:* 773–813.

WEIJ, H. G. VAN DER, 1931. Die quantitative Arbeitsmethode mit Wuchsstoff. *Proc. Kon. Akad. Wetensch.* Amsterdam *34:* 875–892.

WEIJ, H. G. VAN DER, 1932. Der Mechanismus des Wuchsstofftransportes. *Rec. trav. bot. néerl. 29:* 379–496.

WEIJ, H. G. VAN DER, 1933. On the occurrence of growth substance in marine algae. *Proc. Kon. Akad. Wetensch.* Amsterdam *36:* 759–760.

WEIJ, H. G. VAN DER, 1933a. Über Wuchsstoff bei *Elaeagnus angustifolius*. *Proc. Kon. Akad. Wetensch.* Amsterdam *36:* 760–761.

WEIJ, H. G. VAN DER, 1933b. Über das Vorkommen von Wuchsstoff bei Meeresalgen. *Pubbl. Staz. Zool. Napoli 13:* 172–179.

WEIJ, H. G. VAN DER, 1934. Der Mechanismus des Wuchsstofftransportes II. *Rec. trav. bot. néerl. 31:* 810–857.

WEIMANN, R., 1929. Untersuchungen über den Traumatotropismus der *Avena*-koleoptile. *Jahrb. wiss. Bot. 71:* 269–323.

WEISKOPF, B., 1927. Sur les conditions corrélatives de la croissance en longueur des bourgeons chez quelques Papilionacées en voie de germination (résumé). *Publ. biol. école vétér. Brno 6:* 67–103.

WEISS, P., 1935. The so-called organizer and the problem of organization in amphibian development. *Physiol. Rev. 15:* 639–674.

WENT, F. A. F. C., 1927. Groeistoffen. *Jaarb. Kon. Akad. Wetensch.* Amsterdam. 1927.

WENT, F. A. F. C., 1929. Plant movements. *Proc. Int. Congr. Plant Sci.* Ithaca.

WENT, F. A. F. C., 1930. Les conceptions nouvelles sur les tropismes des plantes. *Rev. gén. des Sci. 41:* 631–643.

WENT, F. A. F. C., 1930a. Über wurzelbildende Substanzen bei *Bryophyllum calycinum* Salisb. *Z. f. Bot. 23:* 19–26.

WENT, F. A. F. C., 1931. In: Kostytchew: Pflanzenphysiologie II. Berlin, 1931.

WENT, F. A. F. C., 1932. Pflanzenwachstum und Wuchsstoff (Auxin). *Forsch. und Fortschr. 8:* 371–372.

WENT, F. A. F. C., 1932a. Over groeistoffen bij planten. *Chem. Weekblad 29:* 316–317.

WENT, F. A. F. C., 1932b. Wuchsstoff—Auxin—bei Pflanzen. *Chemiker-Zeit. 56:* 782–783.

WENT, F. A. F. C., 1933. Die Bedeutung des Wuchsstoffes (Auxin) für Wachstum, photo- und geotropische Krümmungen. *Naturwiss. 21:* 1–7.

WENT, F. A. F. C., 1933a. Growth substance (auxin) in plants. *Nature 133:* 452–453.

WENT, F. A. F. C., 1934. Hormone bei Pflanzen. *Verh. Schweiz. Naturf. Ges. 1934:* 220–240.

WENT, F. A. F. C., 1935. The investigations on growth and tropisms carried on in the Botanical Laboratory of the University of Utrecht during the last decade. *Biol. Rev. 10:* 187–207.

WENT, F. W., 1926. On growth-accelerating substances in the coleoptile of *Avena sativa. Proc. Kon. Akad. Wetensch.* Amsterdam *30:* 10–19.

WENT, F. W., 1928. Wuchsstoff und Wachstum. *Rec. trav. bot. néerl. 25:* 1–116.

WENT, F. W., 1928a. Die Erklärung des phototropischen Krümmungsverlaufs. *Rec. trav. bot. néerl. 25a:* 483–489.

WENT, F. W., 1929. On a substance causing root formation. *Proc. Kon. Akad. Wetensch.* Amsterdam *32:* 35–39.

WENT, F. W., 1932. Eine botanische Polaritätstheorie. *Jahrb. wiss. Bot. 76:* 528–557.

WENT, F. W., 1934. On the pea test method for auxin, the plant growth hormone. *Proc. Kon. Akad. Wetensch.* Amsterdam *37:* 547–555.

WENT, F. W., 1934a. A test method for rhizocaline, the root-forming substance. *Proc. Kon. Akad. Wetensch.* Amsterdam *37:* 445–455.

WENT, F. W., 1935. Coleoptile growth as affected by auxin, aging and food. *Proc. Kon. Akad. Wetensch.* Amsterdam *38:* 752–767.

WENT, F. W., 1935a. Hormones involved in root formation. *Proc. 6th Int. Bot. Congr. 2:* 267–269.

WENT, F. W., 1935b. Auxin, the plant growth-hormone. *Bot. Rev. 1:* 162–182.

WENT, F. W., 1936. Allgemeine Betrachtungen über das Auxin-Problem. *Biol. Zentralbl. 56:* 449–463.

WENT, F. W., 1936a. The growth hormone in plants. *Proc. 25th Ann. Celebration, Univ. So. Calif.,* 223–228.

WHITE, P. R., 1933. Concentrations of inorganic ions as related to growth of excised root-tips of wheat seedlings. *Plant Physiol. 8:* 489–508.

WHITE, P. R., 1934. Potentially unlimited growth of excised tomato root tips in a liquid medium. *Plant Physiol. 9:* 585–600.

WIESNER, J., 1878, 1880. Die heliotropischen Erscheinungen im Pflanzenreiche. I, II. Denkschr. *k. Akad. Wiss. Wien 39:* 143–209; *43:* 1–92.

WIESNER, J., 1884. Note über die angebliche Function der Wurzelspitze. *Ber. d. bot. Ges. 2:* 72–78.

WILHELM, A. F., 1930. Untersuchungen über das Chromogen in *Vicia Faba. Jahrb. wiss. Bot. 72:* 203–253.

WILLIAMS, R. J., C. M. LYMAN, G. H. GOODYEAR, J. H. TRUESDAIL, and D. HOLADAY, 1933. "Pantothenic acid," a growth determinant of universal biological occurrence. *J. Am. Chem. Soc. 55:* 2912–2927.

WOLK, P. C. VAN DER, 1911. Onderzoekingen over de geleiding van lichtprikkels bij kiemplantjes van *Avena. Versl. Kon. Akad. Wetensch.* Amsterdam 1911: 258–273.

ZIMMERMAN, P. W., 1930. Oxygen requirements for root growth of cuttings in water. *Am. J. Bot. 17:* 842–861.

ZIMMERMAN, P. W., W. CROCKER, and A. E. HITCHCOCK, 1933. Initiation and stimulation of roots from exposure of plants to carbon monoxide gas. *Contrib. Boyce Thompson Inst. 5:* 1–17.

ZIMMERMAN, P. W. and A. E. HITCHCOCK, 1929. Vegetative propagation of holly. *Am. J. Bot. 16:* 556–570.

ZIMMERMAN, P. W. and A. E. HITCHCOCK, 1935. Response of roots to "root-forming" substances. *Contrib. Boyce Thompson Inst. 7:* 439–445.

ZIMMERMAN, P. W., A. E. HITCHCOCK, and F. WILCOXON, 1936. Several esters as plant hormones. *Contrib. Boyce Thompson Inst. 8:* 105–112.

ZIMMERMAN, P. W. and F. WILCOXON, 1935. Several chemical growth substances which cause initiation of roots and other responses in plants. *Contrib. Boyce Thompson Inst. 7:* 209–229.

ZIMMERMANN, W. A., 1936. Untersuchungen über die räumliche und zeitliche Verteilung des Wuchsstoffes bei Bäumen. *Z. f. Bot. 30:* 209–252.

ZOLLIKOFER, C., 1928. Über Dorsiventralitätskrümmungen bei Keimlingen von *Panicum* und *Sorghum* und den Einfluss der Koleoptile auf das Mesokotylwachstum. *Rec. trav. bot. néerl. 25a:* 490–504.

ZOLLIKOFER, C., 1935. Zur Rolle der Membrandehnbarkeit bei der floralen Bewegung. *Ber. d. bot. Ges. 53:* 152–177.

ADDENDA

CLARK, W. G., 1937. Electrical polarity and auxin transport. *Plant Physiol. 12:* 409–440.

KOEPFLI, J. B., K. V. THIMANN, and F. W. WENT, 1937. Plant Hormones: Structure and physiological activity. I. In press.

ROGENHOFER, G., 1936. Wirkung von Wuchsstoffen auf die Kallusbildung bei Holzstecklingen. I. Sitzungsber. *Akad. Wien I, 145:* 81–99.

AUTHOR INDEX

References to pp. 251–283 are to the Bibliography.

285

SUBJECT INDEX

Page numbers in italics refer to extended or systematic treatment of the subject.

289